OXFORD
WORKSHOP
MATHEMATICS

Student's Manual

Oxford
University
Press

Oxford University Press, Great Clarendon Street, Oxford OX2 6DP

Oxford   New York
Athens   Auckland   Bangkok   Bogota   Bombay
Buenos Aires   Calcutta   Cape Town   Dar es Salaam   Delhi
Florence   Hong Kong   Istanbul   Karachi
Kuala Lumpur   Madras   Madrid   Melbourne
Mexico City   Nairobi   Paris   Singapore
Taipei   Tokyo   Toronto

and associated companies in
Berlin   Ibadan

Oxford is a trade mark of Oxford University Press

© Oxford University Press 1997

First published 1997

ISBN 0 19 9145792

A CIP catalogue record for this book is available from the British Library.

Typeset and illustrated by Tech Set Ltd., Gateshead, Tyne & Wear
Printed in Great Britain by Scotprint Ltd., Musselburgh

Contents

Preface

Aims

This book can be used in two ways:

- As a supplementary text for students using the *Oxford Workshop Mathematics Copymaster Bank*. The chapter numbers in the book allow them to be cross-referenced with the workshop modules. This will enable revision and practice to be carried on away from the workshop whilst directing the student to the appropriate workshop module should a more detailed revision of a topic prove necessary.

- As a revision text in its own right. The book does not set out to teach each topic from scratch but is ideal for students who are resitting GCSE examinations or who are re-encountering mathematical topics in the context of another course such as GNVQ.

This book covers all topics encountered in national Curriculum Levels 4–8 and is therefore suitable for GCSE students at Intermediate level and in GNVQ Application of Number up to Level 3. Some topics, included in the workshop material, and therefore in this book, for the sake of completeness, go beyond these levels.

Because this is a revision text the emphasis has been on providing a brief, clear exposition of each topic, followed by examples and student exercises. In addition there is a 'key facts' panel on most pages, which is designed to highlight the main points covered and, in some cases, to provide an extra commentary on the text. Students requiring a more detailed explanation of a topic should consult their tutor or the relevant workshop module if this is available.

Tony Beadsworth
Brian Jefferson
Wilf Hodgson

N 01 Whole numbers

An **integer** is a whole number

The mathematical word for a whole number is an **integer** (pronounced *in-ti-jer*).

Factors

The result of multiplying two numbers together is called their **product**.

If one integer divides exactly into another, the first integer is a **factor** of the second.

All integers can be expressed as the **product** of two integers in at least one way. For example,

12 can be written as 12×1, 6×2 or 4×3

The integers 1, 2, 3, 4, 6 and 12 are **factors** of 12.

Common factors

If we list all the factors of two or more integers, there will be one or more factors which appear in all the lists. For example, list the factors of 18, 36 and 45.

Factors of 18 are 1, 2, 3, 6, 9, 18
Factors of 36 are 1, 2, 3, 4, 6, 9, 12, 18, 36
Factors of 45 are 1, 3, 5, 9, 15, 45

The largest integer which is a factor of all the integers in a given set is called the **highest common factor (HCF)** of those integers.

The integers 1, 3 and 9 appear in all three lists. These are the **common factors** of 18, 36 and 45.

The largest number in all three lists is 9. This is the **highest common factor (HCF)** of 18, 36 and 45.

Prime numbers

A **prime number** is an integer which has **only two factors** – itself and 1.

Notice that 1 is **not** a prime number because it has only one factor.

We can successively 'split' a given integer into factors until we can go no further. For example,

$$120 = 12 \times 10 \qquad\qquad \text{OR} \quad 120 = 6 \times 20 \qquad\qquad \text{OR}\ldots$$
$$= 3 \times 4 \times 2 \times 5 \qquad\qquad\qquad = 2 \times 3 \times 2 \times 10$$
$$= 3 \times 2 \times 2 \times 2 \times 5 \qquad\qquad\quad = 2 \times 3 \times 2 \times 2 \times 5$$

We can now go no further because 2, 3 and 5 cannot be written as the product of two smaller integers. They are called **prime numbers**.

As 2, 3 and 5 are prime numbers and are factors of 120, they are called **prime factors** of 120.

Writing 120 as $2 \times 2 \times 2 \times 3 \times 5$ is called expressing it as a **product of its prime factors**. Notice that however we choose to go about splitting a number, we always end up with the same product of prime factors.

Index notation

When an integer is multiplied by itself several times, we can write it more compactly by using index notation. For example,

$5 \times 5 = 5^2$ (We say '5 squared')
$5 \times 5 \times 5 = 5^3$ (We say '5 cubed')
$5 \times 5 \times 5 \times 5 = 5^4$ (We say '5 to the power of 4')
$2 \times 2 \times 2 \times 5 \times 5 \times 5 \times 5 \times 5 = 2^3 \times 5^5$

Multiples

If one integer **divides exactly** into another, the second integer is a **multiple** of the first.

Multiplying two integers together gives a number which is called a **multiple** of each of the integers. For example,

$3 \times 4 = 12$ means 12 is a multiple of 3 and a multiple of 4

The multiples of a given integer form the 'times table' of that integer. For example,

6, 12, 18, 24, 30, ... are the multiples of 6

Common multiples

The smallest integer which is a multiple of all the integers in a given set is called the **lowest common multiple (LCM)** of those integers.

If we list the multiples of two or more integers, there will be multiples which appear in all the lists. For example,

Multiples of 4 are 4, 8, 12, 16, 20, 24, 28, 32, 36, ...
Multiples of 6 are 6, 12, 18, 24, 30, 36, 42, 48, ...

The integers 12, 24, 36, ... appear in both of these lists and are the **common multiples** of 4 and 6.

The smallest of these multiples is 12, so 12 is the **lowest common multiple (LCM)** of 4 and 6.

Notice that all the common multiples are multiples of the LCM.

Using prime factors to find HCF and LCM

For example, find the HCF and LCM of 360 and 2100.

Expressing these as products of prime factors gives

$360 = 2 \times 2 \times 2 \times 3 \times 3 \times 5$ or $2^3 \times 3^2 \times 5$
$2100 = 2 \times 2 \times 3 \times 5 \times 5 \times 7$ or $2^2 \times 3 \times 5^2 \times 7$

When two or more integers are expressed as the products of their prime factors:

● their HCF is the product of the **smallest power** of each prime.

The prime factorisation of the HCF must appear in each of these products. The largest product contained in both is

$2 \times 2 \times 3 \times 5$ or $2^2 \times 3 \times 5$

So HCF is 60.

● their LCM is the product of the **largest power** of each prime.

The prime factorisation of the LCM must contain each of the above products. The smallest product which contains both is

$2 \times 2 \times 2 \times 3 \times 3 \times 5 \times 5 \times 7$ or $2^3 \times 3^2 \times 5^2 \times 7$

So LCM is 12 600.

Squares and square roots

$1 \times 1 = 1$

$2 \times 2 = 4$

$3 \times 3 = 9$

$4 \times 4 = 16$

$5 \times 5 = 25$

The result of multiplying an integer by itself is a **square number** or **perfect square**.

The operation **square** is reversed by the operation **taking the square root**.

A perfect square can be identified by takings its square root. The result will be an integer.

When we multiply an integer by itself, the number is a **square number**, as shown. This is why 3^2, for example, is called 'three squared'.

The first ten square numbers are 1, 4, 9, 16, 25, 36, 49, 81, 100.

To square a number on your calculator, use the $\boxed{x^2}$ key.

The reverse operation is **taking the square root** ($\sqrt{\ }$). For example,

$$8^2 = 64 \quad \text{and} \quad \sqrt{64} = 8$$

To take the square root of a number on your calculator, use the $\boxed{\sqrt{\ }}$ key.

EXERCISE N1

1 a List all the factors of
  i 36   **ii** 60   **iii** 80   **iv** 75   **v** 96   **vi** 42

  b List the common factors of 36 and 60.
  c State the highest common factor of 36 and 60.

2 Find the highest common factor of 42, 56 and 70.

3 For each of the following integers state whether it is a square number, a prime number or neither.

  a 37   **b** 42   **c** 144   **d** 729   **e** 39   **f** 61

4 Express the following integers as a product of their prime factors, giving your answer in index notation.

  a 36   **b** 90   **c** 4800

5 Find the value of the following.

  a $2^3 \times 3^2$ **b** $2^4 \times 5^3 \times 7^2$

6 a List the first eight multiples of
  i 3   **ii** 9   **iii** 10   **iv** 15

  b List the first eight common multiples of 10 and 15.
  c State the lowest common multiple of 10 and 15.

7 Find the lowest common multiple of

  a 9, 14 and 21   **b** 12, 15 and 20

8 Find the HCF and LCM of $2^4 \times 3^3 \times 5^2$ and $2^3 \times 3 \times 5^3 \times 7$, leaving your answer as a product of prime factors.

Multiplication without a calculator

When multiplying by a number with two or more digits, we do the calculation in stages as shown below.

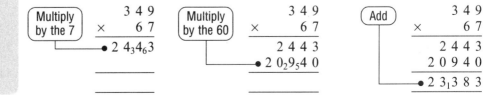

Division without a calculator

'Short' division
Divide successively from the left, carrying the remainder each time.

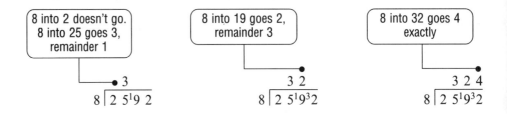

'Long division'
This is a more formal layout for use when dividing by larger numbers: for example, $33\,645 \div 54$.

List the 54 times table: 54, 108, 162, 216, 270, 324, 378, 432, 486. Then

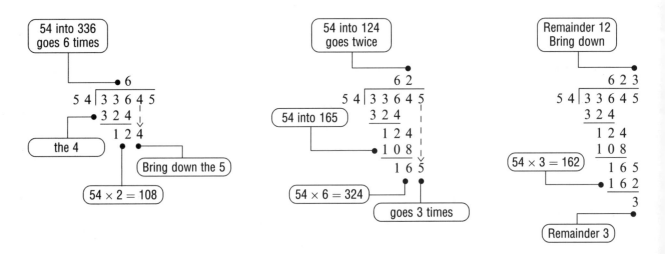

So $33\,645 \div 54 = 623$ remainder 3

EXERCISE N2

1 Complete the following multiplications without using your calculator.

    a 47×83 **b** 452×38 **c** 947×329 **d** 48×6408

2 Complete the following 'short' divisions without using your calculator.

    a $72\,495 \div 9$ **b** $672\,445 \div 5$ **c** $792\,495 \div 11$ **d** $37\,659 \div 7$

3 Complete the following 'long' divisions without using your calculator.

    a $94\,759 \div 37$ **b** $565\,012 \div 62$ **c** $8\,923\,176 \div 125$

If you need more practice, you should make up extra examples to do and check your results with your calculator.

N 02 Directed numbers

On a horizontal scale
- right is positive
- left is negative

On a vertical scale
- up is positive
- down is negative

Positive and negative numbers enable us to label a numerical scale to show both the distance and direction of points from the zero point or **origin**. On a horizontal scale, the positive direction is to the right; on a vertical scale, the positive direction is upwards.

On this scale

+4 (say 'positive 4') means a displacement of 4 to the right
−3 (say 'negative 3') means a displacement of 3 to the left

It is usual to leave out the positive sign and write +4 as just 4.

Order of size

As we move in the positive direction the numbers get larger. This is true at any point on the line. So, for example,

+8 is larger than +3
−2 is larger than −6
+1 is larger than −1

For any pair of numbers, the one which is in the positive direction (to the right or up) from the other is the larger number.

A good example of this is temperature, where we feel warmer when the temperature is −2 °C than when it is −6 °C.

Addition and subtraction

Adding and subtracting are equivalent to moves to the right or left along the number line, starting from zero. For example,

3 − 5 is 3 steps to the right followed by 5 steps to the left

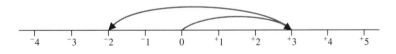

Replacing double signs:

Like signs are replaced with +.

Unlike signs are replaced with −.

When double signs such as −−5 (subtract negative 5) occur in a calculation, they can be replaced by a single sign. The rule is that when the signs are the same we replace them by +, and when they are different we replace them by −. When there are several numbers in the calculation, it is then easiest to find the total 'moves right' and the total 'moves left' before making the final calculation. For example,

$$4 + {}^+3 + {}^-5 - {}^-2 - {}^+6 = 4 + 3 - 5 + 2 - 6$$
$$= 9 - 11$$
$$= {}^-2$$

Multiplication and division

When multiplying or dividing:

Like signs $\Rightarrow$ Positive answer

Unlike signs $\Rightarrow$ Negative answer

When multiplying or dividing, we first complete the calculation ignoring any positive or negative signs, then decide whether the result should be positive or negative.

When the signs are the **same** (positive × positive or negative × negative), the result will be **positive**. When the signs are **different** (positive × negative or negative × positive), the result will be **negative**. For example,

$$^-4 \times {}^-7$$

First multiply the number: $\qquad 4 \times 7 = 28$

Then decide the sign: $\qquad$ negative × negative gives positive

So $\qquad\qquad\qquad {}^-4 \times {}^-7 = {}^+28$

Powers

It is important to remember that powers mean repeated multiplication. For example,

$$(^-2)^3 = {}^-2 \times {}^-2 \times {}^-2$$

$$= {}^+4 \times {}^-2 \quad \text{(Negative} \times \text{Negative gives Positive)}$$

$$= {}^-8 \quad \text{(Positive} \times \text{Negative gives Negative)}$$

Using your calculator

Negative numbers are entered by using a $\boxed{+/-}$ key **after** entering the number, or a $\boxed{(-)}$ key **before** entering the number.

Warning When squaring a negative number using $\boxed{(-)}$, you must enclose it in brackets to get the correct positive answer.

Mixed calculations

The correct order of operations can be remembered by the 'word'

BODMAS

Brackets
Order (powers)
Division
Multiplication
Addition
Subtraction

When a calculation involves several operations, it is important to do things in the **correct order**.

1 Calculations in **brackets** are done first.
2 Any **powers** are done next.
3 **Division** and/or **multiplication** are next, working from left to right.
4 **Addition** and/or **subtraction** are done last.

Warning Some calculators do not obey these rules. Check that yours does by entering '2 + 3 × 4 ='. If the result it gives is not 14, you are strongly advised to replace your calculator.

EXERCISE N3

1 Write the following numbers in increasing order of size,

$^-2$ $^-5$ 0 8 2 $^-7$ 4

2 Complete the following calculations without using your calculator.

a $^-4 + 11$ **b** $6 - 8 + 3 + 2 - 14$ **c** $9 - ^-6$

d $^-2 + ^-9$ **e** $12 - {}^+16 + ^-3$ **f** $^-23 + 18 - {}^+27 - ^-14$

g $17 - 24 + ^-11 - ^-13 - {}^+20$

3 Complete the following calculations without using your calculator.

a $^-6 \times 2$ **b** $^+8 \times ^-5$ **c** $^-7 \times ^-11$ **d** $36 \div ^-9$ **e** $^-56 \div ^-7$

4 a $(3 - 9) \times (7 - {}^+11)$ **b** $(^-4)^2 + ^-3 \times 5$

      c $^-11 - \dfrac{^-8 \times 6}{^-7 + ^-5}$ **d** $(^-2)^2 - (^-3)^3$

You should check that you can also do questions 2, 3 and 4 on your calculator.

N 03 Fractions

Fractions on a calculator

Many calculators can handle fractions. The key is marked $\boxed{\mathbf{a^b/_c}}$ or similar. For example,

     To enter $\frac{3}{4}$ press **3 $\mathbf{a^b/_c}$ 4**

     To enter $5\frac{3}{4}$ press **5 $\mathbf{a^b/_c}$ 3 $\mathbf{a^b/_c}$ 4**

Finding a fraction of a number

For every fraction:
- the top line is the **numerator**
- the bottom line is the **denominator**.

To find a fraction **of** a number:
- **multiply** by the **numerator**
- **divide** by the **denominator**.

Either the multiplying or the dividing may be done first.

The operations 'of' and '×' mean the same.

Finding $\frac{1}{5}$ of 30 is the same as dividing 30 by 5.

Finding $\frac{2}{5}$ of 30 is the same as dividing 30 by 5 and multiplying by 2.

Generally, when we find a fraction of a number, we divide by the bottom number (denominator) of the fraction and multiply by its top number (numerator).

The statements '$\frac{2}{5}$ of 30' and '$\frac{2}{5} \times 30$' mean the same.

Both $\frac{2}{5}$ of 30 and $\frac{2}{5} \times 30$ give $30 \div 5 \times 2 = 12$.

We could reverse the order to give $30 \times 2 \div 5 = 12$.

If you have a fraction key on your calculator you could also enter

     $2 \; a^b/_c \; 5 \times 30 =$

Improper fractions and mixed numbers

Fractions smaller than 1, such as $\frac{3}{4}$, are called **proper fractions**.

Fractions larger than 1 can be written in two ways.

- As an **improper fraction** (the top number larger than the bottom).
- As a **mixed number** (a whole number and a fraction).

EXAMPLES

1 Write $3\frac{3}{4}$ as an improper fraction.

A whole is 4 quarters, so 3 wholes are 12 quarters.

$3\frac{3}{4}$ is 12 quarters plus 3 quarters $= 15$ quarters.

So $3\frac{3}{4} = \frac{15}{4}$.

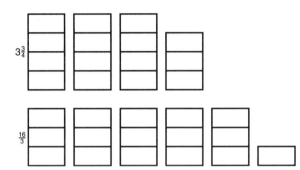

2 Write $\frac{16}{3}$ as a mixed number.

3 thirds make a whole.

16 thirds are 5 lots of 3 thirds (i.e. 5 wholes) plus 1 third.

So $\frac{16}{3} = 5\frac{1}{3}$

On most calculators, using the **INV** (**SHIFT** or **2nd FUNCTION**) key followed by the $\mathbf{a^b/_c}$ key converts between improper fractions and mixed numbers.

For simple calculations, fractions larger than 1 can be used in either form.

EXAMPLE 3

Find $5\frac{3}{4}$ of 8.

Either

$$5\frac{3}{4} \text{ of } 8 = 5 \times 8 + \frac{3}{4} \text{ of } 8$$
$$= 40 + 6$$
$$= 46$$

Or convert $5\frac{3}{4}$ to $\frac{23}{4}$ to give

$$\frac{23}{4} \times 8 = 8 \div 4 \times 23$$
$$= 2 \times 23$$
$$= 46$$

Equivalent fractions

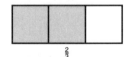   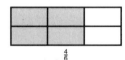

Equivalent fractions
represent the same portion
of a whole one.

The diagrams show that $\frac{2}{3}$ and $\frac{4}{6}$ represent the same fraction. They are called **equivalent fractions**.

All fractions belong to an unlimited set of equivalent fractions. For example,

$$\frac{2}{3} = \frac{4}{6} = \frac{6}{9} = \frac{8}{12} = \frac{10}{15} \cdots$$

When we **multiply** the **top** and **bottom** of a fraction by the **same number**, we get an **equivalent fraction**.

When the top and bottom of a fraction have a **common factor**, we can **divide both** by this and get an equivalent fraction. This process is called **cancelling**.

If we continue cancelling until there is no common factor, the fraction is in its **lowest terms**.

Each of these represents the same portion of a whole. The member of this set with the smallest numerator and denominator (in this case $\frac{2}{3}$) is said to be in **lowest terms**.

Any fraction can be converted into an equivalent fraction by multiplying top and bottom by the same number or, where possible, dividing top and bottom by the same number. For example,

$$\frac{2}{3} = \frac{2 \times 2}{3 \times 2} = \frac{4}{6}$$

$$\frac{6}{9} = \frac{6 \div 3}{9 \div 3} = \frac{2}{3}$$

Note

Your calculator always displays fractions in their lowest terms. For example, when you enter $\boxed{25}$ $\boxed{a^b/_c}$ $\boxed{35}$ $\boxed{=}$, the display will show $\frac{5}{7}$.

Ordering fractions

To decide on the order of size of a set of fractions, we convert them to equivalent fractions having the **same bottom line (common denominator)**.

For example, to decide which of $\frac{5}{6}$ and $\frac{7}{8}$ is the larger, we convert them to fractions with the **same denominator**. Both the 6 and the 8 can be converted to 24 (their LCM).

$\frac{5}{6} = \frac{20}{24}$ (Multiplying top and bottom by 4)

$\frac{7}{8} = \frac{21}{24}$ (Multiplying top and bottom by 3)

So $\frac{7}{8}$ is larger than $\frac{5}{6}$.

EXERCISE N4

1 Complete the following calculations.
  a $\frac{1}{4}$ of 24   **b** $\frac{3}{5}$ of 40   **c** $\frac{1}{6} \times 18$ **d** $\frac{4}{7} \times 21$ **e** $27 \times \frac{5}{9}$

2 Convert the following to improper fractions.
  a $6\frac{3}{4}$ **b** $4\frac{1}{3}$ **c** $3\frac{2}{5}$ **d** $5\frac{5}{6}$ **e** $11\frac{2}{7}$

3 Convert the following to mixed numbers.
  a $\frac{14}{3}$ **b** $\frac{17}{2}$ **c** $\frac{13}{6}$ **d** $\frac{19}{7}$ **e** $\frac{28}{5}$

4 Calculate the following.
  a $5\frac{1}{2} \times 6$ **b** $2\frac{3}{4} \times 12$ **c** $3\frac{2}{3} \times 15$ **d** $4\frac{2}{5} \times 10$

5 Cancel the following to their lowest terms.
  a $\frac{12}{18}$ **b** $\frac{15}{20}$ **c** $\frac{30}{50}$

6 Find the missing number in each of the following.
  a $\frac{3}{4} = \frac{?}{12}$ **b** $\frac{2}{3} = \frac{16}{?}$ **c** $\frac{15}{60} = \frac{3}{?}$

7 Place the following fractions in increasing order of size.
  a $\frac{3}{5}, \frac{5}{8}$ **b** $\frac{5}{9}, \frac{7}{12}$ **c** $\frac{2}{3}, \frac{7}{10}, \frac{3}{5}$

Adding and subtracting fractions

When adding or subtracting fractions, they should first be converted where necessary to equivalent fractions with a **common denominator**.

Where **mixed numbers** are involved, the safest approach is to **convert them to improper fractions before** adding or subtracting.

Fractions with the same denominator can easily be added or subtracted. For example,

$$\frac{2}{9} + \frac{5}{9} = \frac{7}{9}$$

When the fractions have different denominators, we find equivalent fractions so that the denominators are the same. For example,

$$\frac{5}{6} - \frac{7}{9}$$

Convert to fractions with denominator 18 (the LCM of 6 and 9) to give

$$\frac{5}{6} - \frac{7}{9} = \frac{15}{18} - \frac{14}{18}$$
$$= \frac{1}{18}$$

Multiplying fractions

Multiplying fractions gives

$$\frac{\text{Numerator} \times \text{Numerator}}{\text{Denominator} \times \text{Denominator}}$$

To multiply fractions, we simply multiply their numerators and their denominators. For example,

$$\frac{2}{3} \times \frac{4}{5} = \frac{2 \times 4}{3 \times 5} = \frac{8}{15}$$

Dividing fractions

When dividing fraction **turn the second fraction upside down and change ÷ to ×**.

Special cases:
- Always convert mixed numbers to improper fractions first.
- Whole numbers can be thought of as fractions with a denominator of 1.

Problems involving division can be converted to multiplication. For example,

$$\frac{3}{4} \div \frac{7}{8} = \frac{3}{4} \times \frac{8}{7}$$
$$= \frac{24}{28}$$
$$= \frac{6}{7} \quad \text{(Cancelling by 4)}$$

EXERCISE N5

Complete the following manually, then check the results using a calculator if possible.

1 Calculate the following.

   a $\frac{3}{4} + \frac{1}{8}$ **b** $\frac{5}{6} - \frac{1}{3}$ **c** $\frac{5}{6} - \frac{2}{9}$ **d** $\frac{7}{8} + \frac{5}{12}$ **e** $3\frac{3}{10} - 2\frac{2}{5}$

2 Calculate the following.

   a $\frac{4}{9} \times \frac{5}{7}$ **b** $\frac{2}{5} \times \frac{3}{8}$ **c** $1\frac{3}{8} \times \frac{2}{3}$ **d** $2\frac{4}{5} \times 1\frac{3}{7}$ **e** $6 \times \frac{4}{9}$

3 Calculate the following.

   a $\frac{2}{3} \div \frac{3}{4}$ **b** $\frac{3}{5} \div \frac{7}{10}$ **c** $1\frac{1}{4} \div \frac{1}{3}$ **d** $2\frac{5}{8} \div 1\frac{3}{4}$ **e** $2\frac{4}{9} \div 11$

4 Complete the following mixed calculations. Remember to do the operations in the correct order. See p. 6 if you need help.

   a $\frac{2}{3} + \frac{1}{2} \times 5$ **b** $\left(\frac{2}{3}\right)^2 - \frac{1}{6}$ **c** $\left(\frac{4}{5} + 2\frac{1}{2}\right) \div \left(4\frac{1}{4} - \frac{7}{12}\right)$ **d** $3\frac{2}{5} - 1\frac{3}{8} \div 1\frac{1}{4}$

N 04 Decimals

Place value

When we write a number, the value which a given digit represents depends on its position in the number. For example, in the number 385 the digit 3 represents 3 hundreds, the 8 represents 8 tens and the 5 represents 5 ones (units).

Each item is worth **ten items** in the position **to the right of it**.

The system is extended to allow us to indicate fractions. The fractional part is separated from the whole-number part by the **decimal point**. For example,

Each item is worth **one tenth of an item** in the position **to the left of it**.

Thousands 1000	Hundreds 100	Tens 10	Units 1	Tenths $\frac{1}{10}$	Hundredths $\frac{1}{100}$	Thousandths $\frac{1}{1000}$	Ten thousandths $\frac{1}{10000}$
3	7	5	2 .	8	6	4	1

Decimal point

In this example, the digit 8 represents 8 tenths ($\frac{8}{10}$), the digit 6 represents 6 hundredths ($\frac{6}{100}$) and so on.

Converting between fraction and decimal form

Using place value we can write fractions based on 10 in decimal form. For example,

$\frac{7}{10}$ can be written as 0.7

$\frac{3}{100}$ can be written as 0.03

$\frac{349}{1000}$ can be written as 0.349

We can also write decimals in fraction form. For example,

5.3 can be written as $5\frac{3}{10}$

0.55 can be written as $\frac{55}{100}$ and then cancelled to $\frac{11}{20}$

To convert a fraction to decimal form, **divide the top by the bottom**.

Fractions not based on 10 can be converted by dividing the top number (numerator) by the bottom number (denominator).

For example, to write $\frac{3}{8}$ in decimal form, we divide 3 by 8. This can bc done on a calculator or manually as follows. Notice that the 3 can be written as 3.000... with as many zeros as we need.

$$\begin{array}{r} 0\,.\,3\,7\,5 \\ 8\,\overline{\smash{\big)}\,3\,.\,{}^30^60^40} \end{array}$$

To show a recurring decimal, we put **dots above the digits which repeat**.

So $\frac{3}{8} = 0.375$

Sometimes the division never finishes and we get a **recurring decimal**. For example, write $\frac{7}{11}$ in decimal form.

If your calculator has a fraction key, you may find that pressing it repeatedly will cause the displayed number to switch between fraction and decimal form.

$$\begin{array}{r} 0\,.\,6\,3\,6\,3\,6\ldots \\ 11\,\overline{\smash{\big)}\,7\,.\,{}^70^40^70^40^70}\ldots \end{array}$$

So $\frac{7}{11} = 0.\dot{6}\dot{3}$

Adding and subtracting decimals

We must ensure that we add units to units, tenths to tenths etc. by **lining up the decimal points**. Extra zeros can be added as necessary. For example,

Add 234.97 and 15.6135

$$
\begin{array}{r}
2\ 3\ 4\ .\ 9\ 7\ 0\ 0 \\
+\ \ 1\ 5\ .\ 6\ 1\ 3\ 5 \\
\hline
2\,_1 5\,_1 0\ .\ 5\ 8\ 3\ 5
\end{array}
$$

Subtract 19.327 from 38.84

$$
\begin{array}{r}
{}^2 \cancel{3}{}^1 8\ .\ 8\,{}^3 \cancel{4}{}^1 0 \\
-\ 1\ 9\ .\ 3\ 2\ 7 \\
\hline
1\ 9\ .\ 5\ 1\ 3
\end{array}
$$

EXERCISE N6

1 In the number 3592.748 what is the value of
  a the digit 9   **b** the digit 7   **c** the digit 8   **d** the digit 4?

2 Write the following decimals in fraction form, simplifying where possible.
  a 2.7   **b** 0.24   **c** 35.05   **d** 0.875   **e** 1.85   **f** 0.075

3 Write the following fractions in decimal form, without using your calculator.
  a $\frac{3}{10}$ **b** $\frac{37}{100}$ **c** $3\frac{9}{10}$ **d** $14\frac{249}{1000}$

4 Convert the following fractions to decimals, without using your calculator.
  a $\frac{2}{5}$ **b** $\frac{5}{8}$ **c** $\frac{14}{25}$ **d** $\frac{1}{3}$ **e** $\frac{7}{12}$

5 Use your calculator to convert the following fractions to decimals.
  a $\frac{13}{16}$ **b** $\frac{23}{45}$ **c** $\frac{5}{7}$ **d** $3\frac{5}{9}$ **e** $\frac{1}{27}$

6 Complete the following calculations manually then check the results using your calculator.
  a $14.9 + 193.27$ **b** $58.21 - 24.715$
  c $2.95 + 0.536 + 12.7$ **d** $12.67 + 15.924 - 8.7041$

Multiplying and dividing by powers of ten

Multiplying 26.34 by 10 gives 263.4.

The 2 tens have become 2 hundreds, the 6 units have become 6 tens and so on. Each digit has moved one position higher in place value.

Rather than thinking of digits moving to the left, we usually think of the decimal point moving to the right.

Dividing by 10 has the opposite effect. For example, $46.79 \div 10 = 4.679$. Each digit moves one position lower in place value. We think of this as the decimal point moving one place to the left.

Multiplying or dividing by higher powers of ten just moves the decimal point further – one place for each 10 involved. For example,

$$2.673 \times 100 = 267.3$$
$$34.9 \times 1000 = 34\,900$$
$$2.89 \div 100 = 0.0289$$

Notice that where necessary we fill the gap between the decimal point and the digits with zeros to maintain place value.

Multiplying decimals

When multiplying decimals:

When multiplying decimals, we first multiply the numbers as if they were whole numbers, ignoring the decimal points. We then count the **total number** of decimal places in the numbers being multiplied and introduce the same number of decimal places into the answer. For example,

$$0.07 \times 0.013$$

1 Multiply as whole numbers.

Multiply

$$7 \times 13 = 91$$

2 Count the total number of decimal places in the question.

Count decimal places: 0.07 has 2 decimal places
0.013 has 3 decimal places

The answer should have $2 + 3 = 5$ decimal places

3 Introduce the same number of decimal places into the answer.

$$\Rightarrow \quad 0.07 \times 0.013 = 0.00091$$

Notice that when we multiply two numbers which are both smaller than 1, as in the above example, the result is smaller than either of them.

Dividing decimals

When dividing a decimal by a whole number, **line up the decimal points**.

When dividing a decimal by a whole number, we proceed as usual and line up the decimal point in the answer with the one in the question. For example, divide 36.589 by 7.

$$\begin{array}{r} 5.227 \\ 7{\overline{\smash{\big)}\,3\,6\,.^1 5^1 8^4 9}} \end{array}$$

When both numbers in a division problem are multiplied by the same number, the result is unchanged. For example,

$$8 \div 2 = 4 \quad \text{and} \quad 80 \div 20 = 4$$

When **dividing by a decimal**, multiply both numbers by the same power of 10 to make the **divisor a whole number**.

We use this fact when dividing **by** a decimal to change the problem into division by a whole number. Take, for example,

$$3.60942 \div 0.008$$

Multiply both numbers by 1000 to change the divisor to 8. The division then becomes

$$3609.42 \div 8$$

$$\begin{array}{r} 4\,5\,1\,.1\,7\,7\,5 \\ 8{\overline{\smash{\big)}\,3\,6^4 0\,9\,.^1 4^6 2^6 0^4 0}} \end{array}$$

So $3.60942 \div 0.008 = 451.1775$

EXERCISE N7

Complete the following calculations manually, then check the results using your calculator.

1 34.902×10	**2** 19.863×100	**3** 2.62×1000
4 0.00034×100	**5** $67.95 \div 10$	**6** $5.93 \div 1000$
7 $390 \div 100$	**8** $0.0617 \div 10000$	**9** 34.2×6

10 12.3×0.03 **11** 0.0045×1.1 **12** 1.82×0.00032

13 $253.782 \div 6$ **14** $36.427 \div 0.04$ **15** $0.0028756 \div 0.07$

16 $12.388 \div 1.6$

N 05 Percentages: introduction

Percentages are fractions expressed as hundredths.

Per cent means **in each hundred**. So for example, if you invest a sum of money in an account which pays 7% interest each year, this means that for every £100 you invest you will receive another £7 at the end of the first year.

The notation has changed over many years from the normal way of expressing hundredths as $/_{100}$ to the % sign now in every day use.

EXAMPLES

1 Anna invests £900 in an account which pays 4% interest each year. How much money will she receive in interest at the end of the first year?

4% means 4 for every hundred. Anna has £900 which is 9 hundreds. The interest is therefore $4 \times 9 = £36$.

2 Oliver has £450 in a savings account. At the end of one year he receives £27 in interest. What is the percentage interest paid on that account?

£450 is 4 and a half hundreds. Four and a half hundreds earn £27, so one hundred earns $27 \div 4.5 = 6$. So for every hundred pounds Oliver receives an additional £6. The rate of interest is therefore 6%.

3 A tub of margarine usually contains 600 g but a promotional tub offers '10% extra free!'. How much margarine is there in the promotional tub?

600 g is 6 hundreds and 10% means 10 for every hundred. So the extra is $6 \times 10 = 60$ g. The promotional tub contains 660 g altogether.

4 The offer on a box of washing powder is 780 g for the price of 650 g. What extra percentage is being offered free?

The offer is an extra 130 g on top of 650 g. 650 g is 6.5 hundreds. So the offer is $130 \div 6.5 = 20$ g for every hundred. The offer is 20% free.

EXERCISE N8

1 Calculate the interest payable on an investment of £550 when the rate of interest is 7%.

2 Calculate the rate of interest when an investment of £1300 earns £104 interest per year.

3 A television is in a sale which offers a 25% reduction. The television usually costs £900. What is the saving if it is bought in the sale?

4 The offer on a bottle of orange juice is 805 ml for the price of 700 ml. What extra percentage of juice is being offered free?

5 Martha buys a personal stereo, which usually costs £90, in a sale offering 15% off. How much money did she save by buying the stereo in the sale?

Converting percentages to fractions

To convert a percentage to a fraction, we write the percentage as a fraction over a hundred and then cancel where possible to leave the answer in its lowest terms.

EXAMPLE 5

Express 15% as a fraction in its lowest terms.

$$15\% \text{ means } \frac{15}{100}$$

$$= \frac{3}{20} \quad \text{(Dividing top and bottom by 5 to express in lowest terms)}$$

If the percentage itself contains a fraction, we must convert it into an equivalent fraction with whole numbers on the top and bottom before cancelling.

EXAMPLE 6

Express **a** $66\frac{2}{3}\%$ and **b** $8\frac{1}{2}\%$ as fractions in their lowest terms.

a $66\frac{2}{3}\%$ means $\dfrac{66\frac{2}{3}}{100}$

$$= \frac{200}{300} \quad \text{(Multiplying top and bottom by 3)}$$

$$= \frac{2}{3} \quad \text{(Dividing top and bottom by 100)}$$

b $8\frac{1}{2}\%$ means $\dfrac{8\frac{1}{2}}{100}$

$$= \frac{17}{200} \quad \text{(Multiplying top and bottom by 2)}$$

Nothing cancels, so the fraction is already in its lowest terms.

When a fraction is a mixed number, the percentage will be more than 100%.

EXAMPLE 7

Express 445% as a fraction in its lowest terms.

Writing 445% as $\dfrac{445}{100}$

$$= \frac{89}{20} \quad \text{(Cancelling by 5)}$$

$$= 4\frac{9}{20} \quad \text{in its lowest terms}$$

EXERCISE N9

Express the following percentages as fractions in their lowest terms.

1 5%   **2** 55%   **3** 125%   **4** $33\frac{1}{3}$%   **5** 65%

6 530%   **7** $52\frac{1}{2}$%   **8** 80%   **9** $12\frac{1}{2}$%   **10** 19%

Converting percentages to decimals

This is not so difficult if you know that the value of the second decimal place is hundredths. For example,

$$4\% \text{ means } \frac{4}{100} = 0.04$$

Dividing by 100 can be thought of as equivalent to 'moving the decimal point' two places to the left. So, for example,

$$23\% = 0.23 \quad \text{and} \quad 415\% = 4.15$$

$$7\frac{3}{4}\% \text{ means } \frac{(7 + 3 \div 4)}{100} = 0.0775$$

$$18.25\% \text{ means } \frac{18.25}{100} = 0.1825$$

EXERCISE N10

Express the following percentages as decimals.

1 11%   **2** 50%   **3** 9%   **4** 65.3%   **5** 8.3%   **6** $51\frac{1}{2}$%   **7** 125%   **8** $213\frac{1}{3}$%

Converting decimals to percentages

This is simply the reverse process of the above – we multiply the decimal by 100. This can be done by 'moving the decimal point' two places to the right. For example,

$$0.17 = 17\%$$
$$0.1235 = 12.35\%$$
$$3.165 = 316.5\%$$

Converting fractions to percentages

To convert a fraction to a percentage, we multiply it by 100%.

EXAMPLE 8

Write **a** $\frac{3}{20}$ and **b** $\frac{3}{7}$ as percentages.

a $\frac{3}{20} \times 100\%$

$= 3 \times 5\%$ (Cancelling by 20)

$= 15\%$

b $\frac{3}{7} \times 100\%$

$= \frac{300}{7}\%$ (No cancelling possible)

$= 42\frac{6}{7}\%$ or 42.86% (2 dp)

The following table shows the more commonly used percentages with their fraction and decimal equivalents.

Those in **bold** type are particularly useful.

Fraction		Decimal
$\frac{1}{10}$	10%	0.1
$\frac{1}{5}$	20%	0.2
$\frac{1}{4}$	**25%**	**0.25**
$\frac{3}{10}$	30%	0.3
$\frac{1}{3}$	**$33\frac{1}{3}$%**	**0.3̇**
$\frac{2}{5}$	40%	0.4
$\frac{1}{2}$	**50%**	**0.5**
$\frac{3}{5}$	60%	0.6
$\frac{2}{3}$	**$66\frac{2}{3}$%**	**0.6̇**
$\frac{7}{10}$	70%	0.7
$\frac{3}{4}$	**75%**	**0.75**
$\frac{4}{5}$	80%	0.8
$\frac{9}{10}$	90%	0.9

EXERCISE N11

Convert the following to percentages.

1 0.35   **2** $\frac{3}{10}$ **3** 0.875   **4** $\frac{9}{25}$ **5** $\frac{3}{5}$

6 2.25   **7** $\frac{17}{20}$ **8** $\frac{11}{12}$ **9** 0.6532   **10** $\frac{2}{3}$

Putting numbers in order of size

Strictly speaking, these are vulgar fractions, decimals fractions and percentages.

There are three ways of expressing numbers which are smaller than one whole – commonly referred to as fractions, decimals and percentages. If we are given an assortment of these and are asked to place them in order of size, we need to compare them in the same form. The easiest way to do this is to use the methods shown so far and convert all of the numbers into percentages.

The numbers could be compared in decimal form if you prefer.

EXAMPLE 9

Write these in order of size, smallest first: 78%, $\frac{7}{8}$, 0.708.

$$\frac{7}{8} = 7 \div 8 \times 100$$
$$= 87.5\%$$
$$0.708 \times 100 = 70.8\%$$

So in order of size the numbers are 0.708, 78% and $\frac{7}{8}$.

EXERCISE N12

Place the following in order of size, smallest first.

1 0.875 $\frac{7}{9}$ 88%   **2** 45% $\frac{2}{5}$ 0.49 $\frac{4}{9}$

3 $\frac{3}{7}$ 54%   0.44   **4** 85%   0.881 $\frac{11}{13}$

N 06 Units of measurement

Counting and measuring

Some numbers we get by counting, for example: 'How many people get on a train?'

Other number we have to get by measuring, for example: 'How long is that line?'

The number of people travelling on a train is always an **integer** (whole number). The line can be any length.

When we count, we have a number of discrete values – the integers – to which the result is restricted. When we measure, the value is not restricted.

Note The accuracy of instruments used to make a measurement may restrict what the result could be.

All measurements are **continuous**. They can take **any value**.

A **continuous variable** is one that can take any value.

There are two systems of measurement currently used in the UK, the **metric** and the **imperial**, but metric units will soon have replaced all but a few imperial units.

Metric system

Metric system

Distance   1 metre

Mass   1 gram

Capacity   1 litre

Prefixes for decimal multiples

mega	M	1 000 000
kilo	k	1000
deca	da	10
deci	d	$\frac{1}{10}$
centi	c	$\frac{1}{100}$
milli	m	$\frac{1}{1000}$
micro	μ	$\frac{1}{1\,000\,000}$

Note this exception:
1 megagram = 1000 kilograms = **1 tonne**

The term 'megagram' is never used.

Imperial system

Length

1 inch (in)
12 inches = 1 foot (ft)
3 feet = 1 yard (yd)
1760 yards = 1 mile

Mass

1 ounce (oz)
16 ounces = 1 pound (lb)
14 pounds = 1 stone (st)
8 stones = 1 hundredweight (cwt)
20 cwt = 1 ton

Capacity

1 pint
8 pints = 1 gallon (gal)

Equivalents

Length

1 in	is about	2.54 cm
1 ft	is about	30 cm
1 m	is about	39 in
8 km	is about	5 miles

Metric system

Three commonly used metric units are

Distance   1 metre | A long stride is about 1 metre |

Mass   1 gram | A 1p coin is about 4 g |

Capacity   1 litre | Three cans of cola are about 1 litre |

Decimal multiples of units are named by adding the prefixes listed at the side.

EXERCISE N13

1 How many millimetres are in 1 metre?

2 How many centilitres are in 1 litre?

3 How many grams are in 1 kilogram?

4 How many millimetres are in 1 centimetre?

5 How many centimetres are in 1 kilometre?

Imperial system

Some of the imperial units still in daily use are shown at the side.

Equivalents

You should take notice of the sizes of common things (items in your kitchen or shop) and compare metric and imperial measurements. Do not just buy a bag of sugar – see how heavy it is. Is it measured in metric or imperial units? Is the value quoted a 'neat' number or is it an awkward one?

EXERCISE N14

Choose the correct value for each of the following measurements.

1 The mass of a standard sliced loaf.
  a 50 g   **b** 100 g   **c** 800 g   **d** 2 kg

2 The mass of a standard (not large) jar of instant coffee.
  a 30 g   **b** 100 g   **c** 750 g   **d** 1 kg

3 The length of a cricket pitch.
  a 20 m   **b** 50 m   **c** 100 m   **d** 150 m

4 The capacity of a standard can of soft drink.
  a 30 ml   **b** 100 ml   **c** 330 ml   **d** 500 ml

Converting units

To convert from one unit to another you need to know

- the conversion factor
- whether to multiply to divide by the conversion factor.

Remember that | a large number of small things | is the same as | a small number of large things

If you want | a **larger** number of **smaller** things | then | [**multiply**]

If you want | a **smaller** number of **larger** things | then | [**divide**]

Mass
1 lb	is about	454 g
1 kg	is about	2.2 lb
1 tonne	is about	1 ton

Capacity
1 pt	is about	570 ml
1 gal	is about	4.5 l

Converting units
To convert from one unit to another you need to know

- the conversion factor
- whether to multiply or divide by the conversion factor.

If you want	Then
a **larger** number of **smaller** things	multiply
a **smaller** number of **larger** things	divide

EXAMPLE 1

Convert 6342.592 g into kg.

Step 1 Find the conversion factor   There are 1000 g in 1 kg.

Step 2 Do you multiply or divide?   As a kilogram is **larger** than a gram, we want a **smaller** number of **larger** things. So, we divide.

$$6342.592 \, g = \frac{6342.592}{1000} \, kg = 6.342\,592 \, kg$$

EXERCISE N15

Convert the following metric measurements to the form given.

1 2.14 m to cm   **2** 3.56 l to cl   **3** 3826 g to kg

4 1.56 tonnes to kg   **5** 456 mm to cm   **6** 3298 ml to l

7 243 cl to ml   **8** 56.39 kg to g   **9** 2.698 km to m

Write the following imperial measurements in the form given.

10 98 in in ft and in   **11** 57 ft in yd and ft   **12** 10 st 12 lb in lb

13 45 pt in gal and pt   **14** 76 oz in lb and oz   **15** 3000 yd in miles and yd

Area

Metric system
100 mm^2	= 1 cm^2
10 000 cm^2	= 1 m^2
1 000 000 m^2	= 1 km^2
100 m^2	= 1 are
100 are	= 1 hectare (ha)
10 000 m^2	= 1 hectare

Imperial system
144 in^2	= 1 ft^2
9 ft^2	= 1 yd^2
4840 yd^2	= 1 acre

Area

The standard unit of area in either system is the square, whose side is the base unit of length. In the metre system it is the unit square which measures 1 metre by 1 metre. This is called 1 square metre (1 m^2).

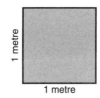

For small measurements, the unit square of 1 cm by 1 cm – 1 square cm (1 cm^2) – is often preferred. For large areas, a more conveniently sized unit is 1 km^2.

In the imperial system, the units of area are the square inch, square foot, square yard etc.

Measuring land area

For measuring the area of fields, units such as the square metre are too small, while others such as the square kilometre are too large. In the metric system, a more conveniently sized unit is defined for this purpose. This is the **are**, which is 10 m by 10 m. Land area is normally given in units of 100 ares, where

100 are = 1 hectare   (hecto = 100)

1 hectare is about the size of 2 football pitches.

In the Imperial system, the unit is the **acre**.

1 acre = 4840 square yards

Volume

Metric system
$$1000\,mm^3 = 1\,cm^3$$
$$1\,000\,000\,cm^3 = 1\,m^3$$
$$1\,000\,000\,000\,m^3 = 1\,km^3$$

Imperial system
$$1728\,in^3 = 1\,ft^3$$
$$27\,ft^3 = 1\,yd^3$$

Volume

In the metric system the unit of volume is the cube whose edge is 1 metre, as shown. This is called 1 cubic metre ($1\,m^3$).

Similarly, there is $1\,cm^3$.

In the imperial system the units of volume are

1 cubic inch ($1\,in^3$)
1 cubic foot ($1\,ft^3$)
1 cubic yard ($1\,yd^3$)

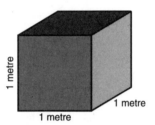

Capacity and volume
1 litre = 1000 cm³
1 ml = 1 cm³

Capacity and volume in the metric system

Capacity usually refers to liquid measure and **volume** to solid measure. In the metric system, there is an equivalence between these.

1 litre = 1000 cm³   So 1 ml = 1 cm³

Converting area and volume measures

The method is as before. The trick is to find the conversion factor.

EXAMPLE 2

Find the conversion factor to convert between square cm and square m.

Each side of a metre square can be divided into 100 cm. So, there are

100×100 $1\,cm^2$ squares in the metre square
$1\,m^2 = 1000\,cm^2$

EXERCISE N16

Convert the following metric measurements to the form given.

1 $2.58\,m^2$ to cm^2 **2** $62.4\,cm^2$ to mm^2 **3** $28\,351\,245\,m^2$ to km^2

4 $5982\,mm^2$ to cm^2 **5** $3.28\,km^2$ to m^2 **6** $43\,829\,561\,cm^2$ to m^2

7 $9.73\,m^3$ to cm^3 **8** $5.39\,m^3$ to litres **9** $62\,951$ litres to m^3

Convert the following imperial measurements to the form given

10 $3\,ft^2$ to in^2 **11** $34\,yd^2$ to ft^2 **12** $189\,ft^2$ to yd^2

13 $2.5\,yd^2$ to in^2 **14** $816\,480\,in^3$ to yd^3 **15** $6\,yd^3$ to ft^3

Time

The units of time are defined as follows:

> 60 seconds = 1 minute
> 60 minutes = 1 hour
> 24 hours = 1 day

The 12-hour clock

In the 12-hour system, there are two starting points – midnight and midday. So any time value occurs twice in 1 day, once in the morning (am) and once in the afternoon (pm). To indicate the minutes, we use two more digits, separated from the hours by a point.

So we write, for example, 9.28 am, 12.05 pm, 3.43 pm.

The 24-hour clock

In the 24-hour system there is only on starting point – midnight. Four digits are used to indicate the time:

> two for the hours between 00 and 23,
> two for the minutes between 00 and 59.

There is no separation between the hours and minutes.

So we write, for example, 0928, 1205, 1543.

Note

We write 12.15 pm for 1215, and 12.15 am for 0015.

EXAMPLE 3

A train leaves London at 1037 and arrives in Edinburgh at 1542. How long did the journey take?

		Hours	Minutes
Break it down into	1037 to 1100		23
easy stages	1100 to 1500	4	
	1500 to 1542		42
	Total	4	65
But	65 minutes is	1 h 5 min	
So the total journey time is		5 h 5 min	

Sidebar:

60 seconds = 1 minute
60 minutes = 1 hour
24 hours = 1 day

12-hour clock		24-hour clock
12.00 am	Midnight	0000
1.00 am		0100
2.00 am		0200
3.00 am		0300
4.00 am		0400
5.00 am		0500
6.00 am		0600
7.00 am		0700
8.00 am		0800
9.00 am		0900
10.00 am		1000
11.00 am		1100
12.00 am	Midday	1200
1.00 pm		1300
2.00 pm		1400
3.00 pm		1500
4.00 pm		1600
5.00 pm		1700
6.00 pm		1800
7.00 pm		1900
8.00 pm		2000
9.00 pm		2100
10.00 pm		2200
11.00 pm		2300
12.00 pm	Midnight	0000

12 hour clock has a point to divide hours from minutes. 24 hour clock has no point.

Note. The point in the 12-hour clock is **not a decimal point**. The numbers after it are sixtieths of an hour, not hundredths.

EXERCISE N17

1 Convert the following from the 12-hour clock to the 24-hour clock.

   a 3.24 pm   **b** 8.48 pm   **c** 12.54 am

2 Convert the following from the 24-hour clock to 12-hour clock.

   a 0025   **b** 1938   **c** 0742

3 A driver starts his journey from Birmingham to Torquay at 7.25 am and arrives at 2.48 pm. How long did the journey take?

Fractions of an hour
Decimal parts of 1 hour can be easily expressed in minutes and seconds.

$$0.1\,h = 0.1 \times 60\,min = 6\,min$$
$$0.25\,h = 0.25 \times 60\,min = 15\,min$$

To convert a **decimal** part of an hour to minutes, **multiply the decimal part by 60**.

To convert a **decimal** part of a minute to seconds, **multiply the decimal part by 60**.

To convert from minutes to a **decimal** part of an hour, **divide by 60**.

To convert from seconds to a **decimal** part of a minute, **divide by 60**.

EXAMPLE 4

Convert 3.14 h to hours, minutes and seconds.

$$0.14\,h \quad \Rightarrow \quad 0.14 \times 60\,min = 8.4\,min$$

To convert the 0.4 min into seconds, multiply by 60 again:

$$0.4\,min = 0.4 \times 60\,s = 24\,s$$

So 3.14 h = 3 h 8.4 min = 3 h 8 min 24 s

To convert from hours, minutes and seconds to hours and decimal parts of an hour, reverse the process and divide. There are three ways this can be achieved using a calculator. **Note** some calculators **do not have these facilities**.

EXAMPLE 5

Convert 4 h 34 min to its decimal form.

Note that this means $\quad 4 + \frac{34}{60} = 4.5\dot{6}$ hours

  i Using the normal $\boxed{+}$ and $\boxed{\div}$ keys:

      4 $\boxed{+}$ 34 $\boxed{\div}$ 60 $\boxed{=}$

  ii Using the fraction key: $\boxed{a^b/_c}$

      4 $\boxed{a^b/_c}$ 34 $\boxed{a^b/_c}$ 60 $\boxed{a^b/_c}$

  iii Using the minute/second conversion key $\boxed{\circ\,{'}\,{''}}$:

      4 $\boxed{\circ\,{'}\,{''}}$ 34 $\boxed{\circ\,{'}\,{''}}$

Experiment with these keys if you have not used them before. Also experiment with the (inv), (shift) or (2nd) functions.

EXERCISE N18

1 Convert these hours and minutes into decimal parts of hours.

   a 2 h 52 min   **b** 7 h 24 min   **c** 23 h 36 min

2 Convert these decimal times into hours and minutes.

   a 2.65 h   **b** 9.45 h   **c** 19.7 h

3 Find the differences between these times.

   a 1428 − 0935   **b** 0549 − 0147   **c** 0238 − 2241

N 07 Approximation

All measurements are approximate. We express them correct to

● the nearest ...
● ... decimal places
● ... significant figures

We can never measure quantities with 100% accuracy and so we have to **approximate** the results.

We use methods such as: the nearest whole number
                            the nearest 100 000
                            3 decimal places
                            4 significant figures

When rounding a number;

1 identify the **target** digit
2 check the **next** digit
3 if the next digit

is	0, 1, 2, 3, 4	5, 6, 7, 8, 9
then	round **down**	round **up**.

The procedure is

Step 1 Find the **target** digit.
Step 2 Look at the **next** digit.
Step 3 Adjust the number according to the size of this next digit.

If the **next** digit is	0, 1, 2, 3, 4	5, 6, 7, 8, 9
the number is	in the **lower** half of the interval	in the **upper** half of the interval
so	round **down**	round **up**

EXAMPLE 1

Write the number 83 462 correct to the nearest thousand.

Step 1 Find the 1000s digit: 8 3̲ 4 6 2

Step 2 Check the next digit: The next digit is 4.

Step 3 Adjust the number: 8 3 0 0 0   (to the nearest 1000)

Note

● The 'next' digit is less than 5 so the number is closer to 83 000 than 84 000.
  It is in the **lower** half of the interval.
● **Three extra zeros are needed** to show where the decimal point is. Without
  them, the number would be only 83.

EXERCISE N19

Write these numbers correct to **a** the nearest 100, **b** the nearest 10 000, **c** the nearest 1 000 000.

1 5 673 863	**2** 9 573 852	**3** 4 657 358
4 7 438 926	**5** 2 344 678	**6** 3 141 592

Decimal places

> The **first decimal place** is the **first position after the decimal point**.

The rounding process is exactly the same when we require decimal places. To find the target digit, we count **from the decimal point**.

EXAMPLE 2

Write the number 38.4239 correct to 3 decimal places.

Step 1 Find the target digit   3 8 . 4 2 ⒊ 9

Step 2 Check the next digit   The next digit is 9.

Step 3 Adjust the number   3 8 . 4 2 4   (to 3 dp)

Note
- The 'next digit' is 5 or more, so the number is closer to 38.424 than to 38.423. It is in the **upper** half of the interval.
- **Extra zeros** are **not** needed because we know where the decimal point is.

EXERCISE N20

Write the following numbers correct to **a** 2 decimal places, **b** 1 decimal place, **c** 3 decimal places.

1 18.462 8	**2** 1.414 21	**3** 452.176 2
4 7.335 4	**5** 112.785 5	**6** 85.747 3
7 394.857 2	**8** 25.725 6	**9** 3.141 59
10 34.638 2	**11** 2.718 28	**12** 923.684 9

Significant figures

Significant means **important**.

> The first **significant figure** is the first **figure** that is not zero.

The **first** significant figure is the first figure that is **not zero**.
The **second** significant figure is the next figure to the right.
And so on... .

EXAMPLE 3

Write 32.487 2 correct to 3 significant figures.

Step 1 Find the target digit   3   2 . ⒋ 8   7   2

Step 2 Check the next digit   The next digit is 8.

Step 3 Adjust the number   3   2 . 5   (to 3 sf)

EXAMPLE 4

Write 48.635 correct to 3 significant figures.

Step 1 Find the target digit   4 8 6̄ 3 5

Step 2 Check the next digit   The next digit is 3.

Step 3 Adjust the number   4 8 6 0 0   (to 3 sf)

Note

- The 'next digit' is 5 or more in Example 3, so the number is closer to 32.5 than to 32.4. It is in the **upper** half of the interval. In Example 4, the number is in the **lower** half of the interval.
- **Extra zeros** are **not** needed in Example 3 because we know where the decimal point is. In Example 4, we needed 2 extra zeros to indicate where the decimal point is.

Zeros

A zero in a number has one of two functions:

- to show the position of the decimal point
- to be a significant digit

EXAMPLE 5

0.**0**350   This zero shows the position of the decimal point

0.035**0**   This zero does not show the position of the decimal point. It is significant and shows that the number is correct to 3 significant figures

---

EXAMPLE 6

Write 1.039 72 correct to 4 significant figures.

Step 1 Find the target digit: 1 . 0 3 9 7 2

Step 2 Check the next digit: The next digit is 7.

Step 3 Adjust the number: 1 . 0 4 0   (to 4 sf)

Note: Both zeros are significant.

EXERCISE N21

Write these numbers correct to **a** 2 significant figures, **b** 1 significant figure, **c** 3 significant figures.

1 82 693	**2** 0.837 25	**3** 34.968 1
4 0.019 452	**5** 9.794 19	**6** 437.8
7 81.73	**8** 147.963	**9** 0.008 3629

A zero can either show the position of the decimal point, or be a significant digit.

A zero as the first digit of a decimal fraction or at the end of an integer is not significant.

In a decimal number, all zeros after the first significant figure **and** after the decimal point **must be significant**.

Accuracy of measurement

Measurements are never 100% accurate and it is necessary to decide what is a **sensible** value to quote.

The distance to London would be better expressed as 125 miles.

London
123 miles
875 yards
2 feet 7 inches

A recipe that asked for 147.62 g of flour or 1.48 eggs would not be sensible.

Sale Price – £1299.99 is equally not sensible but is used for psychological reasons.

In most circumstances, measurements need only be accurate to **3 significant figures**. Sometimes fewer are sufficient and sometimes 4 or 5 are required.

EXERCISE N22

Write the following values more sensibly.

1 The Eurostar train took 2 hours 58 minutes 36.79 seconds to travel from London to Paris.

2 The distance from London to Manchester is 199 miles 275 yards.

3 Make this dress – you only need 2.769 m^2 of material!

4 $\sqrt{2} = 1.414\,2136$.

Intervals and errors

When we quote a number with a degree of accuracy, there is always a range of possible values for it. For example:

The number of people ... was 15 400, correct to the nearest 100.

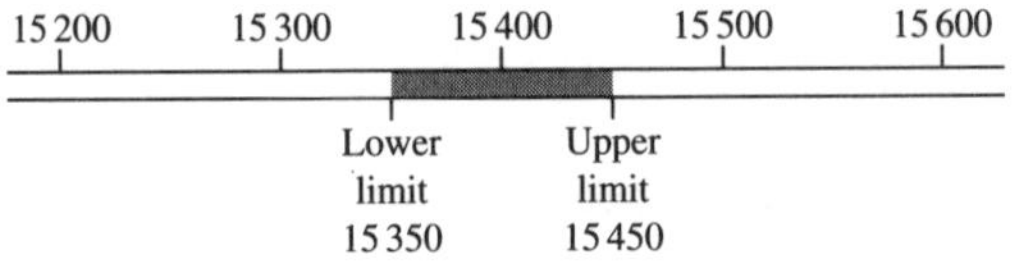

```
  15 200     15 300     15 400     15 500     15 600
    |          |          |          |          |
  ──┴──────────┴──────────┴██████████┴──────────┴──
                        Lower      Upper
                        limit      limit
                        15 350     15 450
```

The correct value could lie anywhere between 15 350 and 15 450, but not **exactly** equal to 15 450. In other words, 15 350 ⩽ correct value < 15 450.

In the example, the **maximum error** in quoting the value as 15 400 is 50 people.

Sidebar notes:

Always quote the accuracy of your measurements and calculations.

Choose a **sensible** value.

In most cases, **3 significant figures** are sufficient.

All quoted values are representative of a range of values. The value quoted is **usually** in the centre of the range.

So, for example, 6.7 cm really means any value between 6.65 cm and 6.75 cm, or

6.65 cm ⩽ value < 6.75 cm

In general:

Accuracy	Maximum error
nearest 1000	500
nearest 100	50
nearest 10	5
1 decimal place	0.05
2 decimal places	0.005
3 decimal places	0.0005
1 significant figure	5 in the 2nd figure place-value
2 significant figures	5 in the 3rd figure place-value

> The **maximum error** is half of the quoted accuracy.

The maximum error is always half of the level of accuracy stated.

EXERCISE N23

What are the maximum possible errors in the following measurements?

1 The length of a line is 9 cm.

2 A person contains 8 pints of blood.

3 The number of people attending a football match was 15 600 to the nearest hundred.

Errors in calculation

> Your answer can never be **more accurate** than the **least accurate** of the numbers in the calculation.

When a series of calculations are performed with rounded values, the maximum possible error increases with every calculation. So be careful not to claim an unjustified degree of accuracy in your answers.

Find the accuracy of the numbers in the calculation and choose the least accurate of these.

> **Note** When a number in a calculation is the result of **counting**, it should be 100% accurate.
> So, if we have 5 pieces of wood, each 1.57 m long, the least accurate number is 1.57. The answer should be given to 3 significant figures.

EXAMPLE 7

4.2×3.124

4.2 is accurate to 2 significant figures   ← Least accurate number

3.124 is accurate to 4 significant figures

The answer given by a calculator is 13.1208.
This should be quoted to **2 significant figures**. It is 13 (to 2 sf)

If you are in any doubt about how accurately to quote a result, particularly when you do not know the accuracy of the numbers in the calculation, then **3 significant figures** are usually sufficient.

N 08 Estimation and calculation

We often need to make a rough estimate of a calculation before finding the accurate answer, or sometimes just to see how large the result is likely to be.

1 Write each value correct to **1 significant figure**.

2 Perform the calculation in your head or on paper using the **rounded values**.

The idea is quickly to get a feel for the **size** of the result. It does not have to be accurate.

One way is to approximate each value to 1 significant figure and then perform a calculation in our head, approximating each result as we go.

Do not waste time trying to get an accurate result. You need a quick answer just to get a feel for the magnitude of the correct result.

> **EXAMPLE 1**
>
> $$\frac{485 \times 7.942}{62.24} \quad \text{would become} \quad \frac{500 \times 8}{60}$$
>
> $$\approx \frac{4000}{60}$$
>
> $$\approx 70$$

EXERCISE N24

In questions 1–6, round each of the numbers to 1 significant figure and use these values to find a rough estimate of the correct result for each expression.

1 52.34×769.2

2 0.0264×0.8423

3 $638.9 \div 18.523$

4 $\dfrac{48.62 \times 632.9}{37.26 \times 9.83}$

5 $\dfrac{5.27^2 \times \sqrt{62.47}}{1.852 \times 9.853}$

6 $\dfrac{\sqrt{16.94} \times 7.26^2}{1.973^3 \times \sqrt{29.27}}$

In questions 7–14, the decimal point has been omitted from the result of each calculation. By making a rough estimate of each result decide on the position of the decimal point.

7 $\sqrt{856.3} = 29\,262\,604$

8 $0.064\,58^2 = 41\,705\,764$

9 $9.872 \times 5.294 = 5226\,237$

10 $486.57 \div 5.19 = 93\,751\,445$

11 $\dfrac{15.258 \times 49.643}{0.139 \times 0.0473} = 11\,520\,722$

12 $\dfrac{0.257 \times 739.2}{56.38 \times 19.94} = 1689\,837$

13 $8.942^3 = 71\,499\,663$

14 $\dfrac{\sqrt{95.42} \times 56.78^2}{\sqrt{0.0735} \times 529.8} = 2192\,577$

15 In a pop festival, 87 952 people paid £57 each for a ticket. What was the approximate total income for the event?

Trial and improvement

1 Estimate a solution.
2 Test it.
3 Try to improve the estimate.

Try integer values first, making them more accurate as you go along.

We can solve some problems by guessing an answer and then seeing how wrong we are. This enables us to improve the guess. We repeat this process until we obtain an accurate answer or an answer accurate enough for our purpose.

This process is called **trial and improvement**.

EXAMPLE 2

What is the cube root of 100?

1 | Try a rough search |

Number	4	5
Cube	64	125

The answer must lie somewhere between 4 and 5.

2 | Improve your Estimate |

Try 4.5: $4.5^3 = 91.125$ Too small
Try 4.7: $4.7^3 = 103.823$ Too large
Try 4.6: $4.6^3 = 97.336$ Too small
Try 4.65: $4.65^3 = 100.544\,63$ Too large

You carry on in this way until either

- your solution is accurate, or
- your solution is sufficiently accurate for your purpose.

EXERCISE N25

1 Find the cube root of 400 correct to 2 decimal places.

2 Use a trial-and-improvement method to find the square root of 0.5 correct to 3 decimal places.

3 I choose a positive number.
I square it.
I then add the number I started with.
The result is 1.

Use a trial-and-improvement method to find my number correct to 3 decimal places.

4 I choose a positive number.
I square it.
I then subtract the number I started with.
The result is 1.

Use a trial-and-improvement method to find my number correct to 3 decimal places.

5 What do I get if I multiply together the final results of questions 3 and 4?

N 09 Ratio and proportion

Ratio is a way of comparing two or more numbers (or quantities).

: means 'compared with'

15 m compared with 25 m is a ratio which can be written as 15 : 25.

Ratios are usually expressed in their simplest integer (whole number) form

Ratios can be simplified in the same way as fractions are cancelled. For example,

$\frac{15}{25} = \frac{3}{5}$ (Cancelling by 5)

In the same way, 15 : 25 = 3 : 5 expressed in its simplest form.

Ratios **never** include units of measurement but the quantities **must** be in the same units when the ratio is expressed in order to compare like with like.

(£1 to £10 and £1 to 10p are obviously not both the same as 1 : 10!)

Ratios can be **multiplied up** as well as cancelled in order to express them in integer form

---

EXAMPLES

1 Express £100 : £275 as a ratio in its simplest form.

$$£100 : £275$$
$$= 100 : 275 \quad \text{(Leaving out the units)}$$
$$= 4 : 11 \quad \text{(Cancelling by 25)}$$

2 Express the ratio 5p to £25 as a ratio in its simplest form.

$$5p : £25$$
$$= 5p : 2500p \quad \text{(Expressing the quantities in the same units)}$$
$$= 5 : 2500 \quad \text{(Leaving out the units)}$$
$$= 1 : 500 \quad \text{(Cancelling by 5)}$$

3 Express the ratio $\frac{2}{3}$ to $\frac{3}{10}$ as a ratio in its simplest form.

$$\frac{2}{3} : \frac{3}{10} \quad \text{(Find the LCM of the denominators)}$$
$$\frac{2}{3} \times 30 : \frac{3}{10} \times 30 \quad \text{(Multiply both by the LCM)}$$
$$= 20 : 9 \quad \text{(Already in its simplest form)}$$

4 Express the ratio 0.75 : 2.25 in its simplest form.

$$0.75 : 2.25$$
$$= 75 : 225 \quad (\times 100 \text{ to express in integer form})$$
$$= 15 : 45 \quad \text{(Cancelling by 25)}$$
$$= 1 : 3 \quad \text{(Cancelling by 15)}$$

Ratios are used to show the relative amounts needed when various ingredients are combined in some set way to produce the correct mixture.

For example, flaky pastry can be made from 8 oz of flour, 4 oz of margarine and 2 oz of lard. This simplifies from 8 : 4 : 2 to 4 : 2 : 1, which means for a given amount of lard you need twice as much margarine and four times as much flour. Knowing this we can make smaller or greater quantities of flaky pastry than the original recipe intended:

Flour	*Marg*	*Lard*
800 g	400 g	200 g
16 kg	8 kg	4 kg

EXERCISE N26

1 Express each as a ratio in its simplest terms.

   a 35 : 45   **b** 2.9 : 8.7   **c** $\frac{3}{4} : \frac{5}{12}$

2 Express each as a ratio in its simplest form.

   a 6 litres to 21 litres   **b** £4 to 65p   **c** 25 mm to 3 m

3 This year Tony is 38 years old and his daughter, Joanna, is 14 years old. Express their ages as a ratio in its simplest terms

   a this year,   **b** in 6 years

4 A potting compost is mixed from 4 kg of peat, 6 kg of loam and 8 kg of sand.

   a Express this as a ratio in its simplest form.

   b How many kilograms of loam are needed to make a smaller amount which uses 1 kg of peat and 2 kg of sand?

Dividing a quantity in a given ratio

Express the ratio in its **simplest form**.

Add the components of the ratio to get the total number of parts.

Divide the amount by this total to obtain the value of one part.

Multiply the components of the ratio by the value of one part to get the amounts.

Always check that the amounts which you have calculated add up to the original total.

EXAMPLE 5

Alice, Bob and Cherry are aged 15, 21 and 28 respectively. They receive £200 which is to be shared in the same ratio as their ages. Calculate the amount each will receive.

$$15 : 21 : 28 \quad \text{(ratio of their ages)}$$
$$= 5 : 7 : 8 \quad \text{(cancelling by 3)}$$

We now add these together to find the number of parts into which the £200 must be divided.

$$5 + 7 + 8 = 20 \text{ 'parts'}$$

One 'part' is worth £200 ÷ 20 = £10
Alice receives 5 'parts' $5 \times £10 = £50$
Bob receives 7 'parts' $7 \times £10 = £70$
Cherry receives 8 'parts' $8 \times £10 = £80$

(Check: £50 + £70 + £80 = £200)

EXERCISE N27

1 I divide my daily activities of sleeping, working and leisure in the ratio of $3 : 4 : 5$. How many hours do I spend each day doing each activity?

2 Aneena, Baljit and Carlos form a syndicate to pool their winnings on National Lottery tickets. Each week Aneena buys 7 tickets, Baljit buys 10 tickets and Carlos buys 5 tickets. One week they win £1100 and the winnings are shared in the same ratio as the number of tickets each buys. How much does each person receive?

3 An allotment is shared by Meg and Jack in the ratio of $3 : 7$. How much area does Jack have if Meg's share is $27 \, \text{m}^2$?

4 An alloy is formed by combining aluminium, zinc and copper in the ratio $1 : 2 : 11$. How much alloy can be produced using 5 kg of zinc?

Map scales

Map scales are always expressed in the form $1 : n$, not in their simplest integer form.

For example, a scale of $1 : 2.5$ would be used rather than $2 : 5$.

When a ratio is used to describe the scale of a map, it is usually given in the form $1 : n$, where n represents the number of units of real distance represented by one unit on the map.

EXAMPLE 6

A map is drawn using a scale whereby 3 cm represents a distance of 150 m. Express this scale in the form $1 : n$. What distance, in metres, is represented on the map by 7 cm?

$$3 \, \text{cm} : 150 \, \text{m}$$
$$= 3 \, \text{cm} : 15\,000 \, \text{cm} \quad \text{(in the same units)}$$
$$= 3 : 15\,000 \quad \text{(omitting the units)}$$
$$= 1 : 5000 \quad \text{(in its simplest form)}$$

1 cm on the map represents 5000 cm in real distance.

So 7 cm represents $7 \times 5000 = 35\,000 \, \text{cm}$
                                      $= 350 \, \text{m}$

EXERCISE N28

1 Write each of the following as a ratio in the form 1 : *n*.

  a 5 cm : 3 km   **b** 12 cm : 3600 m   **c** 1 cm : 1 km

2 A map has a scale whereby 8 cm represents 64 km.

  a Express this as a scale in the form 1 : *n*.
  b Calculate the distance on the map which represents 24 km.

Direct proportion

When a number of articles is purchased and they each cost the same, the total cost is **proportional** to the number of articles bought. So, for example, if 10 articles were bought the total would be 10 times the price of one. This is an example of **direct proportion**.

Problems involving direct proportion can best be solved by referring to a single unit, and so this method is known as the **unitary method**.

If two quantities are in direct proportion as one of them increases by 1, the other will increase by some constant, k (you can think of k as the 'price' per item).

EXAMPLE 7

15 m of rope cost £11.70. How much does 24 m of the same rope cost?

  15 m cost £11.70
  1 m costs £11.70 ÷ 15 = £0.78
  24 m cost 24 × 0.78 = £18.72

---

*Find the cost of 1 m (the **unit cost**), then multiply this by the quantity required.*

Foreign exchange

Foreign exchange is a common application of direct proportion. When we visit a foreign country, we have to 'buy' some of that country's currency to use there. The 'price' of each foreign currency varies from day to day. The amount of a particular currency you can buy for £1 sterling is called the **exchange rate**. This is the 'unit cost' when applying direct proportion to foreign exchange.

You have to pay to change your money – you are charged commission.

EXAMPLE 8

I buy 127.2 US dollars ($) for £80.

a What is the exchange rate?
b How many dollars can I buy for £150?
c If I bring back a $50 bill to the UK, how much is it worth in £s Sterling (to the nearest penny)?

a £80 buys $127.2
    £1 buys 127.2 ÷ 80 = $1.59
  The exchange rate is $1.59 to the £.
b £150 buys 150 × 1.59 = $238.5.
c $1.59 buys £1
    $1 buys 1 ÷ 1.59 = £0.628 9308...
    $50 buys 50 × 0.628 930 8 = £31.45

---

*c Although we would round off to say $1 is worth 63p, you **must not** use this rounded value to calculate with. You should use the **full value on your calculator display**.*

EXERCISE N29

1 A car uses 50 litres of petrol when travelling 315 miles. How far could it go on 70 litres of petrol?

2 It costs £8.68 to feed a horse for 7 days. How much would it cost to feed it for 12 days?

3 In a recipe for buns, 500 g of flour are needed to make 12 buns. How much flour is needed to make 20 buns?

4 Toni travels to Italy and buys 154 500 lire for £60.

  a What is the exchange rate?
  b How many lire can she buy for £75?

5 Manoli arrives on holiday from Spain with 25 000 pesetas. The exchange rate is 192 pesetas to the £. How many £s sterling can she buy?

Inverse proportion

Inverse proportion occurs when an increase in one quantity leads to a decrease in the other quantity.

As the number of chickens increase, the number of days a bag of food will last will decrease

Using the unitary method, we find out for how many days **we** could **feed one chicken**

EXAMPLE 9

An economy bag of chicken food is enough to feed 6 chickens for 40 days. For how many days would the same sized bag feed 10 chickens?

  6 chickens can feed for 40 days
  1 chicken can feed for $6 \times 40 = 240$ days
  10 chickens can feed for $240 \div 10 = 24$ days

EXERCISE N30

1 Three combine harvesters can harvest a field in 5 hours. How long would the harvest take if one of the machines was broken down?

2 A group of 5 mountaineers take enough food to last them on an expedition lasting 12 days. How long would the same amount of supplies last 4 mountaineers?

3 A 30-piece band can play the national anthem in 2 minutes. How long would a 60-piece band take?

4 Twelve bricklayers can complete a wall in 8 hours. How long would it take 16 bricklayers to build the same wall?

5 A car can complete a particular journey in 3.5 hours travelling at 60 mph. How long, in hours and minutes, would the same journey take travelling at 50 mph?

N 10 Use of percentages

Calculating a percentage of a quantity

'**Per cent**' means **for each hundred** and **of** means $\times$ in mathematics.

EXAMPLE 1

Find 45% of £600.

$$45\% = \frac{45}{100}$$

So 45% of $600 = \dfrac{45}{100} \times 600$

$$= \frac{45}{100} \times \frac{600}{1}$$

$$= \frac{45}{1} \times \frac{6}{1} \quad \text{(Cancelling by 100)}$$

$$= £270$$

When using a calculator you key in

$$45 \div 100 \times 600 =$$

It may be necessary to change the units in some cases.

EXAMPLE 2

Express 5% of 3 km in metres.

$$3\,\text{km} = 3000\,\text{m}$$

5% of $3\,\text{km}$

$$= \frac{5}{100} \times \frac{3000}{1}\,\text{m}$$

$$= \frac{5}{1} \times \frac{30}{1} \quad \text{(Cancelling by 100)}$$

$$= 150\,\text{m}$$

EXERCISE N31

1 Find **a** 10% of £30, **b** 65% of £140, **c** $66\frac{2}{3}\%$ of £18.60.

2 Find 150% of 700 ml, giving your answer in litres.

3 In a survey on smoking, 82% of the 1700 people surveyed had given up smoking. How many people is this?

4 The cost of a twin room in a hotel is £170 per person per week. If a child shares a room with its two parents, the child is charged at 25% of the adult rate. How much is paid for the child per week?

5 It costs an amateur operatic company £15 000 to put on a production. The company hope to raise 40% of this through sponsorship. How much more money would they have to find?

Expressing one quantity as a percentage of another

Step 1 Write the first quantity as a fraction of the second.

Step 2 Express this fraction as a percentage by multiplying by 100.

EXAMPLE 3

In a test a student scored 48 out of a possible 60 marks. Express this as a percentage.

Step 1 48 out of 60 as a fraction is $\dfrac{48}{60}$

Step 2 $\dfrac{48}{60} \times 100\% = \dfrac{48}{3} \times 5\%$ (Cancelling by 20)

$\qquad\qquad = 80\%$

On a calculator
$48 \div 60 \times 100 = 80\%$

EXAMPLE 4

Express 640 g as a percentage of 4 kg.

$4\,\text{kg} = 4000\,\text{g}$

Step 1 $\dfrac{640}{4000}$

Step 2 $\dfrac{640}{4000} \times 100\% = \dfrac{64}{4}\%$

$\qquad\qquad = 16\%$

Note When the units are different, we must change them so that both quantities are in the same units

EXERCISE N32

1 Express the first quantity as a percentage of the second.
  a 18 ft, 72 ft   **b** 70p, £2   **c** 34 seconds, 2 minutes

2 There are 320 people at a disco and 144 are boys. What percentage are girls?

Using percentages to compare proportions

EXAMPLE 5

Last year, 96 pupils in a school took GCSE mathematics, 72 of whom attained a grade C or better. This year, 85 pupils took the examination, 68 of whom attained a grade C or better. In which year were the results more successful?

Last year $\dfrac{72}{96} \times 100\% = 75\%$

This year $\dfrac{68}{85} \times 100\% = 80\%$

So the results were more successful this year.

EXERCISE N33

A slimmers society tried two different diets for one month. Of the 26 on the M-plan diet, 21 lost 10 pounds or more. Of the 24 on the N-plan diet, 18 lost 10 pounds or more. Which was the more effective diet?

Percentage increase and decrease

There are two ways of tackling these problems. You should use the one you feel more comfortable with.

EXAMPLE 5

An electronic keyboard costs £850. Next month the price is expected to rise by 15%. What will the new price be?

METHOD 1

Find the increase: 15% of $850 = \dfrac{15}{100} \times 850$

$$= £127.50$$

Add this increase to the original price:

$$£127.50 + £850 = £977.50$$

The new price will be £977.50.

METHOD 2

The current price is 100%.
Increasing this by 15% means the new price will be 115% of the current price.
So the problem becomes 'Find 115% of £850'.

$$\text{New price} = \dfrac{115}{100} \times 850$$

$$= £977.50$$

EXAMPLE 6

A three-piece suite is advertised at £700 but a sale offers 20% off. What is the sale price of the suite?

METHOD 1

Find the amount to be taken off:

$$20\% \text{ of } £700 = \dfrac{20}{100} \times 700$$

$$= £140$$

Subtract this reduction from the original cost:

$$£700 - £140 = £560$$

The sale price is £560.

METHOD 2

20% off means we only pay 80% of the original price.
So the problem becomes 'Find 80% of £700'.

$$\text{Sale price} = \dfrac{80}{100} \times 700$$

$$= £560$$

EXERCISE N34

1 A sales assistant earns £8500 per year. He is given a pay rise of 3%. What is his new annual salary?

2 A car cost £13 500 when new. After three years, its trade-in value is 40% less than the cost of the car when it was new. What is the trade-in value of this car after three years?

3 Because of severe flooding there is a shortage of lettuces this year. It is expected that the price of a lettuce will rise by 35%. Last year a lettuce cost 40p. What is the expected price of a lettuce this year?

4 It is claimed that a new type of central heating system reduces annual heating bills by 22%. If my annual heating costs are £1200, what should I expect them to be if I install this new system?

Percentage change

Percentage change is always calculated by

The actual change in amount may be an increase or a decrease.

$$\frac{\text{Actual change in amount}}{\textbf{Original amount}} \times 100\%$$

EXAMPLE 7

The price of a picnic table increases from £90 to £108. Express this increase as a percentage of the original price.

$$\text{The actual change in amount} = £108 - £90$$
$$= £18$$

$$\text{Percentage change} = \frac{18}{90} \times 100\%$$
$$= 20\%$$

EXAMPLE 8

In a sale the price of a lawn mower is reduced from £130 to £91. Calculate the percentage reduction.

$$\text{The actual change in amount} = £130 - £91$$
$$= £39$$

$$\text{Percentage change} = \frac{39}{130} \times 100\%$$
$$= 30\%$$

EXERCISE N35

1 A jacket is reduced in price from £65 to £55.25. Calculate the percentage reduction.

2 A school organised a sponsored 10 km 'Push and Pull' in order to raise funds for the new school minibus. The event raised £4500. The fund already had £7500 in it. By what percentage did this event raise the total fund?

3 Last year a Beavers group had 45 members. This year the membership is 36. By what percentage has the membership fallen?

4 Because of a signalling problem the train journey from Plyton to Taunmouth took 3 hours and 21 minutes instead of the usual 2 hours and 50 minutes. Calculate as a percentage the increase in the journey time caused by the delay.

Hint with 4
3 hours and 21 minutes is **not** *3.21 hours.*

Finding the original amount

EXAMPLE 9

A company employs 1428 females, who represent 68% of the total workforce. How many people does the company employ altogether?

$$68\% = 1428$$

So
$$1\% = 1428 \div 68$$
$$= 21$$

$$\Rightarrow \quad 100\% = 21 \times 100$$
$$= 2100$$

The total workforce is 2100.

EXAMPLE 10

A bookshop makes 30% profit on each book it sells. What is the original cost, to the nearest penny, of a book which the shop sells for £13.99?

If the cost of the book to the shop is 100%, then the shop sells the book for 130% of this cost.

$$130\% = £13.99$$

So
$$1\% = 13.99 \div 130$$
$$= £0.107\,6153$$

$$\Rightarrow \quad 100\% = 0.107\,6153 \times 100$$
$$= £10.76 \text{ to the nearest penny}$$

A common **mistake** *is to find 30% of £13.99!!! You should* **avoid this** *by reading the question carefully so that you are clear about which quantity the given percentage refers to (in this case the original cost, not the selling price).*

EXERCISE N36

1 An ice-cream company employs 25% more workers during the summer months. There are 35 people working for the company during the summer. How many people work there during the rest of the year?

2 A technical manual contains pages which are either wholly illustrations or wholly text. 45% of the pages are wholly illustrations and the other 110 pages are wholly text. How many pages are there in the manual?

3 My wages this week include an annual productivity bonus which is 6% of my annual earnings. The bonus is £702. How much do I earn per year excluding this bonus?

4 A mail order company charge a 9% delivery charge on all orders whatever the value of the goods you buy. The bill for my order is £1369.04. What was the cost of the goods I ordered?

N 11 Everyday finance

Household bills

For a telephone bill the standing charge is for the rental of the line and possibly the hire of the telephone and other equipment.
The cost of each call is calculated from the duration of the call using a rate (pence per minute) which varies according to the type of call (local, national or international), the time of day, and the day of the week.

Among the main households bills are those for gas, electricity and telephone. Each consists of a fixed **standing charge** plus the cost of the **quantity of supply** (gas and electricity) or the **calls made** (telephone). The quantity of gas or electricity is given as **units**, read from a meter at the house. Telephone calls are metered at the telephone exchange and are charged for individually. Gas and electricity meters are mostly digital but some are still clockmeters.

The **digital meter** is a series of windows showing **single digits**.

8	5	3	7	2

The **clockmeter** has a set of **dials**, each with a pointer. The pointers rotate alternately clockwise and anticlockwise.

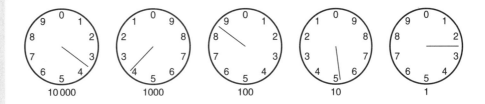

For each dial we **read the digit which the pointer has just passed**. So in this case the reading is 33 852.

To calculate the bill we first find the number of units used.

Units used = Current reading − Previous reading

We next find the cost of these units by multiplying by the unit price (tariff)

Cost = Units used × Unit price

Finally, we add the **standing charge**.

EXAMPLE 1

In March, Ms Smith's electricity meter reading was 16 046. The diagram below shows the dials when the meter was read in July. The standing charge was £18.70 and the tariff is 5.1p per unit (kWh). Calculate Ms Smith's bill before VAT.

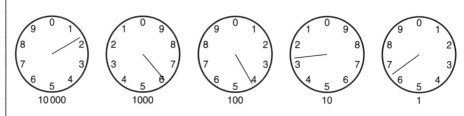

| 10 000 | 1000 | 100 | 10 | 1 |

July reading = 16 426   March reading = 16 046

Units used = 16 426 − 16 046 = 380 kWh

Cost of electricity used = 380 × £0.051 = £19.38

Standing charge   £18.70

Total electricity bill (excluding VAT)   £38.08

Note The tariff is usually in **pence per unit**. Make sure you allow for this in your calculation. In this example the 5.1p was entered as £0.051.

EXERCISE N37

1 In August, Mr Uzzell's gas meter showed the following number of units. Each unit is equivalent to 100 cubic feet of gas.

| 1000 | 100 | 10 | 1 |

In November the reading was 6048.

100 cubic feet of gas is equivalent to 30.1 kilowatt-hours (kWh).

Gas is charged at a tariff of 1.52p per kWh.

The standing charge is £11.65.

Calculate Mr Uzzell's bill for this period, excluding VAT.

On a gas meter the readings show 100s of cubic feet of gas. On the bill this is converted to cubic metres, which in turn is converted to kilowatt-hours (kWh). The conversion factor may vary slightly depending on the energy value of the gas supplied. The tariff is given in pence per kWh.

2 Mrs Greatorex pays a standing charge of £13.47 per quarter for her electricity.

In April her meter reading was 62 458 and in the following July it was 63.067.

Electricity is charged at a tariff of 4.6p per unit.

Calculate Mrs Greatorex's electricity bill for this period, excluding VAT.

Value Added Tax (VAT)

Value Added Tax is a tax on goods and services, though certain goods, such as food and children's clothing, do not carry VAT (they are 'zero-rated').

For most goods the standard rate of VAT is $17\frac{1}{2}\%$. The exception is fuel, for which the rate is 8%.

Prices are sometimes quoted *exclusive* of VAT. In this case, the price paid by the customer is $17\frac{1}{2}\%$ more than the quoted price.

EXAMPLE 2

The price of a washing machine is shown in the catalogue as £565 plus VAT. How much would a customer pay for the washing machine when VAT is charged at $17\frac{1}{2}\%$?

METHOD 1 $17\frac{1}{2}\%$ of £565 $= \frac{17\frac{1}{2}}{100} \times 565$

$$= £98.875$$

The customer pays £565 + £98.875 = £663.88 (to the nearest penny).

METHOD 2   The customer pays $117\frac{1}{2}\%$ of £565

$$\frac{117\frac{1}{2}}{100} \times 565 = £663.88 \text{ (to the nearest penny).}$$

EXAMPLE 3

It will not effect the final answer if the VAT is added first and then the discount is calculated.

A builder gets 15% discount off the list price of goods in a local **DIY** shop but still has to pay the VAT at $17\frac{1}{2}\%$ on the discounted price. How much does the builder pay for a drill whose list price is £78.45?

	£
List price	78.45
Less 15% discount	−11.77
Discounted price	66.68
Add $17\frac{1}{2}\%$ VAT	+11.67
Builder pays	78.35

EXERCISE N38

1 Calculate the amount of VAT at $17\frac{1}{2}\%$ which is to be added to

   a a camera priced at £399.99

   b a tent priced at £876.50

   c a box of chocolates priced at £2.45

   d a car priced at £14 500.

2 A bistro levies a service charge of 10% of the cost of a meal before adding $17\frac{1}{2}\%$ VAT. What is the total bill for a meal which costs £34.67?

3 An employee of a fashion trader is entitled to 20% discount on items sold in the shop but must include $17\frac{1}{2}\%$ VAT after the discount has been subtracted. How much does she pay for a skirt listed at £32.35?

Hire purchase (HP)

Hire purchase is a method of buying goods by spreading their cost over several months. The result is that the goods cost more. This extra cost to the customer pays for the loan from which the shop gets its money for the goods.

The normal HP arrangement is to pay a **deposit** at the time of purchase and to then to pay the **balance** in a number of equal monthly **instalments**.

EXAMPLE 4

A tumble dryer can be bought for £270 or, under a hire purchase agreement, for 12 monthly payments of £21.60 and a 20% deposit. How much more does the tumble dryer cost when bought under the HP scheme?

The deposit is 20% of £270 = £54
The instalments come to 12 × £21.60 = £259.20
Total HP price = £54 + £259.20 = £313.20
Extra paid under HP scheme = £313.20 − £270 = £43.20

EXERCISE N39

1 A stereo system costs £456.75. It can be bought under an HP scheme for a 10% deposit and 24 monthly payments of £21.40. How much more does it cost under the HP scheme?

2 A boat can be bought for £15 890 cash or under one of two HP schemes.
Scheme 1 25% deposit and 12 monthly payments of £1241.
Scheme 2 15% deposit and 24 monthly payments of £765.
Which is the more costly scheme and how much more would you pay?

Mortgages

The amount which can be borrowed is based upon the joint income of the purchasers.

A mortgage is the money borrowed from a bank or a building society to buy a flat or a house. As this is usually a large amount, the loan is usually repaid over a long period of time, typically 20 or 25 years. Sometimes it is possible to borrow the whole amount of the purchase price. This is a 100% mortgage but it is more usual to be required to pay a deposit of between 5% and 10% and borrow the rest as a mortgage.

EXAMPLE 5

Janet and John decide to buy a house costing £45 000. Their building society agrees to a 95% mortgage. **a** How much deposit do they have to pay?
b How much do they borrow?

a   A 95% mortgage means they have to pay a 5% deposit.
5% of £45.000 = £2250

b   They pay £2250, so they borrow
£45 000 − £2250 = £42 750

EXAMPLE 6

Marion obtains a 20 year mortgage of £85 000. Her monthly repayments are £7.21 per £1000 borrowed. Calculate **a** her monthly repayments, **b** the total amount repaid over 20 years.

a   Monthly repayments are 85 × £7.21 = £612.85

b   Total annual repayment is 12 × £612.85 = £7354.20
Total repayment over 20 years is 20 × £7354.20 = £147 084

EXERCISE N40

1 Andre and Andrea are offered a 90% mortgage on a flat costing £78 000.

 a How much deposit do they have to pay?

 b Their monthly repayments are £5.24 per £1000 borrowed. How much do they pay per month?

2 Pam and Sam are buying a house costing £112.500. They have £34 500 from a previous house sale but need to borrow the rest. The bank agrees a mortgage for this amount, repayable over 15 years at a monthly rate of £7.83 per £1000 borrowed. Calculate **a** the amount borrowed, **b** the monthly repayments.

Insurance

Some insurance, especially motor insurance, offer a reduction on a premium if you do not make any claims. For motor insurance this is called a 'no-claims bonus'.

Insurance is a method of covering the cost of some unforeseen catastrophe. You can to choose whether to take out insurance on most things, such as your life or house contents but some types of insurance are not voluntary. For example, motor insurance is a legal requirement, and usually a mortgage is granted on the condition that the property is insured.

Insurance is based upon a regular, usually monthly or annual, payment called the **premium**. The size of the premium depends on the risk involved and the 'value' of the item insured. If the item is damaged or lost, you can claim compensation from the insurance company. If the company rejects your claim, you have wasted your premium!

EXAMPLE 7

Veronica insures her house for £65 000 and the contents for £22 500. The insurance company offers the following rates:

 Buildings insurance £1.54 per £1000 insured
 Contents insurance £3.86 per £1000 insured

Calculate her annual premium.

 Premium for buildings = 65 × 1.54 = £100.10
 Premium for contents = 22.5 × 3.86 = £86.85
 Total premium due = £186.95

EXERCISE N41

1 Troy owns a motorcycle and the insurance premium is £896 per year. He is entitled to a 55% no-claims bonus. How much does Troy pay to insure his machine?

2 An insurance company offer the following rates for home insurance:

 Buildings £1.78 per £1000 insured
 Contents £4.23 per £1000 insured

Calculate the annual premium paid by Mr and Mrs Amin if their house is valued at £58 500 and the contents at £19 000.

Interest

Interest is the amount which you will be paid if you invest a sum of money in a savings account. It is also the extra you have to pay if you borrow a sum of money. It is expressed as a percentage and is referred to as the **rate of interest** per annum (p.a.).

If you withdraw the interest earned each year, then the amount earning interest each year does not change. This is an example of **simple interest**. If, however, you leave the interest in the savings account, then the amount earning interest will continue to grow. This is an example of **compound interest**.

EXAMPLE 8

If the monthly repayments do not work out to an exact amount, then the first or last payment is adjusted to make sure the total amount is met exactly.

Jim borrows £245 to buy a bicycle and agrees to repay the loan with 22% interest over 12 equal monthly payments. **a** How much does he repay?
b What are his monthly repayments:

a   22% of 245 = £53.90
       Total repayment of £245 + £53.90 = £289.90

b   Monthly repayments of £289.90 ÷ 12 = £24.91

EXAMPLE 9

Christine has £875 in a savings account which pays interest at 7% p.a. Calculate how much interest she will earn over three years **a** if she withdraws the interest each year, **b** if she adds the interest to the account each year.

b can be calculated more directly, if using Method 2 on page 36 since we have
$\{[(875 \times 1.07) \times 1.07] \times 1.07\}$

$= 875 \times (1.07)^3$
$= £1071.91$
(the annual amounts were rounded off each time, which earned 1p extra!)

a   Interest at 7% on £875 = £61.25 per year
       Over three years this is $3 \times £61.25 = £183.75$

b   Interest for the first year is £61.25, making a total of
       £875 + £61.25 = £936.25 in the account.
       Interest at 7% on £936.25 = £65.54 for the second year, making a total of £1001.79 in the account.
       Interest at 7% on £1001.79 = £70.13 for the third year, making a total of £1071.92 in the account after three years.

Total interest earned this way is £1071.92 − £875 = £196.92

EXERCISE N42

1 Calculate the interest earned on £3275 at a rate of 4% p.a.

2 Calculate **a** the simple interest, **b** the compound interest earned on £525 over two years in an account which pays interest at 8.5% p.a.

3 Lionel buys a new suit which costs £276. He buys it on a hire purchase scheme which requires a 20% deposit. The remaining amount is repaid in 12 monthly instalments after 30% interest has been added to the outstanding amount. Calculate

   a the deposit required
   b the amount of interest charged on the balance
   c the monthly repayments.

Profit and loss

The amount a shop pays for a product is called the **cost price**. The amount for which it sells the product is called the **selling price**, which is usually more than the cost price. The money made is called **profit**. If the selling price has, for some reason, to be less than the cost price, the difference is then a **loss**. Profit and loss are expressed as a **percentage of the cost price**.

$$\frac{\text{Amount of profit (or loss)}}{\text{Cost price}} \times 100\%$$

EXERCISE N43

1 David buys a computer for £740 and two years later sells it for £333. Calculate the percentage loss.

2 Honest John buys a car for £450 and sells it for £585. Calculate his percentage profit.

3 Mr Pears buys a box of 64 apples for £1.92 and sells them for 7p each. Calculate his profit if he sells all of the apples.

4 Brian buys six boxes of 24 choc ices for £3.25 per box. He sells the choc ices at 22p each except for the last 12, which he sells at 5p each because they are slightly melted. Calculate his profit and express it as a percentage of his initial outlay.

N 12 Income

People in work are paid in a variety of ways. They are all paid for the amount of work they do but the method of payment is different for different types of job. The main methods of payment are

Wages
Salary
Piecework
Commission
Combination of wages or salary plus bonus or commission

Wages

Basic wage =
Hours worked × Hourly rate

A wage is based upon a contracted number of hours of work and an **hourly rate of pay**. Many wage earners are contracted to work a fixed number of hours per week and are paid a basic weekly wage.

EXAMPLE 1

Toby works in a factory as a maintenance engineer. He is paid £5.30 per hour for a 40-hour week. Calculate his weekly earnings.

Weekly wage is $40 \times £5.30 = £212$

> **EXAMPLE 2**
>
> Nicky is employed as a mechanic in a garage. She works a 36-hour week and her wage is £228.60 per week. How much is she paid per hour?
>
>   Hourly rate is £228.60 ÷ 36 = £6.35

Overtime

Hourly rate × 1.5 is called **time and a half**

Hourly rate × 2 is called **double time**

Overtime worked = actual hours − normal hours

When employees work more than their contracted hours in a given week, the extra time worked is called overtime. They are usually paid at a rate higher than their normal hourly rate. This is often 1.5 times or twice the normal hourly rate and is referred to as 'time and a half' or 'double time', respectively.

> **EXAMPLE 3**
>
> Mr Gmiterlek works a basic 38-hour week and is paid £5.84 per hour. He is paid overtime at time and a half and one week he worked 45 hours. What was his wage that week?
>
>   Basic wage is 38 × £5.84 = £221.92
>   Overtime rate is 1.5 × £5.84 = £8.76
>   Amount of overtime is 45 − 38 = 7 hours
>   Overtime pay is 7 × £8.76 = £61.32
>   Total wage is £221.92 + £61.32 = £283.24

Salary

Monthly salary = Annual salary ÷ 12

Always calculate monthly and weekly incomes from the **annual total**

An employee who is paid a salary receives a fixed amount of money per year. This is usually paid monthly. Some salaried employees also have the opportunity to earn bonuses.

> **EXAMPLE 4**
>
> Tom and Diana are both working. Tom earns a £1298 per month and Diana earns £21 564 per year. Calculate their joint   **a** monthly income,   **b** annual income,   **c** weekly income (1 year = 52 weeks).
>
> **a** Diana earns £21 564 ÷ 12 = £1797 per month
>   Joint monthly income is £1298 + £1797 = £3095
>
> **b** Tom earns £1298 × 12 = £15 576 per year
>   Joint annual income is £15 576 + £21 564 = £37 140
>
> **c** Joint weekly income is £37 140 ÷ 52 = £714.20

EXERCISE N44

1 Bernard is paid £3.78 per hour for a 42-hour week as a security officer. Calculate his weekly wage.

2 Siobhan is paid £4.12 per hour and her weekly wage is £160.68. Calculate the number of hours she works per week.

3 Guy is paid £4.60 per hour for a 36-hour week. Overtime is paid at time and a half except on Sundays when it is double time. One week Guy works a total of 51 hours, including 5 hours on a Sunday. Calculate his wage for that week.

4 Isobella receives a monthly salary of £1528. Calculate her annual salary.

5 Calculate the monthly salary, to the nearest pound, for someone whose annual salary is **a** £36 750, **b** £16 460.

6 Keith earns £6.25 per hour for a 40-hour week. His wife Val earns an annual salary of £18 980. Calculate their joint income **a** per year, **b** per month, **c** per week.

Piecework

When a rate of production is set which is not per item it is assumed that payment is 'pro rata', which means 'at the same rate'
So if a bricklayer is paid £10 for every 50 bricks laid, he would be getting 20p per brick pro rata. It does not mean if he laid only 49 bricks he wouldn't get paid!

Some employees, particularly in manufacturing industries, are paid an amount for each item they produce. This is called **piecework**.

Earnings can sometimes consist partly of a basic wage and partly of a piecework payment. Also, in some jobs, if the employees produce more than a certain number of items, they are paid a bonus or at a higher rate for the extra output.

EXAMPLE 5

Melanie works as a machinist in a handbag factory. For sewing zips onto handbags, she is paid a basic wage of £25 per week and 7p per zip. If she sews more than 150 zips per day, the rate goes up to 12p per zip. Her output one week is shown below. Calculate her wage that week.

Day of the week	Mon	Tues	Wed	Thurs	Fri
Number of zips	215	197	135	177	162

Monday	215 zips earn	$150 \times £0.07 + 65 \times £0.12$	= £18.30
Tuesday	197 zips earn	$150 \times £0.07 + 47 \times £0.12$	= £16.14
Wednesday	135 zips earn	$135 \times £0.07$	= £9.45
Thursday	177 zips earn	$150 \times £0.07 + 27 \times £0.12$	= £13.74
Friday	162 zips earn	$150 \times £0.07 + 12 \times £0.12$	= £11.94
		Basic wage	£25.00
		Total	£94.57

Commission

Commission is similar to piecework except it applies to people who are employed to sell goods or services. Part or all of their earnings will depend upon the value of the sales they achieve. Commission is usually calculated as a percentage of the value of the goods or services sold.

EXAMPLE 6

Rich Gottsell works as a car salesperson. He is paid £35 per week plus a commission of 4% of the value of the cars he sells. Calculate his earnings in a week when he sells two cars for £8675 and one for £6540.

Total sales $= 2 \times £8675 + £6540 = £23\,890$
Commission $= 4\%$ of $23\,890 = £955.60$
Total earnings that week $= £35 + £965.60 = £1000.60$

EXERCISE N45

1 Winnie works in a factory on an assembly line soldering components to a circuit board. She is paid £10 per day plus 8 p for each completed board. If she completes more than 175 boards per day, she is paid 11 p per board for the extras. Calculate how much Winnie earns on a day when she completes 205 boards.

2 An auctioneer earns 3% commission on all the goods sold at the auction. Calculate her commission on sales valued at £345 560.

3 Omar works in a music shop. He earns £90 per week plus 5% commission on the value of sales over £1200 in any one week. Calculate his earnings in a week when he sold £2345 of sheet music and equipment.

4 Sharon works for a firm of bathroom fitters as a tiler. She gets no basic wage but each day earns £12 per 20 tiles fixed for the first 60 tiles, then £17 per 20 tiles fixed after that. Calculate Sharon's earnings on a day when she fixes 95 tiles.

Gross pay and net pay

Employees do not receive all the money they earn. Deductions are made from their pay, which can include income tax, National Insurance and pension contributions.

Gross pay is the amount earned **before** any deductions are made.

Net pay is the amount actually received **after** any deductions have been made. (Net pay is often referred to as 'take home' pay.)

> Net pay =
>   Gross pay – Deductions

Taxable income

Some amounts of a person's income are free from income tax. These are called **allowances**. They are set each year in the Budget by the Chancellor of the Exchequer.

> This is to protect low earner's income, since they can earn £3765 before they pay any income tax.

The main allowances for 1996/97 were

> Personal allowance   £3765
> Married allowance   £1790

> Married allowance actually gives relief at 15% but for the sake of simplicity this has been ignored in what follows.

(Married allowance can be against the husband's or wife's income but not both.)

Whatever you earn above your allowances is called **taxable income**.

> Taxable income =
> Gross income – Allowances

The amount of income tax you pay depends on how much you earn. The tax rates for 1996/97 were

> 20% on the first £3900 of taxable income
> 24% on £3901–£25 500
> 40% over £25 500

> Tax is deducted from 'the top down' rather than from 'the bottom up' so

It is important to divide annual earnings into the amounts subject to each tax rate when carrying out these calculations.

1 Start with the taxable income.
2 Subtract the first applicable 'tax-rate boundary'.
3 Calculate the tax payable on that amount.
4 Go to the next boundary and so on.

Always check that the **amounts** you have used to calculate the tax **plus the allowances** add up to the **gross earnings**.

EXAMPLE 7

Calculate the tax payable on a salary of £30 000 in 1996 with no additional allowances to the personal allowance.

Allowances   3765   tax free
Taxable income is   30 000–3765   = £26 235
                                 26 235–25 500 = £735 taxed at 40%
                                 25 500–3900   = £21 600 taxed at 24%
                                                       £3900 taxed at 20%

(Check: 3765 + 3900 + 21 600 + 735 = 30 000)

40% of 735   = £294
24% of 21 600 = £5184
20% of 3900   = £780
Total tax payable is £6258

National Insurance

Once calculated, the NI contribution will probably be a fixed amount deducted each week or month, unless earnings fluctuate widely from week to week.

There is a maximum NI contribution which is the same for everyone earning more than £455 per week or £1972 per month.

National Insurance contributions are another form of tax but the revenue raised is used specifically to help pay for the National Health service, sick pay, the state pension and unemployment benefits. The amount of NI paid by an employee depends upon his or her gross pay. The National Insurance contribution is deducted either weekly or monthly, depending on how the employee is paid.

National Insurance Contributions 1996/97

Weekly earnings £s	Monthly earnings £s	NI contributions
0–60.99	0–264.99	Nil
61–455	265–1972	2% of the first £61 per week (or £265 per month) plus 10% of the remainder
over 455	over 1972	2% of the first £65 per week (or £265 per month) plus 10% of £394 per week (or £1707 per month)

£2650 – £265 = £2385 but the **maximum** NI monthly contribution still applies: 2% of £265 + 10% of £1707.

EXAMPLES

8 Craig earns £86 per week before deductions. Calculate his National Insurance contribution.

2% of £61 + 10% of £(86 − 61) = £3.72

9 Sonya earns £1250 per month gross. Calculate her National Insurance contribution.

2% of £265 + 10% of £(1250 − 265) = £103.80

10 Harry earns £2650 per month before deductions. Calculate his monthly National Insurance contributions.

2% of £265 + 10% of £1707 = £176.00

EXERCISE N46

Use the 1996/97 tax rates and NI contributions information on pages 48–49.

1 Calculate
  i the taxable income,
  ii the amount of tax paid in each of the following:

	Income	Standard allowance	Extra allowance
a	£24 500	£3765	£750
b	£17 600	£5555	£600
c	£19 300	£4910	£50
d	£38 400	£5555	£830
e	£11 250	£3765	none

2 Calculate the National Insurance contributions payable for each of the following gross incomes:

a £235 per week   **b** £1495 per month

c £320 per week   **d** £475 per week

3 Ali earns £26 350 per year. He has a personal allowance, a married allowance and an extra allowance of £425. Calculate

a his annual taxable income

b the amount of tax he should pay per year

c the amount of tax he pays per month

d his gross monthly salary

e his monthly NI contribution

f his net monthly salary.

N 13 Compound measures

Combining measures

The measures for many physical quantities are formed by combining base measures. For example, an area is found by multiplying a length by a length; a volume by multiplying three lengths together.

Some combined measures are obtained by dividing one base measure by another. This is expressed by the term **per** in the new measure so formed.

The term 'per' means **for each** and, mathematically, is associated with **division**.

Speed

The speed of a car is often expressed in **miles** *per* **hour**. This is the distance travelled **for each** hour.

Speed is calculated by   **Distance travelled** $\div$ **Time taken**
For example   miles **per** hour
                                                         m **per** second

$$\text{Speed} = \frac{\text{Distance travelled}}{\text{Time taken}}$$

EXAMPLE 1

A cyclist covers a distance of 36 miles in a time of 3 hours. What was her average speed?

$$\text{Speed} = \frac{\text{Distance travelled}}{\text{Take taken}} = \frac{36}{3} \text{ miles per hour}$$
$$= 12 \text{ miles per hour}$$

Calculating distance travelled or time taken

The formula for speed can be rearranged to give

$$\text{Time taken} = \frac{\text{Distance travelled}}{\text{Speed}}$$

$$\text{Distance travelled} = \text{Speed} \times \text{Time taken}$$

EXERCISE N47

Copy and complete this table, filling in the blank spaces.

	Distance travelled	Speed	Time taken
1	160 km		2.5 h
2		9.4 m/s	45 s
3	216 miles	54 mph	
4	1500 m		4 min
5	370 km	125 kph	

Average speed

Because vehicles hardly ever travel at a constant speed for long periods, we calculate their **average speed**.

For this, we need to know the **total distance travelled** and the **total time taken**.

Staged journeys

EXAMPLE 2

A vehicle travels along the motorway at 65 mph for 2 hours. It then leaves the motorway and covers the final 30 miles at a speed of 25 mph. What is its average speed?

Step 1
Make a table and fill in the known values.

	Distance	Speed	Time
Stage 1		65	2
Stage 2	30	25	
Total			

Step 2
Calculate the missing values in the table.

Stage 1
$$\text{Distance travelled} = \text{speed} \times \text{time taken}$$
$$= 65 \times 2$$
$$= 130 \text{ miles}$$

Stage 2
$$\text{Time taken} = \frac{\text{Distance travelled}}{\text{Speed}}$$
$$= \frac{30}{25}$$
$$= 1.2 \text{ hours}$$

Note You get nothing sensible by adding together the speeds for the two stages of the journey.

Step 3
Fill in the values to complete the table.

	Distance	Speed	Time
Stage 1	**130**	65	2
Stage 2	30	25	**1.2**
Total	**160**		**3.2**

Step 4
Calculate the average speed.

Stage 1
$$\text{Average speed} = \frac{\text{Total distance travelled}}{\text{Total time taken}}$$
$$= \frac{160}{3.2}$$
$$= 50 \text{ mph}$$

EXERCISE N48

1 A motorist travelling to a holiday resort covers the first 150 miles at an average speed of 65 mph along the motorway. The final part is along narrow country roads and the average speed is only 18 mph. This section takes 2 hours 30 minutes to complete. What is his average speed for the whole journey?

2 A cyclist takes a total of 8 hours to complete a journey at an average speed of 9 mph. The first part, on the flat, was completed at an average speed of 15 mph and took 3 hours. The second part, in the hills, was heavier going. Find the average speed for this second part of the journey.

3 A rally driver loses one point for each minute late at a control. Minutes lost on a stage cannot be recovered later. All times are calculated to the previous whole minute. If cars arrive early, they can wait for their due time. Clocking in early earns a double penalty, i.e. 2 points per minute. On Stage 1, distance 25.3 miles, an average speed of 55 mph was specified. Junju took 32 minutes. On Stage 2, a hilly, rocky section, distance 15.7 miles, a speed of 43 mph was specified. Junju was timed at 19 minutes on this section. Stage 3 is a fairly flat but dusty 28-mile section, with a specified average speed of 72 mph. However, a swollen river delays progress and the section takes 35 minutes.
What is Junju's penalty score so far?

Acceleration

Acceleration is a measure of how quickly speed is changing. Like speed, this often changes continuously and we can find only the **average acceleration**.

$$\text{Average acceleration} = \frac{\text{Change in speed}}{\text{Time taken}}$$

Units m/s^2, km/h^2, ft/s^2.

To do this we need to know the **overall change in speed** and the **total time taken**.

Some units of acceleration are

(metres per second) per second = metres per second^2 (m/s^2)
(feet per second) per second   = feet per second^2 (ft/s^2)
(miles per hour) per hour   = miles per hour^2 ($miles/h^2$)

Note Always keep the two time units the same.

EXERCISE N49

1 A boy throws a stone into the air. Its initial speed, vertically upwards, is $24\,m/s$ and it takes 2.4 seconds to reach the top of its flight. What is its acceleration?

2 A car travelling at $45\,m/s$ accelerates at a rate of $7\,m/s^2$ for 6 seconds. What is its new speed?

Density

Density is another compound measure. It explains why a bag of feathers is lighter than the same sized bag of coal.

$$\text{Density} = \frac{\text{Mass}}{\text{Volume}}$$

Units g/cm^3, kg/m^3

The density of a substance is the mass of one unit of volume of the substance. That is

$$\text{Density} = \frac{\text{Mass}}{\text{Volume}}$$

So, one way of expressing the unit of density is

grams   per   cubic centimetre (g/cm^3)
(mass)   ÷   (volume)

EXERCISE N50

1 A small iceberg has a mass of 50 tonnes. If ice has a density of $900\,kg/m^3$, what is the volume of the iceberg?

2 An aluminium block, 5 cm by 8 cm by 12 cm, has a density of $2.7\,g/cm^3$. What is its mass.

3 The density of steel is $8.5\,g/cm^3$. Express this quantity in kg/m^3.

4 Which has the larger volume, a block of ice of mass 190 g and density $0.9\,g/cm^3$, or a lump of aluminium of mass 560 g and density $2.7\,g/cm^3$?

Simple equivalent problems

You may often forget the formula needed to solve a compound measure problem. One way of helping yourself is to make your own simple equivalent problem. It can be the same one every time. What you are trying to achieve here is not to work out the answer (you know that already) but to use it to work out the formula you need for the actual problem you have to solve.

EXAMPLE 3

You know that if you travel for 2 hours at 3 mph, you will cover 6 miles.

From this information work out the formula for:

a distance in terms of speed and time
b time in terms of distance and speed.

a Question   How do we get the value for distance (6) from the other two values?

Answer	6	=	3	×	2
	⇑		⇑		⇑
So	Distance	=	Speed	×	Time

b Question   How do we get the value for time (2) from the other two values?

Answer	2	=	6	÷	3
	⇑		⇑		⇑
So	Time	=	Distance	÷	Speed

Or   Time $= \dfrac{\text{Distance}}{\text{Speed}}$

Once you have the formula, you can apply it to your situation.

EXAMPLE 4

You know that an object whose volume is $2\,\text{cm}^3$ and whose density is $3\,\text{g/cm}^3$, will have a mass of 6 g.

From this information work out the formula for:

   volume in terms of mass and density

Question   How do we get the value for volume (2) from the other two values?

Answer	2	=	6	÷	3
	⇑		⇑		⇑
So	Volume	=	Mass	÷	Density

Or   Volume $= \dfrac{\text{Mass}}{\text{Density}}$

Do use this technique if you have any difficulties with questions like this.

N 14/D 16 Charts and tables

When a large amount of numerical information needs to be presented so that it is easily accessible, it is usually laid out in table or chart form. We will examine some common examples, but the skills needed for these will carry over into reading less familiar tables and charts.

Distance charts

Road atlases often show the distances between major towns in the form of a chart. Here is an extract from one such chart.

Table 1

		Distance in miles
Belfast	141	

Cork	134	264
Dublin	78	104	160
Galway	58	190	130	136
	Athlone	Belfast	Cork	Dublin

The distance between Dublic and Cork, for example, is found where the row labelled Dublin crosses the column labelled Cork, that is 160 miles. This is the distance using the most likely main road route, and is not necessarily the shortest distance between the two places.

Here are two further examples, one giving the distances in both miles and kilometres.

Table 2

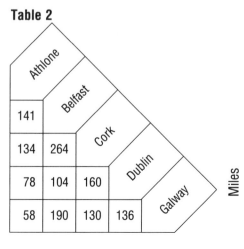

Table 3

Miles \ Kilometres	Athlone	Belfast	Cork	Dublin	Galway
Athlone		226	215	125	98
Belfast	141		422	166	304
Cork	134	264		256	208
Dublin	78	104	160		218
Galway	58	190	130	136	

EXERCISE N51

1 Use Table 1 to find the distance of a journey from Athlone to Cork then to Galway and then back to Athlone.

2 Use the information in Table 2 to find the time taken, to the nearest minute, to travel from Dublin to Cork and then to Athlone at an average speed of 40 mph

3 Use Table 3 to find the distance in kilometres from Cork to Belfast via Dublin.

Conversion charts

Charts are often used for quick reference when converting from one set of units to another. Here are two examples. Table 4 converts tyre pressures from pounds per square inch (PSI) to kilograms per square centimetre. Table 5 converts gallons to litres.

Table 4 Pounds/square inch to kilograms/square centimetre

psi	16	18	20	22	24	26	28	30
kg/cm^2	1.12	1.26	1.4	1.54	1.68	1.82	1.96	2.1
psi	32	36	40	45	50	55	60	65
kg/cm^2	2.24	2.52	2.8	3.15	3.5	3.85	4.2	4.55

Table 5 Gallons to litres

Gallons	0.2	0.4	0.6	0.8	1	2	3	4	5	10
Litres	0.91	1.82	2.73	3.64	4.55	9.09	13.64	18.18	22.73	45.46
Litres	1	2	3	4	5	10	20	30	40	50
Gallons	0.22	0.44	0.66	0.88	1.1	2.2	4.4	6.6	8.8	11

EXAMPLE 1

Convert   **a** 37 litres to gallons,   **b** 34 psi to kg/cm^2

a 37 litres $= 30 + 5 + 2$ litres
$\qquad\qquad\quad = 6.6 + 1.1 + 0.44$ gallons
$\qquad\qquad\quad = 8.14$ gallons

b 34 psi $= 16 + 18$ psi   (or halfway between 32 and 36 psi)
$\qquad\quad\ \, = 1.12 + 1.26$ kg/cm^2 (or halfway between 2.24 and 2.52 kg/cm^2)
$\qquad\quad\ \, = 2.38$ kg/cm^2 ($\frac{1}{2}[2.24 + 2.52] = 2.38$ km/cm^2)

EXERCISE N52

1 Convert to kg/cm^2

     a 26 psi   **b** 17 psi   **c** 54 psi

2 Convert

     a 20 litres to gallons   **b** 20 gallons to litres   **c** 6.2 gallons to litres

Financial and other tables

There are many tables of information related to the commercial world. Table 6 is an extract from a table which shows the monthly repayments when money is borrowed from this finance house over three different periods of time. The repayments for amounts other than those shown can be found by combining values from the table.

Table 6

Amount borrowed (£)	Monthly instalments (£)		
	12 months	24 months	36 months
5	0.51	0.30	0.23
20	2.02	1.18	0.90
50	5.04	2.95	2.25
100	10.08	5.91	4.52
500	50.40	29.55	22.60
900	90.72	53.19	40.68

EXAMPLE 2

Find the monthly repayments on a loan of £775 over 36 months.

$$£775 = £500 + £100 + £100 + £50 + £20 + £5$$
Repayments are   £22.60 + £4.52 + £4.52 + £2.25 + £0.90 + £0.23
$$= £35.02 \text{ per month over 36 months}$$

Table 7 shows the cost of sending mail since July 1996.

Table 7 UK inland letter rates from July 1996

Weight not over	First class	Second class	Weight not over	First class	Second class
60 g	26p	20p	500 g	£1.30	£1.05
100 g	39p	31p	600 g	£1.60	£1.25
150 g	49p	38p	700 g	£2.00	£1.45
200 g	60p	45p	750 g	£2.15	£1.55
250 g	70p	55p	800 g	£2.30	Not
300 g	80p	64p	900 g	£2.55	admissible
350 g	92p	73p	1000 g	£2.75	over 750 g
400 g	£1.04	83p	Each extra 250 g of part		
450 g	£1.17	93p	thereof 65p		

EXAMPLE 3

Find the cost of sending **a** a 325 g letter second class, **b** a 785 g package first class.

a 325 g is not over 350 g, so the cost is 73p

b 785 g is not over 800 g, so the cost is £2.30

Table 8 shows the returns on National Savings Certificates over a five-year maturity period.

Table 8 Growth of National Savings Certificates

Interest added at end of year	£100 Certificate	£1,000 Certificate	£10,000 Certificate
Year 1	£3.65	£36.50	£365.00
Year 2	£4.20	£41.98	£419.78
Year 3	£5.82	£58.24	£582.38
Year 4	£7.28	£72.75	£727.50
Year 5	£9.13	£91.31	£913.15
Maturity value	£130.08	£1300.78	£13 007.81

As with other tables, any information which cannot be read from the table directly can be obtained from the values shown.

EXAMPLE 4

What is the value of a £10.200 National Savings Certificate **a** cashed after 3 years, **b** left for the full five years?

a £10 200 = £10 000 and 2 × £100
After 3 years, £10 000 earns £365 + £419.78 + £582.38 = £1367.16
After 3 years, £100 earns £3.65 + 4.20 + £5.82 = £13.67
So total earned is £1367.16 + 2 × £13.67 = £1394.50

b £10 000 earns £13 007.81
£100 earns £130.08
So, total earnings after full maturity are
£13 007.81 + 2 × £130.08 = £13 267.97

EXERCISE N53

For questions 1 and 2, use the information in Table 6.

1 Find the monthly repayments when £330 is borrowed over 24 months.

2 How much more does it cost to borrow £1895 over 36 months rather than 12 months?

For questions 3, 4 and 5, use the information in Table 7.

3 Find the total cost of a 313 g letter sent first class and a 634 g package sent second class.

4 I want to send two presents to the same address, one weighs 125 g and the other weighs 235 g. How much will I save if I send them second class as one package rather than two?

5 Find the cost of sending a 1600 g package.

For questions 6 and 7, use the information in Table 8.

6 Find the value of a £25 500 National Savings Certificate after five years.

7 How much is lost by cashing in a £2800 National Savings Certificate after two years instead of five?

Timetables

Train, bus and other travel services run to a regular time schedule which is published as a timetable. Some of the points to be aware of are

- Times are usually, though not always, given according to the 24-hour clock.
- Ensure that you use the table for the direction you wish to go in.
- There are often different sections of the timetable for Saturdays, Sundays, Bank Holidays, etc.
- Not all trains/buses call at every stop on a route.
- Often at major railway stations, the timetables show separate times for arrival and departure (labelled **a** and **d**).
- Other letters placed in a timetable refer to footnotes giving details of connections and other information.

Calculating journey times

We need to be careful when calculating time gaps, especially if we use a calculator. For example, to find the gap between 1345 and 1407, we *do not* enter 14.07 − 13.45 on the calculator. This would give us 0.62, whereas the correct answer is 22 minutes. The reason is that the calculator works in decimals, but the 24-hour clock notation is not decimal (see page 21). The safe way to calculate time gaps is to count on to the next full hour, as in the following example.

EXAMPLE 5

A bus leaves the central bus station in Manchester at 2322 and arrives in Rochdale at 0153. Calculate the journey time.

Counting on from 2322 to 0000 is 38 min.
From 0000 to 0153 is 1 h 53 min
Total journey time is 1 h 53 min + 38 min = 2 h 31 min

The following example and exercise refer to the railway timetable, Table 9, below.

EXAMPLE 6

Geoff lives within a 20 minutes walk of Sherringham station. One Wednesday he leaves home at 9 am to catch the train to Norwich. He must be home by 5 pm.

a What is the earliest train he can catch and what time does he arrive?

b What is the latest train he can catch home?

c At what time will he get home and how long has he been away from home?

a 0936 train arriving at 1037.

b 1345 (the 1545 train gets into Sheringham at 1646 but he then has a 20 min walk home, which would get him home at 5.06 pm – too late!)

c The 1345 train arrives at 1446 which, with his 20 min walk, means he arrives home at 1506. From 9 am until 1300 is 3 h. From 1200 until 1506 is 3 h 6 min, so he has been away for 6 h 6 min altogether.

Table 9 (Continued on next page)

Norwich – Cromer and Sheringham   Monday to Saturday

					SO		SO	SO		SO		SO
Norwich	d	0525	0545	0720	0810	0828	0936	1025	1045	1125	1145	1225
Salhouse	d	.....	0555	0731	0820	0838	0946	1035	1055	1135	1155	1235
Hoveton & Wroxham	d	.....	0600	0736	08a25	0844	09a51	10a40	1100	11a40	1200	1240
Worstead	d	.....	0607	0743	.....	0851	.....	.....	1107	.....	1207	1247
North Walsham	d	.....	0614	0751	.....	0859	.....	.....	1114	.....	12e21	12a53
Gunton	d	.....	0620	0575	.....	0905	.....	.....	1120	.....	1227	.....
Roughton Road	d	.....	0627	0804	.....	0912	.....	.....	1127	.....	1234	.....
Cromer	a	0605	0633	0810	.....	0918	.....	.....	1133	.....	1240	.....
	d	0608	0638	0813	.....	0921	.....	.....	1136	.....	1243	.....
West Runton	d	0613	0643	0818	.....	0926	.....	.....	1141	.....	1248	.....
Sheringham	a	0618	0648	0823	.....	0932	.....	.....	1146	.....	1255	.....

Norwich – Cromer and Sheringham   Monday to Saturday

			SO					SX	SO	SX	SO	FO
Norwich	d	1345	1454	1545	1650	1535	1815	1900	1935	2040	2040	2255
Salhouse	d	1355	.....	1555	1700	1745	1825	1910	1945	2050	2050	2305
Hoveton & Wroxham	d	1400	1509	1601	1706	1751	1831	1916	1950	2055	2055	2311
Worstead	d	1407	.....	1608	1713	1758	1838	1923	1957	2102	2102	2318
North Walsham	d	1414	1522	1614	17f22	1804	1844	1929	2004	2108	21h11	23a24
Gunton	d	1420	1528	1620	1728	1810	1850	1935	2010	2114	2117	.....
Roughton Road	d	1427	1535	1627	1735	1817	1857	1942	2017	2121	2124	.....
Cromer	a	1433	1541	1633	1741	1823	1903	1948	2023	2127	2130	.....
	d	1436	.....	1636	1744	1826	1906	1951	2026	2130	2133	.....
West Runton	d	1441	.....	1641	1749	1831	1911	1956	2031	2135	2138	.....
Sheringham	a	1446	.....	1646	1754	1837	1917	2002	2036	2141	2144	.....

Sheringham – Cromer and Norwich   Monday to Saturday

				SO		SO		SO	SO		SO	
Sheringham	d	0622	0719	.....	0828	.....	0936	.....	.....	1150	.....	1310
West Runton	d	0626	0723	.....	0832	.....	0940	.....	.....	1154	.....	1314
Cromer	a	0631	0728	.....	0837	.....	0945	.....	.....	1159	.....	1319
	d	0634	0731	.....	0840	.....	0948	.....	.....	1202	.....	1322
Roughton Road	d	0639	0736	.....	0845	.....	0953	.....	.....	1207	.....	1327
Gunton	d	0646	0743	.....	0852	.....	1000	.....	.....	1214	.....	1334
North Walsham	d	0653	0750	.....	0859	.....	1017	.....	.....	1221	1310	1341
Worstead	d	0658	0755	.....	0904	.....	1012	.....	.....	1226	1315	1346
Hoveton & Wroxham	d	0706	0803	0900	0912	0958	1020	1058	1158	1234	1323	1354
Salhouse	d	0711	0808	0905	0917	1003	1025	1103	1203	1239	1328	1359
Norwich	a	0724	0821	0917	0930	1015	1037	1115	1215	1252	1340	1412

Sheringham – Cromer and Norwich   Monday to Saturday

		SO				SO	SX	SO	SX	SX	SO	SX	SO
Sheringham	d	1450	.....	1650	1813	1850	1850	1932	1935	2010	2040	2145	2150
West Runton	d	1454	.....	1654	1817	1854	1854	1936	1939	2014	2044	.....	.....
Cromer	a	1459	.....	1659	1822	1859	1859	1941	1944	2019	2049	2153	2158
	d	1502	1554	1702	1826	1904	1907	1944	1950	2022	2052	2156	2201
Roughton Road	d	1507	1559	1707	.....	1910	1912	1949	1955	2027	2057	.....	.....
Gunton	d	1514	1606	1714	.....	1917	1919	1956	2020	2034	2104	2208	2213
North Walsham	d	1521	1615	1721	1845	1924	19p31	20q05	2009	2041	2111	2214	2219
Worstead	d	1526	.....	1726	.....	1929	1936	2010	2014	2046	2116	.....	.....
Hoveton & Wroxham	d	1534	1626	1734	1855	1937	1944	2018	2022	2054	2124	2225	2230
Salhouse	d	1539	.....	1739	.....	1943	1950	2023	2027	2059	2129	.....	.....
Norwich	a	1552	1642	1752	1912	1955	2002	2036	2040	2112	2142	2242	2247

Norwich – Cromer & Sheringham   Sheringham – Cromer & Norwich
Sundays   Sundays

Norwich	d	1030	1135	1410	1625	1730
Salhouse	d	1040	1145	1420	1635	1740
Hoveton & Wroxham	d	1046	1150	1426	1640	1745
Worstead	d	1053	1157	1433	1647	1752
North Walsham	d	1059	12t07	1439	1653	18v01
Gunton	d	1105	1213	1445	1659	1807
Roughton Road	d	1112	1220	1452	1706	1814
Cromer	a	1118	1226	1457	1711	1819
	d	1121	1229	1501	1714	1822
West Runton	d	1126	1234	1506	1719	1827
Sheringham	a	1131	1239	1511	1725	1833

Sheringham	d	1135	1245	1515	1730	1840
West Runton	d	1139	1249	1519	1734	1844
Cromer	a	1144	1254	1524	1739	1849
	d	1147	1257	1527	1742	1852
Roughton Road	d	1152	1302	1532	1747	1857
Gunton	d	1159	1309	1539	1754	1904
North Walsham	d	1206	1316	1546	1801	1911
Worstead	d	1211	1321	1551	1806	1916
Hoveton & Wroxham	d	1219	1329	1559	1814	1924
Salhouse	d	1225	1334	1604	1819	1929
Norwich	a	1237	1347	1617	1832	1942

Notes SO – Saturdays only, SX – Saturdays excepted, FO – Fridays only

a	arrive	p	Arr 1926
d	depart	q	Arr 2002
e	Arr 1213	t	Arr 1203
f	Arr 1719	v	Arr 1758
h	Arr 2108		

EXERCISE N54

1 At what time does the Saturday Only train, leaving Cromer at 1904, arrive in Norwich?

2 Chris lives 15 minutes walk from Hoveton and Wroxham station. She must see her bank manager at 0950 in Norwich on Thursday. The bank is a 5-minute walk from the railway station in Norwich. At what time must she leave home to make sure she is on time for her appointment?

3 Grace and Rob have a holiday home in Cromer, where they spend their weekends away from London. Their train from London arrives in Norwich station at 8.15 pm on Friday and the latest train they can catch back to London from Norwich on Sunday is at 7.08 pm.

    a At what time will they arrive in Cromer if they catch the first available train from Norwich?

    b What is the latest train they can catch from Cromer to make their London connection on Sunday?

4 Matthew lives in Norwich but runs an antiques shop in Worstead, 20 minutes walk from the station. He has to open the shop at 9.15 am and close it at 5 pm each day from Monday to Saturday.

    a At what time must he catch the train in the morning?

    b What is the first train he can catch home in the evening?

    c How long does he spend on the train each day?

    d He lives 15 minutes walk from Norwich station. How long is he away from home each day?

5 The distance from Norwich to Sheringham is 48 km. Calculate the average speed of the first train on Saturday from Norwich to Sheringham in km/h.

N 15/D16 Conversion and travel graphs

Conversion of units

Even when we know the conversion factor between two units, a visual method of making the conversion is often more convenient. For example, we know that 1 inch ≈ 2.54 cm. Suppose we want an easy visual way to convert between inches and centimetres. One way is to draw parallel scales, like this:

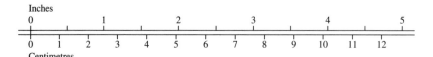

We can see from this that, for example, 3 inches is about 7.6 cm or that 10 cm is about 3.9 inches.

Such number lines are difficult to draw accurately. A better way is to draw the two scales at right angles to each other on millimetre graph paper. The scales can then be conveniently fitted to the graph grid. Points representing corresponding inch and centimetre values then form a straight line through the origin.

To draw the line, we only need to know one pair of values besides the origin. Knowing that 1 inch ≈ 2.54 cm, we calculate that, for example, 5 inches ≈ 12.7 cm. We can then draw our conversion line by joining the point (5, 12.7) to the origin.

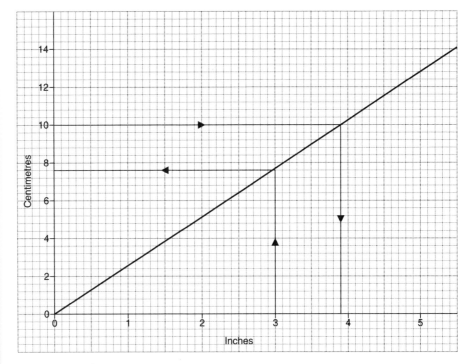

We can now read off required inches values. For example, 3 inches ≈ 7.6 cm and 10 cm ≈ 3.9 inches can be read off, as shown by the arrows on the graph.

Travel graphs

Displacement is the amount by which the position of an object moved relative to a fixed reference point (origin). Displacement can be positive or negative, depending on the direction of motion.

We can illustrate the movement of an object by drawing a graph relating its displacement from some fixed point (usually the starting point) to the time taken.

For example, a woman walking a dog along a straight path stops and releases the dog. It runs 100 m forwards in 10 seconds, stops and sniffs for 10 seconds, runs a further 50 m forwards in 20 seconds then, spotting another dog in the distance, runs back past her to a point 100 m behind her in 40 seconds. Assume that all speeds are constant.

Distance is the amount of 'ground' covered by a moving object, disregarding its direction of motion. Distance is always positive.

For example, a person walking 100 m along a path and then returning to the starting point achieves a total distance of 100 + 100 = 200 m, but a total displacement of 100 + (⁻100) = 0 m.

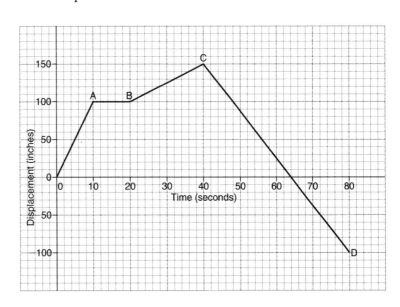

Velocity is the rate of change of displacement and may be positive or negative depending on the direction of motion. The velocity is the **gradient of the travel graph**.

Speed is the rate of change of distance. Speed is always positive.

Average speed =
Total distance
———————
Total time

Average velocity =
Total displacement
————————
Total time

When velocity is constant, the graph is a straight line. When velocity varies, the graph is a curve. The gradient of the curve at any point is the velocity at that instant. Average speed and average velocity are still found in the same way.

On the graph we have a series of straight lines because the dog makes each run at constant speed, so each displacement changes at a uniform rate.

Section OA represents the first stage of the dog's journey – a displacement of 100 m. The gradient of OA is 10, corresponding to a velocity of 10 m/s.

Section AB represents the period when the dog was stationary. There is no displacement and the gradient is zero (zero velocity).

Section BC represents the second forward stage – a displacement of 50 m. The gradient of BC is 2.5, corresponding to a velocity of 2.5 m/s.

Section CD represents the final stage. The displacement during this section was $^-250$ m. The gradient of CD is $^-6.25$, corresponding to a velocity of $^-6.25$ m/s. The **negative sign** indicates that the dog was travelling in the **opposite direction**.

The **total distance** the dog travelled $= 100 + 50 + 250 = 400$ m
The **total displacement** the dog achieved $= 100 + 50 + {}^-250 = -100$ m

The dog's **average speed** $= 400 \div 80 = 5$ m/s
The dog's **average velocity** $= {}^-100 \div 80 = {}^-1.25$ m/s

EXERCISE N55

1 Given that $1\,\text{kg} = 2.205\,\text{lb}$, draw a graph to convert up to 20 kg to lb. Use your graph to convert **a** 14.5 kg to lb, **b** 26.2 lb to kg.

2 $0\,°\text{C} = 32\,°\text{F}$ and $100\,°\text{C} = 212\,°\text{F}$. Use these to draw a graph to convert between temperature values in Celsius and in Fahrenheit. Use your graph to convert **a** 56 °C to °F, **b** 100 °F to °C.

3 A driver in a treasure hunt sets out at 10.00 am. He drives 5 km to the first clue, arriving at 10.10 am. He takes 3 minutes to solve the clue and then drives towards the next clue, which is 8 km further on. He misses this next clue and goes an extra 2 km before he realises his mistake. The time is then 10.28 sm. He turns round and returns to the second clue, reaching it at 10.30 am.

    a Draw a graph to show the driver's journey.
    b State the driver's total distance travelled and his total displacement.
    c Calculate the driver's average speed and average velocity.

4 A tortoise and a hare have a 100 m race. The tortoise is given a 40 m start and when the starting pistol sounds he sets off at a steady speed of 0.6 m/s. The hare dawdles over the first 60 m, taking 10 seconds, but then gets bored and just sits around for 85 seconds. The hare finally realises her predicament and runs the remainder of the race to achieve a dead heat with the tortoise.

    a Draw a graph to illustrate this contest.
    b At what times after the start are the tortoise and the hare level?
    c What is the hare's speed over the final stage of her journey?
    d What is the hare's average speed?

5

Madeleine gets off the bus at midday. She walks to the shop in 8 minutes and spends 5 minutes there shopping. She then walks to the post office at 60 m/min. Her business there takes 6 minutes. Finally, she walks home in 4 minutes.

Taking left to right on the diagram to be the positive direction

a Draw a graph to illustrate Madeleine's journey.
b Calculate her average speed for the journey.
c Calculate her average velocity for the journey.

N 16 Indices and standard form

Powers

$4^2 = 1 \times 4 \times 4$ $4^3 = 1 \times 4 \times 4 \times 4$ and so on.

The most common powers of numbers are shown in the table. For higher powers, use your calculator. Check how to use the keys:

x^2 for squares

x^3 for cubes (you may not have this key)

x^y for powers in general

Number	Power				
	2	3	4	5	6
2	4	8	16	32	64
3	9	27	81	243	729
4	16	64	256		
5	25	125	625		
6	36	216			
7	49				
8	64				
9	81				
10	100	1000			
11	121				
12	144				
13	169				

EXERCISE N56

Find the values of the following, using a calculator where necessary

1 4^5 **2** 2^{10} **3** 9^3 **4** 3^6 **5** 10^6

6 5^3 **7** 2^7 **8** 7^4 **9** 8^3

Multiplication

EXAMPLE 1

Find $3^5 \times 3^2$.

$$3^5 \times 3^2 = (3 \times 3 \times 3 \times 3 \times 3) \times (3 \times 3 \times 3)$$
$$= 3^7$$
$$\Rightarrow \quad 3^5 \times 3^2 = 3^{5+2} = 3^7$$

The rule is: when **multiplying** two powers of the **same** number, **add the powers**.

Rules for combining powers

Multiplication rule

$$a^m \times a^n = a^{m+n}$$

Division rule

$$a^m \div a^n = a^{m-n}$$

Powers rule

$$(a^m)^n = a^{mn}$$

Division

> EXAMPLE 2
>
> Find $5^8 \div 5^3$.
>
> $$5^8 \div 5^3 = \frac{5 \times 5 \times 5 \times 5 \times 5 \times \not{5} \times \not{5} \times \not{5}}{\not{5} \times \not{5} \times \not{5}}$$
> $$= 5^3$$
> $$\Rightarrow \quad 5^8 \div 5^3 = 5^{8-3} = 5^3$$

The rule is: when **dividing** one power by another power of the **same** number, **subtract the second power from the first**.

Powers of powers

> EXAMPLE 3
>
> Find $(4^3)^2$
>
> $$(4^3)^2 = 4^3 \times 4^3$$
> $$= 4^6 \text{ by the rule for multiplying powers.}$$
> $$\Rightarrow \quad (4^3)^2 = 4^{3 \times 2} = 4^6$$

The rule is: when a power of a number is raised to another power, **multiply the powers**.

Negative and zero powers

Consider this sequence:

$$3^4 = 81$$
$$3^3 = 27$$
$$3^2 = 9$$
$$3^1 = 3$$

At each stage the index is reduced by 1 and the result is divided by 3. If the process is continued, we get

$$3^0 = 1$$
$$3^{-1} = \frac{1}{3^1} = \frac{1}{3}$$
$$3^{-2} = \frac{1}{3^2} = \frac{1}{9}$$

and so on

From this we can see that

- any number, raised to the **power 0**, is equal to **1**.
- a **negative power** indicates a **reciprocal** of the number.

> **Example 4**
>
> Find 2^{-5}.
>
> $$2^{-5} = \frac{1}{2^5}$$
>
> $$= \frac{1}{32}$$

Fractional powers

Suppose we want to find $9^{\frac{1}{2}}$.

Zero index rule	We note that $(9^{\frac{1}{2}})^2 = 9^{\frac{1}{2} \times 2}$
$a^0 = 1$	$= 9^1$
Negative index (reciprocal) rule	so $(9^{\frac{1}{2}})^2 = 9$
$a^{-n} = \dfrac{1}{a^n}$	which gives $9^{\frac{1}{2}} = \sqrt{9} = 3$

Negative index (reciprocal) rule
$$a^{-n} = \frac{1}{a^n}$$

Fractional index rule
$$a^{1/n} = \sqrt[n]{a}$$

We note that $(9^{\frac{1}{2}})^2 = 9^{\frac{1}{2} \times 2}$
$$= 9^1$$
so $(9^{\frac{1}{2}})^2 = 9$
which gives $9^{\frac{1}{2}} = \sqrt{9} = 3$

By a similar argument we could show that, for example,

$$8^{1/3} = \sqrt[3]{8} = 2$$

and so on.

From this we can see that

- a **fractional power** indicates a **root** of the number.

> **EXAMPLE 5**
>
> Find $81^{\frac{1}{4}}$.
>
> $$8^{\frac{1}{4}} = \sqrt[4]{81}$$
>
> $$= 3$$

EXERCISE N57

Find the value of the following. Use a calculator where necessary.

1 $144^{\frac{1}{2}}$ **2** 6^0 **3** $(2^4)^2$

4 6^{-1} **5** $16^{-\frac{1}{2}}$ **6** $32^{\frac{3}{5}}$

Simplify the following, leaving your answer in index form.

7 $6^3 \times 6^2$ **8** $9^4 \div 9^6$ **9** $(5^5)^3$

10 $(\sqrt{3})^5$ **11** $4^6 \times 4^2 \div 4^4$ **12** $2^7 \times 2^3 \div 2^{-5}$

Using the facts that $4 = 2^2$ and $9 = 3^2$, simplify the following, leaving your answer in index form.

13 $4^3 \div 2^5$ as a power of 2   **14** $3^5 \times 9^2$ as a power of 3

15 $2^6 \times 4^3$ as a power of 4   **16** $9^3 \times 3^3 \div 3^5$ as a power of 9

17 2^5 as a power of 4   **18** 3^9 as a power of 9

Standard form

The number 3456 can be written as
$$
\begin{array}{rcl}
345.6 & \times & 10^1 \\
\text{or} \quad 34.56 & \times & 10^2 \\
\text{or} \quad 3.456 & \times & 10^3 \\
\text{or} \quad 0.3456 & \times & 10^4 \\
\text{or} \quad 0.034\,56 & \times & 10^5
\end{array}
$$

and so on.

The third of these, 3.456×10^3, is called the **standard form** of the number 3456. This is made up of two parts:

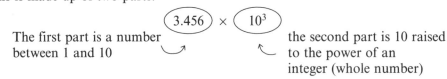

The first part is a number between 1 and 10   the second part is 10 raised to the power of an integer (whole number)

Notice that the digits in the first part are the same as those in the original number.

This notation is especially useful when very large or very small numbers are being used, particularly in scientific measurements. You will find that if you try to calculate a large result with your calculator, it will display the result in standard form, but showing **only the power** without the base 10. Some calculators display E before the power.

EXAMPLE 6

Write the following numbers in standard form.

a 87 359   **b** 0.024 68

a   87.359   Put the decimal point after
    Find A 8.7359   the first significant figure.
                    ↓
    Find n 8.7359×10.000 What power of ten do you
                                         need to move the decimal
    So $87\,359 = 8.7359 \times 10^4$ point back to where it was?

b   0.024.68   Put the decimal point after
    Find A 2.468   the first significant figure.
                    ↓
    Find n 2.468×0.01 What power of ten do you
                                         need to move the decimal
                                         point back to where it was?

    So $0.024\,68 = 2.468 \times 10^{-2}$

EXERCISE N58

Write the following numbers in standard form.

1 46.329   **2** 0.015 738 1   **3** 7.853 942

4 0.000.136 5   **5** 456.283   **6** 0.142 857

7 The mean radius of the earth is 6.4×10^6 m. Write this as an ordinary number.

8 The earth is travelling at approximately 6.7×10^4 miles per hour as it orbits the sun. Write this as an ordinary number.

Sidebar:

The **standard form** of a number is defined as $A \times 10^n$, where

- A is a number in the range $1 \leqslant A < 10$
- n is a positive or negative integer (whole number).

Remember:
$$
\begin{array}{rcl}
10^{-6} & = & 0.000\,001 \\
10^{-5} & = & 0.000\,01 \\
10^{-4} & = & 0.000\,1 \\
10^{-3} & = & 0.001 \\
10^{-2} & = & 0.01 \\
10^{-1} & = & 0.1 \\
10^{0} & = & 1 \\
10^{1} & = & 10 \\
10^{2} & = & 100 \\
10^{3} & = & 1000 \\
10^{4} & = & 10\,000 \\
10^{5} & = & 100\,000 \\
10^{6} & = & 1\,000\,000
\end{array}
$$

Standard form on a calculator

Most calculators have a key labelled $\boxed{\text{EXP}}$ or $\boxed{\text{EE}}$. If your calculator does not, check in your manual.

This key is used to input numbers in standard form. For example,

You would write 2.456×10^3

But you key in 2.456 $\boxed{\textbf{EXP}}$ 3

Note that the $\boxed{\text{EXP}}$ key replaces $\times 10$. This is not displayed on most calculators.

Standard form	Key in
3.256×10^5	3.256 $\boxed{\text{EXP}}$ 5
-8.917×10^{15}	8.917 $\boxed{\pm}$ $\boxed{\text{EXP}}$ 15
1.235×10^{-5}	1.235 $\boxed{\text{EXP}}$ 5 $\boxed{\pm}$
-9.287×10^{-13}	9.287 $\boxed{\pm}$ $\boxed{\text{EXP}}$ 13 $\boxed{\pm}$

Note. Your calculator may use a $\boxed{\pm}$ key after the negative number or a $\boxed{(-)}$ key before it.

Forcing standard form display

Your scientific calculator will display results in standard form to any degree of accuracy. Check in your manual how to achieve this. It probably comes under the heading of *Scientific Notation*.

When the result of a calculation is very large or very small, your calculator will present the result in standard form. Otherwise it will display the result normally unless you select the standard-form display.

Calculating with numbers in standard form

EXAMPLE 7

Find

a $(2.4 \times 10^5) \times (3.2 \times 10^2)$

b $\dfrac{(2.4 \times 10^5)}{(3.2 \times 10^2)}$

a $(2.4 \times 10^5) \times (3.2 \times 10^2)$
$= (2.4 \times 3.2) \times (10^5 \times 10^2)$
$= \quad 7.68 \quad \times \quad 10^7$
$= 7.68 \times 10^7$

> Rearrange the order and calculate each bracket separately.

b $\dfrac{(2.4 \times 10^5)}{(3.2 \times 10^2)}$
$= \quad \left(\dfrac{2.4}{3.2}\right) \quad \times \left(\dfrac{10^5}{10^2}\right)$
$= \quad 0.75 \quad \times \quad 10^3$
$= (7.5 \times 10^{-1}) \times \quad 10^3$
$= \quad 7.5 \quad \times \quad 10^2$
$= 7.5 \times 10^2$

> Treat the number part separately from the index part.

We cannot use the index laws to add or subtract. We must either use a calculator, or write the numbers in their normal form, add or subtract, then write the answer in standard form.

EXERCISE N59

Give all answers in standard form.

1 Find, without using a calculator,

    a $(3 \times 10^3) \times (4 \times 10^5)$ **b** $(4.2 \times 10^6) \div (1.4 \times 10^2)$

    c $(1.5 \times 10^4) \times (5 \times 10^{-2})$ **d** $(6.4 \times 10^3) \div (1.6 \times 10^{-4})$

    e $(3.2 \times 10^2) \times (6.4 \times 10^4)$ **f** $(1.5 \times 10^{-3}) \div (3 \times 10^{-5})$

    g $(5 \times 10^2)^2$ **h** $(6 \times 10^{-3})^2$

2 Find, using a calculator if necessary,

    a $(3 \times 10^3) + (4 \times 10^5)$ **b** $(4.2 \times 10^6) - (1.2 \times 10^2)$

    c $(1.5 \times 10^{-4}) + (5 \times 10^{-2})$ **d** $(6.4 \times 10^3) - (1.6 \times 10^4)$

    e $(3.2 \times 10^2) + (6.4 \times 10^4)$ **f** $(1.5 \times 10^{-3}) - (3 \times 10^{-5})$

3 Place these numbers in order of size, **smallest** first.

    a (3×10^3) **b** (4×10^5) **c** (4.2×10^6)

    d (1.2×10^2) **e** (1.5×10^4) **f** (5×10^{-2})

    g (6.4×10^3) **h** (1.6×10^{-4}) **j** (1.5×10^{-3})

4 The mass of the earth in kg can be found from the formula

$$M = \frac{gR^2}{G}$$

where

    G is the universal constant of gravitation $\approx (6.7 \times 10^{-11})\,\mathrm{N\,m^2\,kg^{-2}}$

    g is the acceleration due to gravity $\approx (9.81 \times 10^0)\,\mathrm{m\,s^{-2}}$

    R is the radius of the earth $\approx (6.4 \times 10^6)\,\mathrm{m}$

Calculate the mass of the earth.

A 01/D 15 Flow charts

Flow charts are a way of giving a set of instructions in the correct order. This is indicated by the direction of the arrows between the boxes through the flow chart.

Conventionally flow charts begin with a 'Start' box and end with a 'Stop' box, both of which are either ellipses or rounded rectangles. 'Instruction' boxes are rectangles and 'Decision' (question) boxes are diamonds.

The box $N = N + 1$ may seem strange but it is a way of saying 'the value of N is increased by 1'.

A decision box has two exits, one for a 'Yes' answer, the other for a 'No' answer.
You exit from the box in the direction which answers the question in the box correctly each time you pass through it.

This allows us to have the 'loop' on the right-hand side, which means the flow chart can keep on generating outputs until the condition in the decision box is met.

The operation then stops.

'Variables' are letters whose value changes as we work through the flow chart.

In this flow chart, the variables are N and A.

EXAMPLE 1

Here is a flow chart which is used to generate all the square numbers between 1 and 200.

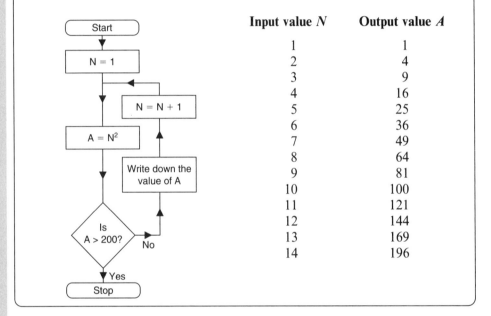

Input value N	Output value A
1	1
2	4
3	9
4	16
5	25
6	36
7	49
8	64
9	81
10	100
11	121
12	144
13	169
14	196

The table next to the flow chart helps to keep a check on the values of the variables as we go through the operations of the flow chart.

EXERCISE A1

For each of these flow charts, write down the value of each of the variables as you work through the flow chart (as in the above example).

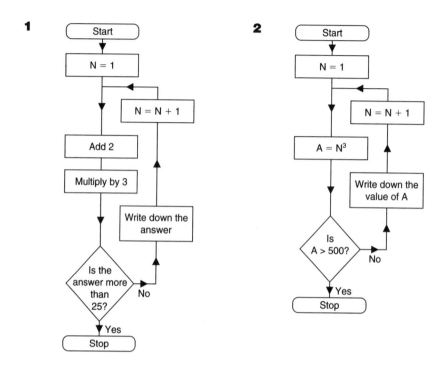

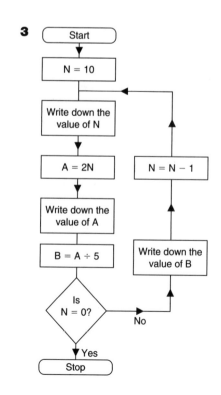

Reversing the flow

If we know the output value of a flow chart, we can retrace our route through the flow chart to find out what the input value was. This involves

Step 1 Working through the flow chart from the Stop box back up to the Start box.

Step 2 Carrying out the **inverse** operation of the instruction in each box.

> An inverse operation **undoes** what the original operation does.

Inverse operations

An inverse operation 'undoes' what the original operation 'does'
For example, if the box said 'add 4', the inverse operation would be 'subtract 4'. Here are some common inverse operations.

Operation	*Inverse*
Add	Subtract
Subtract	Add
Multiply by	Divide by
Divide by	Multiply by

> **a** Work through the flow chart as it is presented
>
> **b** **Step 1** means that we operate the flow chart from the bottom to the top. In the diagram, the flow chart has the flow reversed
>
> **Step 2** means we carry out the inverse operation in each box
>
> After some practice you will be able to do this without redrawing the flow charts

EXAMPLE 1

From the flow chart below   **a** find the output when the input is **i** 6, **ii** 1;
b find the input when the output is **i** 17, **ii** 5.

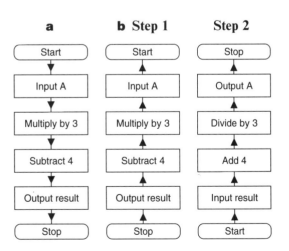

a   **i** $6 \times 3 - 4 = 14$ **b**   **i** $17 + 4 \div 3 = 7$
    ii $1 \times 3 - 4 = {}^{-}1$ **ii** $5 + 4 \div 3 = 3$

EXERCISE A2

1 From the flow chart, find   **a** the output when the input is **i** 2, **ii** 14.5;
b the input when the output is **i** 3, **ii** 1.8.

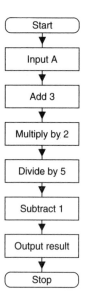

A 02 Algebra: introduction

Order of arithmetic operations

The 'word' BODMAS is
useful to help remember
this

Brackets
Order (powers)
Division
Multiplication
Addition
Subtraction

Multiplication before
addition.

Division before subtraction.

Brackets first
then powers
before + or −
then subtraction and
addition, working from left
to right.

There is a conventional order in which arithmetic operations **must be carried out**.

1 Start with any calculations in **brackets**.
2 Then any **powers**.
3 Then any **multiplication** and/or **division**.
4 Then any **addition** and/or **subtraction**.

Any operations at the same level of priority are carried out **working from left
to right**.

EXAMPLE 1

Evaluate

a $3 + 2 \times 5$

b $10 - 6 \div 2$

c $(3 + 5)^2 - 2^2 + 6 \times 3$

a $3 + 2 \times 5$
   $= 3 + 10$
   $= 13$

b $10 - 6 \div 2$
   $= 10 - 3$
   $= 7$

c $(4 + 5)^2 - 2^2 + 6 \times 3$
   $= 9^2 - 2^2 + 6 \times 3$
   $= 81 - 4 + 6 \times 3$
   $= 81 - 4 + 18$
   $= 77 + 18$
   $= 95$

EXERCISE A3

Work out the following without using your calculator.

1 $7 + 3 \times 2$ **2** $8 - 12 \div 4$ **3** $(3 + 2) \times 5 - 6$

4 $4^2 + 2 \times 3$ **5** $(3 + 6) - 4 \times 2$ **6** $5 + 2^2 - 3$

7 $(8 - 3)^2 + 2^2 \times 3$ **8** $5^2 \times (6 + 4) + 3^2$ **9** $10 - 6 \div 3 \times 4 + 3$

10 $3 \times 2 - 15 \div (3 + 2) \times 6^2$

The division which is in the form of one quantity **over** another quantity is always done **last**.

> This seems like a contradiction of BODMAS unless you think of there being brackets above and below the division line.

EXAMPLE 2

a Evaluate $\dfrac{12}{6 - 2}$ *Solution* $\dfrac{12}{6 - 2}$

$$= \frac{12}{4}$$

$$= 3$$

b Evaluate $\dfrac{7^2 - 4}{3 \times 2 + 3}$ *Solution* $\dfrac{7^2 - 4}{3 \times 2 + 3}$

$$= \frac{49 - 4}{6 + 3}$$

$$= \frac{45}{9}$$

$$= 5$$

> $\dfrac{7^2 - 4}{3 \times 2 + 3}$
>
> is the same as
>
> $(7^2 - 4) \div (3 \times 2 + 3)$

EXERCISE A4

Work out these expressions without using your calculator.

1 $\dfrac{15}{11 - 6}$ **2** $\dfrac{7 + 3}{5 - 3}$ **3** $\dfrac{7 + 3 \times 7}{(9 - 2) \times 2}$

4 $\dfrac{(7 + 3) \times 7}{9 - 2 \times 2}$ **5** $\dfrac{(72 - 6^2) \div 9}{20 \div (2 + 3)}$ **6** $\dfrac{10 \div 2 + 3 \times 5}{8^2 - 6^2 - 4 \times 2}$

Letters representing numbers

> Remember BODMAS

Algebra is concerned with the generalisation of arithmetic operations. The order in which operations are carried out remains the same when dealing with letters or other symbols which represent numbers.

Notation

ab means $a \times b$

$3a$ means $3 \times a$

$3ab$ means $3 \times a \times b$

a^2 means $a \times a$

$(3a)^2$ means $3 \times a$ **then** square the answer

$3a^2$ means $a \times a$ **then** multiply by 3

EXAMPLE 3

When $p = -2$, $q = 3$ and $r = 4$, evaluate

a $\dfrac{3p^2}{qr}$ **b** $2r^2 - (q-p)^2 + qr$

a $\dfrac{3p^2}{qr} = \dfrac{3 \times (-2)^2}{3 \times 4}$

$= \dfrac{3 \times 4}{12}$

$= 1$

b $2r^2 - (q-p)^2 + qr = 2 \times 4^2 - [3 - (-2)]^2 + 3 \times 4$

$= 2 \times 16 - 5^2 + 12$

$= 32 - 25 + 12$

$= 7 + 12$

$= 19$

---

a Powers before multiplication. Division of the top by the bottom is the last operation.

b Brackets before powers. Powers before multiplication. Then addition and subtraction working from left to right.

EXERCISE A5

Evaluate the following when $x = 5$, $y = -4$ and $z = 2$.

1 xz **2** $x + y$ **3** $3z$

4 $2y - x$ **5** $5z^2$ **6** $(3y)^2$

7 $3x - 2y$ **8** $\dfrac{10z}{x}$ **9** $2xy - 3z^2$

10 $3x^2 - (yz)^2$ **11** $x^2 + y^2 \times z^2$ **12** $\dfrac{x+y+z}{x^2 + (y^2 \div z^2)}$

13 $3x^2 + 2x + 6$ **14** $\dfrac{2x^2 y}{25z}$ **15** $\dfrac{x + (y+z)^2}{x^2 + y - 20}$

Simplifying algebraic expressions – collecting like terms

An algebraic term often consists of a number, one or more variables (represented by letters) and the sign in front of them. A collection of algebraic terms is called an **expression**. Algebraic expressions can be reduced to their simplest form by collecting 'like' terms.

The expression $3x + 7xy + 5x$ has three terms, which may be 'boxed':

$$\boxed{+3x} \quad \boxed{+7xy} \quad \boxed{+5x}$$

You can use this method of 'boxing' each term to make sure you only combine 'like' terms. Don't forget to include the sign in front!

When the letters in two or more boxes are **exactly the same** (the order in which they appear doesn't matter), the terms are 'like' terms which can be combined to simplify the expression.

$$\boxed{+3x} + \boxed{+5x} = \boxed{+8x} \quad \text{but} \quad \boxed{+7xy} \text{ has no like terms.}$$

The expression in its **simplest form** is $8x + 7xy$

EXAMPLE 4

Simplify by collecting like terms

a $2p - 3q + 4p + q + 7$ **b** $3r^2 - 2rs + r^2 - 3sr + r$

a $2p - 3q + 4p + q + 7$

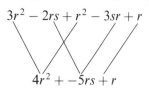

$2p - 3q + 4p + q + 7$ in its **simplest form** is $6p - 2q + 7$

b
$$3r^2 - 2rs + r^2 - 3sr + r$$

$$4r^2 + -5rs + r$$

$3r^2 - 2rs + r^2 - 3sr + r$ in its **simplest form** is $4r^2 - 5rs + r$

Note that *rs* and *sr* are like terms – the boxes would contain the same letters.

EXERCISE A6

Simplify the following expressions by collecting like terms.

1 $2a - a + 3a$ **2** $3b - 2a + b$ **3** $5d - 3 - 3d$

4 $6m - 2m + n + 3n$ **5** $4p + q + 3p + 4q$ **6** $2r^2 - r^2 + 3 - 2s$

7 $4 - 3pq - 5 + pq$ **8** $2ab - 3ab + 5$ **9** $6pqr - 3pqr + pq$

10 $4xy - x^2 + xy + 4x^2$ **11** $5st - 2ts + t^2 - 3st$ **12** $11a - 2ab - a + 4ab$

13 $5 - 2y + xy - y$ **14** $4mn - 3n + 2m + 4m + 2n - mn$

Using algebraic expressions – generalisations

Algebraic expressions often occur as **formulae** (the plural of formula) and are used to state facts. A formula will contain letters to represent numbers and the formula is used to express a true statement whatever values the letters take.

EXAMPLE 5

Pencils cost 12 p each. Write down the cost of   **a** 2 pencils,   **b** 5 pencils, **c** n pencils.

a 2 pencils cost $12\,p \times 2 = 24\,p$

b 5 pencils cost $12 \times 5 = 60\,p$

c $12\,n$ pence

We can see that the total cost will always be 12 × number of pencils

An algebraic expression or formula for this is 12n (which is how we write 12 × n), where n can stand for any positive whole number.

EXAMPLE 6

Wendy is 26 years younger than her mother. How old will Wendy be when her mother is   **a** 40 years old,   **b** x years old?

a Wendy's age $= 40 - 26 = 14$ years old

b Wendy's age $= x - 26$ years old

If we know her mother's age, we can find Wendy's age each time by subtracting 26.

An algebraic formula shows this for any value of x.

EXERCISE A7

1 Rope costs 34 p per metre. Find the cost of   **a** 2 m,   **b** 7 m,   **c** x m of rope.

2 Jim is 12 years old. How old will he be   **a** 5,   **b** 15,   **c** y years from now?

3 In a certain service station unleaded petrol is always 5 pence per litre less than the price of leaded petrol. What is the price of a litre of unleaded petrol when the price of a litre of leaded petrol is   **a** 52 p,   **b** 57 p,   **c** x pence?

4 Winston is having a party. He sends out 32 invitations. How many guests will he have if   **a** 7,   **b** 12,   **c** r guests cannot make it?

5 A recipe uses twice as much margarine as it does butter. How much butter is used when   **a** 10 oz,   **b** 6 oz,   **c** M oz of margarine are used?

6 I have £36 in my bank account. How much will be in the account if I **a** write a cheque for £8 and another for £x,   **b** deposit £z and withdraw £18,   **c** deposit £n and withdraw £m?

Formulae and units

When working with algebraic formulae, it is essential to have all the variables in the same units. If the units are different, you will have to include a conversion factor in the formula to overcome this. **You must not mix units**.

In each case here, we cannot mix pounds and pence so we must work in either one or the other unit. In pence, we simply write £5 as 500 pence.
In pounds, we can write the amounts in **a** and **b** as decimals but we cannot do this in **c**. In this problem we have to write the pence as hundredths of a pound – the conversion factor.

EXAMPLE 7

How much change will I get from £5 if I buy 4 items which cost
a 55 p, **b** 75 p, **c** x pence each?

a $5 - 4 \times 0.55 = £2.80$ or $500 - 4 \times 55 = 280$ pence

b $5 - 4 \times 0.75 = £2.00$ or $500 - 4 \times 75 = 200$ pence

c $5 - 4 \times \dfrac{x}{100} = £\left(5 - \dfrac{4x}{100}\right)$ or $500 - 4 \times x = 500 - 4x$ pence

---

EXERCISE A8

1 I have 14 m of ribbon. I cut off 17 pieces each a cm long. Write an expression for the length, in cm, of ribbon left.

2 Write down an expression for the cost in pounds of 125 items which cost x pence each.

3 Bicycle lights cost £h each and batteries cost g pence each. Write down an expression for the cost of two lamps and four batteries.

4 In a youth club cafe a canned drink costs four times as much as a packet of crisps. Write down an expression for the change I get from £5 when I buy two canned drinks and two packets of crisps if crisps cost y pence per packet.

A 03 Sequences, mappings and generalisations

Sequences

A sequence is an ordered set of numbers, or terms. Every term in the sequence is given by applying the same 'rule' to the preceding term or terms.

The numbers in a sequence are called **terms**.

Finding the rule

If you think that you can see the rule at once, check carefully that it applies to each term.

Check 1 Is the sequence produced by adding (or subtracting) the same number to each term to get the next term?

The sequence below is produced by successively adding 2.

    1, 3, 5, 7, 9, 11, …

Check 2 Is the sequence produced by multiplying (or dividing) each term by the same number to get the next term?

The sequence below is produced by successively multiplying by 3.

    1, 3, 9, 27, 81, …

Some sequences have a rule which involves more than one operation. We can sometimes deal with these as follows.

The differences are what you get when you subtract each term from the next one.

Check 3 Can we see a pattern in the differences between the terms?

For example, consider this sequence.

Differences
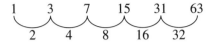

The pattern of the differences can indicate what to multiply by.

We see that the differences are doubled each time. This gives us the clue to try doubling each term. We find that by then adding 1 we obtain the next term of the sequence in each case.

It may then be necessary to add or subtract the same number n each case to produce the actual sequence.

Multiply by 2

Add 1
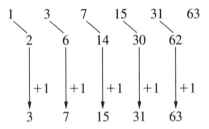

We have found the rule, which is 'multiply by 2 than add 1'.

EXERCISE A9

Find the rule and the next three terms in the following sequences.

1 1 5 9 13 17...   **2** 1 4 16 64 256...   **3** 3 1 -1 -3 -5...

4 2 -6 18 -54 162...   **5** 1 5 13 29 61...   **6** 8 4 2 1...

7 0 $\frac{1}{3}$ $\frac{2}{3}$ 1 $\frac{4}{3}$ $\frac{5}{3}$...   **8** 1 2 0 4 -4 12 -20...

Mappings

A mapping is a rule which connects two sets of numbers. One set of numbers is the 'input' set, called the **domain** of the mapping. The mapping relates the domain to an 'output' set of numbers, called the **range**. Each **object** in the domain has an **image** in the range.

Mappings are represented in diagrams like this.

Mappings are described concisely by stating 'algebraically' what happens to a general term *x*.

This is expressed as $x \rightarrow \ldots$

Under this mapping

   1 is mapped to 2

   2 is mapped to 3
and so on

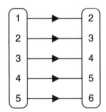

Or we say, for example, that 6 is the image of 5.

We can describe the mapping in words as 'add one', or more neatly as an algebraic generalisation $x \rightarrow x + 1$.

In this form, *x* can be any number in the domain and its image under this mapping is the result of adding 1 to the value of *x*.

EXERCISE A10

Draw diagrams to show the following mappings. Use the numbers 1, 2, 3, 4, 5 as the domain in each case.

1 $x \rightarrow x - 1$ **2** $x \rightarrow x + 2$ **3** $x \rightarrow 2x - 1$ **4** $x \rightarrow 4 - x$

Finding the mapping rule

We may be required to find the rule which connects a domain to its range. Check to see if the rule is

1 Adding or subtracting the same number to each member of the domain to produce its image.
2 Multiplying or dividing each member of the domain by the same number to produce its image.
3 Obtained by examining the differences in the range.

EXAMPLE 1

Find the mapping in the form $x \rightarrow \ldots$ for each of the following.

a 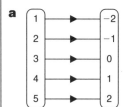   **b** 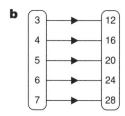   **c**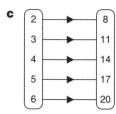

a By using Check 1, we see that the mapping is 'subtract 3' or 'add negative 3', written in the required form $x \rightarrow x - 3$.

b By using Check 2, we see that the mapping is 'multiply by 4', written in the required form as $x \rightarrow 4x$.

c Since neither Check 1 nor 2 works, we find the differences between consecutive pairs of terms in the range.

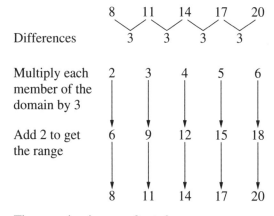

> This approach only works if the domain consists of consecutive whole numbers.

The mapping is $x \rightarrow 3x + 2$.

EXERCISE A11

Find the mapping in the form $x \rightarrow \ldots$ for each of the following.

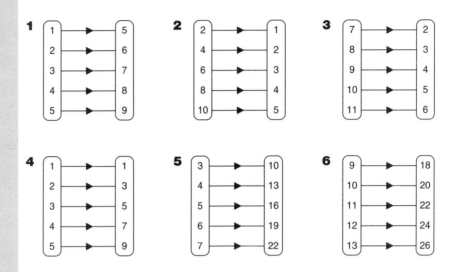

Mappings and sequences – finding the nth term

The *n*th term of a sequence is also referred to as the **general term**.

Find the *n*th term of this sequence.

    7 11 15 19...

In this case, it is not enough to find the rule and be able to generate the next few terms by using it. We are asked to relate the value of the term to its place in the sequence and generalise this as the *n*th term. If someone tells you the position of a term in the sequence, you should be able to find the value of that term.

1st term	2nd term	3rd term	4th term ... 10th ... 15th ... 50th ... *n*th ...
1	11	15	19 ? ? ? ?

We can see this as another form of mapping with the domain as the positions in the sequence and the range as the values of the terms.

Position in sequence   Value of term

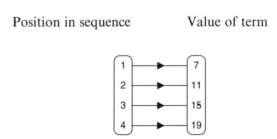

Having decided that the mapping is not a simple case of addition/subtraction or multiplication/division, we check the differences between consecutive pairs of terms in the range.

We can see that the differences in the range are all 4, so we start by multiplying the terms in the domain by 4.

Adding 3 gives
the range

1	× 4 = 4	+ 3 =	7
2	× 4 = 8	+ 3 =	11
3	× 4 = 12	+ 3 =	15
4	× 4 = 16	+ 3 =	19
n	× 4 = $4n$	+ 3 =	$4n + 3$

> **Check that the rule applies to the terms you are given.**

The nth term is $4n + 3$.

We can now use this expression for the general term to find the value of any term in the sequence specified by its position. So the tenth term in the sequence above is

$$4 \times 10 + 3 = 43$$

The fifteenth term is

$$4 \times 15 + 3 = 63$$

The 50th term is

$$4 \times 50 + 3 = 203$$

EXERCISE A12

Find the nth term of each of the following sequences and use it to find the ninth term in each case.

1 3 5 7 9   **2** 1 4 7 10   **3** 7 8 9 10

4 4 8 12 16   **5** −1 1 3 5   **6** 11 12 13 14

7 1 5 9 13   **8** 7 5 3 1

If we find that the first differences of the terms in the range are not the same, we can check the second differences. If these are the same, we start with the position (n) of the term in the domain and calculate the values of

$$\frac{n^2}{2} \times \text{2nd difference}$$

EXAMPLE 2

Find the nth term of the sequence   5 11 21 35 ...

Position in sequence (domain)	Terms of sequence (range)	1st diff.	2nd diff.	$\dfrac{n^2}{2} \times 4$
1	5			$\dfrac{1^2}{2} \times 4 = 2 \quad +3 = 5$
		6		
2	11		4	$\dfrac{2^2}{2} \times 4 = 8 \quad +3 = 11$
		10		
3	21		4	$\dfrac{3^2}{2} \times 4 = 18 \quad +3 = 21$
		14		
4	35			$\dfrac{4^2}{2} \times 4 = 32 \quad +3 = 35$

The nth term is $4 \times \dfrac{n^2}{2} + 3 = 2n^2 + 3$

EXERCISE A13

Find the nth term of each of the following sequences and use it to find the seventh term in each case.

1 2 5 10 17   **2** 2 11 26 47   **3** -4 -1 4 11

4 -1 2 7 14   **5** -1 5 15 29

A 04 Linear equations

What is an equation?

An equation is a mathematical statement. The statement is either **true** or **false**, depending upon the values of the variables in the equation.

A **solution** of an equation in one variable is a value of the variable which makes the equation true.

An **equation** is a mathematical statement. That is, something that can be either **true** or **false**. Whether it is true or false depends upon the values of the variables in the equation.

   For example, $x + 2 = 7$ is an equation.

If x takes the value 1, the equation is false.
If x takes the value 5, the equation is true.

$x = 5$ is the only value which makes the equation true. It is called the **solution** of the equation. We say that the value 5 **satisfies** the equation.

Finding a solution

Equivalent equations have exactly the same solutions.

To find a solution to an equation, we simplify the equation in such a way that we do not change the solution. Equations with the same solutions are called **equivalent**.

We can
- add the same thing to both sides
- subtract the same thing from both sides
- multiply both sides by the same thing
- divide both sides by the same thing

except that you **cannot multiply or divide by zero.**

Always **check your solutions**.

LHS = left-hand side
RHS = right-hand side

To solve an equation:

1 Decide what you want to get rid of.
2 Decide what process gets rid of it.
3 Make a note at the side saying what you are going to do.
4 Do this to **both sides**.
5 Simplify both sides of the equation.

Repeat the above until a solution is found.

To make an equivalent equation, we do the **same thing to both sides**.

- add the same thing to both sides
- subtract the same thing from both sides
- multiply both sides by the same thing, **except zero**
- divide both sides by the same thing, **except zero**

EXAMPLE 1

Solve the equation $x + 3 = 9$.

Subtract 3 from both sides		$x + 3 = 9$
		$x + 3 - 3 = 9 - 3$
		$\Rightarrow \quad x = 6$	Simplify

Check the solution	LHS $\quad x + 3 = (6) + 3 = 9$
	RHS $\qquad\qquad\qquad = 9$

EXAMPLE 2

Solve the equation $4x = 12$.

Divide both sides by 4		$4x = 12$
		$\dfrac{4x}{4} = \dfrac{12}{4}$
		$\Rightarrow \quad x = 3$	Simplify

Check the solution	LHS $\quad 4x = 4 \times (3) = 12$
	RHS $\qquad\qquad\qquad = 12$

EXERCISE A14

Solve the following equations.

1 $a - 3 = 12$ **2** $8 + b = 17$ **3** $c + 16 = 7$

4 $24 = e - 7$ **5** $3 = 8 + f$ **6** $9 = g + 15$

7 $3h = 18$ **8** $5k = 25$ **9** $4m = 36$

10 $15 = 5n$ **11** $30 = 6p$ **12** $49 = 7q$

13 $\dfrac{r}{4} = 5$ **14** $\dfrac{s}{6} = 9$ **15** $\dfrac{t}{7} = 3$

16 $\dfrac{v}{3} = 6$ **17** $\dfrac{w}{5} = 8$ **18** $\dfrac{x}{9} = 4$

More complicated equations

Remember that the process of solving equations consists of forming simpler equivalent equations. You may meet more complicated equations but they can always be converted, using the rule, to one of the types you have already met.

EXAMPLE 3

Solve the equation $4x + 3 = 23$.

Subtract 3 from both sides

$$4x + 3 = 23$$

$$4x + 3 - 3 = 23 - 3$$

$$4x = 20 \quad \text{Simplify}$$

Divide both sides by 4

$$\frac{4x}{4} = \frac{20}{4}$$

$$\Rightarrow \quad x = 5 \quad \text{Simplify}$$

Check this solution for yourself to make sure that it is correct.

EXAMPLE 4

Solve the equation $8 - 5x = 32 + 3x$.

Subtract 32 from both sides

$$8 - 5x = 32 + 3x$$

$$8 - 5x - 32 = 32 + 3x - 32$$

$$-5x - 24 = 3x \quad \text{Simplify}$$

Add $5x$ to both sides

$$-5x - 24 + 5x = 3x + 5x$$

$$-24 = 8x \quad \text{Simplify}$$

Divide both sides by 8

$$\frac{-24}{8} = \frac{8x}{8}$$

$$\Rightarrow \quad -3 = x \quad \text{Simplify}$$

$$\text{Or} \quad x = -3$$

Check this solution for yourself to make sure that it is correct.

EXERCISE A15

Solve the following equations.

1 $2a - 4 = 12$ 2 $5 + 3b = 17$ 3 $5c + 22 = 7$

4 $15 = 3e - 9$ 5 $34 = 6 + 4f$ 6 $9 = 23 - 2g$

7 $3h - 4 = 17$ 8 $9 - 5k = 24$ 9 $7 + 4m = 31$

10 $18 - 3n = 5n + 2$ 11 $4p + 21 = 7p - 12$ 12 $49 + 7q = 3q + 25$

13 $5r - 19 = 8r + 11$

Doing and undoing

Another method for solving linear equations where the unknown variable **appears only once** is to construct a flow chart.

For example, in the expression $2x + 7$, what is happening to x?

The answer is

Stage 1 Multiply it by 2
Stage 2 Add 7 to the result

We can construct a flow chart showing this.

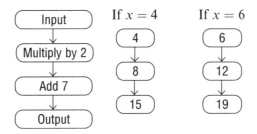

At every stage, you must ask the question 'What is happening **to** x?'

If the expression were part of the equation $2x + 7 = 15$, we could solve the equation by reversing the flow chart. To do this we need to follow these steps:

Step 1 Change the direction of the arrows
Step 2 Find the inverse of each operation

Some common inverses are

Operation	Inverse
Add	Subtract
Subtract	Add
Multiply	Divide
Divide	Multiply

EXAMPLE 5

Draw the flow chart representing the expression $4x - 7$ and use it to solve the equation $4x - 7 = 5$.

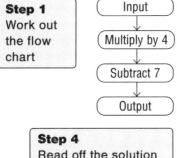

Step 1 Work out the flow chart

Step 2 Reverse the flow chart
1 Change the arrows
2 Invert the operations

Step 3 Use the original output (5) as the new input

Step 4 Read off the solution as the output from the reversed flow chart

The solution is $x = 3$.

(sidebar)

At every stage, ask the question 'What is happening **to** x?'

Some common inverses are

Operation	Inverse
Add	Subtract
Subtract	Add
Multiply	Divide
Divide	Multiply

To solve a simple equation using the flow chart method, follow these four steps.

Step 1 Work out the flow chart for the expression on the left-hand side.

Step 2 Reverse the flow chart.
1 Change the direction of the arrows.
2 Find the inverse of each operation.

Step 3 Use the original output as the input of the reversed flow chart.

Step 4 Read off the solution as the output from the reversed flow chart.

EXAMPLE 6

Draw the flow chart representing the expression $32 - 3x$ and use it to solve the equation $32 - 3x = 5$.

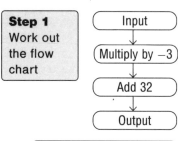
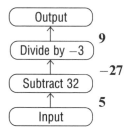

The solution is $x = 9$.

EXERCISE A16

1 $3n - 5 = 13$ **2** $8 + 4p = 24$ **3** $2q + 13 = 7$

4 $28 = 5r - 7$ **5** $49 = 7 + 6t$ **6** $11 = 29 - 2v$

7 $6w - 7 = 23$ **8** $17 - 5x = 32$ **9** $14 + 3y = 5$

A 05 Brackets and factorisation

Brackets

Remember BODMAS

Brackets are used to tell us to perform the operations inside the brackets first.

So $4 \times (3 + 2) = 4 \times 5 = 20$

But $4 \times 3 + 2 = 12 + 2 = 14$

Consider the following.

$$2 \times (1 + 3) = 2 \times 4 = 8$$
$$(2 \times 1) + (2 \times 3) = 2 + 6 = 8$$

We can see that

$$2 \times (1 + 3) = (2 \times 1) + (2 \times 3)$$

Also check that $5 \times (4 + 2) = (5 \times 4) + (5 \times 2)$

and $8 \times (6 - 1) = (8 \times 6) - (8 \times 1)$

An algebraic generalisation is a statement about a sequence of numerical operations which is true for any numbers we may use to replace *a*, *b* and *c*

Remember in algebra

xy means $x \times y$

We can express these as algebraic generalisations:

$$a \times (b + c) = (a \times b) + (a \times c)$$

and $\quad a \times (b - c) = (a \times b) - (a \times c)$

We do not usually include $\times$ in algebraic formulae, so we write these expressions as

$$a(b + c) = ab + ac$$

and $\quad a(b - c) = ab - ac$

This process is called 'multiplying out' or 'expanding' brackets.

EXAMPLE 1

Expand   **a** $-3(m + n)$ **b** $2(5y - 2z)$.

a $-3(m + n) = -3m + -3n$
$$= -3m - 3n$$

b $2(5y - 2z) = (2 \times 5y) - (2 \times 2z)$
$$= 10y - 4z$$

EXERCISE A17

Expand the brackets in the following expressions.

1 $3(p - 2)$ **2** $-4(a + 5)$ **3** $2(5x - 3)$ **4** $5(4m + 2n)$

5 $10(3a - 4b)$ **6** $\frac{1}{2}(2p - 6q)$ **7** $-3(6g - 2h)$ **8** $-4(\frac{1}{2}x - y)$

When there is an algebraic term in front of a bracket, the same operations are used.

EXAMPLE 2

Expand   **a** $x(x - y)$, **b** $-2p(3p + 5q)$.

$-2p \times 3q = -2 \times p \times 3 \times q$
$\qquad\qquad = -2 \times 3 \times p \times q$
$\qquad\qquad = -6 \times pq$
$\qquad\qquad = -6pq$

a $x(x - y) = (x \times x) - (x \times y)$
$$= x^2 - xy$$

b $-2p(3p + 5q) = (-2p \times 3p) + (-2p \times 5q)$
$$= -6p^2 + -10pq$$
$$= -6p^2 - 10pq$$

EXERCISE A18

Expand the following brackets.

1 $a(b - a)$ **2** $2x(x + y)$ **3** $3m(2n - 5m)$

4 $-h(3g - h^2)$ **5** $-3x(4y + x)$ **6** $7q(4q - 3p)$

Simplifying

Expanding two or more brackets in an algebraic expression often involves collecting like terms. The expanded expression can then be reduced to its **simplest terms**.

a $2a$ is **not** involved in the expansion of the brackets.

b When there is more than one set of brackets in an expression, expand each one separately by what is immediately in front of it (see **a** above), then collect the like terms from the results.

EXAMPLE 3

Simplify   **a** $2a + a(3 + 7b)$, **b** $2(3x - 2y) - 3(x + 6y)$

a $2a + a(3 + 7b) = 2a + 3a + 7ab$
$$= 5a + 7ab$$

b Expanding the brackets separately gives
$$2(3x - 2y) = 6x - 4y$$
$$-3(x + 6y) = -3x - 18y$$
Collecting like terms gives
$$6x - 3x = 3x \quad \text{and} \quad -4y - 18y = -22y$$
so we have $3x - 22y$ or $-22y + 3x$

EXERCISE A19

Expand and simplify the following expressions.

1 $4x + x(3 - 2y)$ **2** $5b - 3(2b + a)$ **3** $3m + n(m + 2)$

4 $q - q(2p - 5)$ **5** $3 + 4(a + 6)$ **6** $2(2a + 3b) - 5(5a + 2b)$

7 $3(x - y) + 2(x + y)$ **8** $m(n + 3) - m(4 - n)$ **9** $2r(3 + 2s) - s(3r - 4s)$

10 $a(2b + 7c) - a(3b - 2c)$

Factorising

A product is the result of multiplying two or more numbers together.

We can write any number as the **product** of two or more numbers. For example, $15 = 1 \times 15$ or 3×5, where 1, 3, 5 and 15 are **factors** of 15. When we **factorise** an algebraic expression, the result is a **product of its factors**, one at least of which is bracketed.

Factorising can be thought of as the reverse process of expanding brackets.

Expanding $a(b + c) = ab + ac$

Factorising $ab + ac = a(b + c)$

We have to look for **common factors** in every term in the expression. It is the common factors which are 'taken out' to the front of the bracket.

EXAMPLE 4

You can always check a factorisation by expanding the brackets to see if you get what you started with.

Factorise   **a** $3x + 3y$, **b** $5a - 10b$.

a $3x = 3 \times x$ and $3y = 3 \times y$
So both terms have a common factor 3 and we can factorise the expression as $3(x + y)$.

b In $5a - 10b$
$$5a = 5 \times a \quad \text{and} \quad 10b = 5 \times 2 \times b$$
So both terms have a common factor 5 and we can factorise the expression as $5(a - 2b)$.

EXERCISE A20

Factorise

1 $4a - 4b$ **2** $6x + 9y$ **3** $5p + 10q$ **4** $7e + 28f$

5 $11m - 11n$ **6** $14f - 2g$ **7** $18x + 3y$ **8** $42v - 36w$

9 $54a + 108b$ **10** $72r - 132s$

A factor can sometimes be an algebraic variable or a combination of a number and a variable.

EXAMPLE 5

Factorise $2mn - 5mp$.

$$2mn = 2 \times m \times n$$
$$5mp = 5 \times m \times p$$

So both terms have a common factor m and we can factorise the expression as $m(2n - 5p)$.

EXAMPLE 6

Factorise   **a** $4ab + 12ac$, **b** $6xy + 3y$.

a $4ab$ is $4 \times a \times b$
$12ac$ is $4 \times 3 \times a \times c$

So both terms have a common factor $4a$ and we can factorise this as $4a(b + 3c)$.

b $6xy$ is $2 \times 3 \times x \times y$
$3y$ is $3 \times y \times 1$

So both terms have a common factor $3y$ and we can factorise this as $3y(2x + 1)$

> It can be confusing when one term is entirely the common factor itself. In this case, we leave a 1 inside the bracket to be multiplied by the common factor.

It is wise to take out one factor at a time as you 'spot' them and then to check the bracket for further factors.

EXAMPLE 7

Factorise fully $12pq - 28qr$.

2 is a factor so we get

$$2 \times (6pq - 14qr)$$

This is factorised because we now have a product but it is not **fully** factorised. You may spot q is a factor of the bracket, so we now have

$$2 \times q \times (6p - 14r)$$

We finally notice that each number in the bracket is '2× something', so we can take out another 2 as a factor to get

$$2 \times q \times 2 \times (3p - 7r)$$

which we of course write as $4q(3p - 7r)$.

EXERCISE A21

Factorise fully

1 $2ab + 3ac$	**2** $5xy - 2yz$	**3** $7pq - p$
4 $4m + 11km$	**5** $3ab - 3ac$	**6** $3y + 6yz$
7 $15ab - 25bc$	**8** $14mn + 28mp$	**9** $5a^2 - 20ab$

10 $30x^2y + 48yz$

Sometimes the common factor can be an expression in a bracket.

Remember $a^2 = a \times a$

EXAMPLE 8

Factorise

a $2x(a + b) + 3y(a + b)$ **b** $3a(m - n) + 2b(n - m)$

a In the expression $2x(a + b) + 3y(a + b)$, both terms have a common factor $(a + b)$.

We therefore factorise this as $(a + b) \times (2x + 3y)$ with the bracketed common factor appearing in front of the bracketed expression like any other common factor would, but this does look different from what we have seen so far. We do not need $\times$, so we get $(a + b)(2x + 3y)$.

b This is a **special case** of factorisation which is well worth noting.
There may not appear to be a common factor when we first look at this expression. However, if we write $(n - m)$ as $-(m - n)$, then

$$2b(n - m) = -2b(m - n)$$
$$\Rightarrow \quad 3a(m - n) + 2b(n - m) = 3a(m - n) - 2b(m - n)$$
$$= (m - n)(3a - 2b)$$

with $(m - n)$ as a common factor.

$-(m - n)$ can be thought of as
$-1(m - n) = -1 \times m$
and $-1 \times -n$
$= -m + n$
$= n - m$

EXERCISE A22

Factorise fully

1 $3x(m + n) - 2y(m + n)$ **2** $4a(x - y) + 7b(x - y)$

3 $a(b - c) + 2(c - b)$ **4** $3p(4s - 3t) - 2q(3t - 4s)$

5 $12n(p + 2q) - 13(p + 2q)$ **6** $5p(a + b) - 3q(a + b)$

7 $5w(w - v) + 3v(v - w)$ **8** $11x(3u - v) + 12(3u - v)$

9 $2x(y - z) - 3(z - y)$ **10** $s(2t - w) + r(2t - w)$

Sometimes an expression with four terms can be factorised as follows but this is a special case.

EXAMPLE 9

Factorise fully $6ab + 4a + 15bc + 10c$.

Take pairs of terms which have a common factor to get

$$6ab + 4a = 2a(3b + 2)$$
$$15bc + 10c = 5c(3b + 2)$$

giving $2a(3b + 2) + 5c(3b + 2) = (3b + 2)(2a + 5c)$

using the methods in Example 8.

EXERCISE A23

Factorise fully

1 $ac + ad + bc + bd$

2 $2xw - 2xz + wy - yz$

3 $12mp - 3mq + 8np - 2nq$

4 $10cf - 5cq - 2df + dq$

5 $4ad - 3bd - 4ac + 3bc$

6 $8wy + 12xy + 10wz + 15xz$

A 06 More linear equations

To solve an equation, you must do the **same thing to both sides**

There is no 'right' way to solve an equation. Some methods are quicker than others.

Expand all brackets first.

There is no 'right' way to solve an equation. The process is one of repeated simplification whilst keeping the same solution until we eventually arrive at the solution.

Equations with brackets

Simplify such equations by first expanding the brackets.

EXAMPLE 1

Solve the equation $5(3x - 2) = 35$.

$$5(3x - 2) = 35$$

Expand the bracket
$$15x - 10 = 35$$

Add 10 to both sides
$$15x - 10 + 10 = 35 + 10$$
$$\Rightarrow \quad 15x = 45 \quad \boxed{\text{Simplify}}$$

Divide both sides by 15
$$\frac{15x}{15} = \frac{45}{15}$$
$$\Rightarrow \quad x = 3$$

Always **check your solutions**.

Check the solution
LHS $= 5(3x - 2) = 5(3 \times 3 - 2) = 5 \times 7 = 35$
RHS $= 35$

EXAMPLE 2

Solve the equation $3(4 - 7x) = 2(5 - 11x)$.

$$3(4 - 7x) = 2(5 - 11x)$$

Expand the brackets

$$12 - 21x = 10 - 22x$$

Add 22x to both sides

$$12 - 21x + 22x = 10 - 22x + 22x$$

$$\Rightarrow \quad 12 + x = 10$$

Simplify

Subtract 12 from both sides

$$12 + x - 12 = 10 - 12$$

$$\Rightarrow \quad x = -2$$

Simplify

Check the solution

$$\text{LHS} = 3(4 - 7x) = 3[4 - 7 \times (-2)] = 3 \times 18 = 54$$
$$\text{RHS} = 2(5 - 11x) = 2[5 - 11(-2)] = 2 \times 27 = 54$$

EXERCISE A24

Solve the following equations.

1 $4(x + 5) = 28$ **2** $3(5 + y) = 12$ **3** $5(1 - 2z) = -25$

4 $2(2x - 3) = 14$ **5** $2(3 + 2p) = -10$ **6** $4(3t + 9) = 12$

7 $45 = 5(4 + 5w)$ **8** $-30 = 3(6 - 4r)$ **9** $99 = 9(2 - 3k)$

EXERCISE A25

Solve the following equations.

1 $2(1 + 3x) = 13(6 - x)$ **2** $4(1 - 2x) = 7(2x + 10)$

3 $6(2x + 7) = 9(2 + 4x)$ **4** $3(3x - 2) = 4(5 - x)$

5 $3(1 - 2x) + 4(3x - 1) = -7$ **6** $2(5 + 2x) + 4(3x - 1) = -58$

7 $5(3x - 2) + 3(1 - 2x) = 20$ **8** $4(4x + 5) - 5(2x + 3) = -7$

Equations with fractions

For an equation containing a fraction, multiply both sides by the denominator of the fraction

The way to simplify an equation containing a fraction is to multiply both sides by the denominator of the fraction.

EXAMPLE 3

Solve the equation $\dfrac{x - 4}{3} = 1$.

$$\frac{x - 4}{3} = 1$$

Multiply both sides by 3

$$3 \times \left(\frac{x - 4}{3}\right) = 3 \times 1$$

$$\Rightarrow \quad x - 4 = 3$$

$$x = 7$$

Do not forget to check your solutions.

EXERCISE A26

Solve the following equations.

1 $\dfrac{x}{2} = 3$ **2** $\dfrac{y}{3} = 5$ **3** $\dfrac{z}{7} = 3$

4 $\dfrac{2x-3}{7} = 3$ **5** $\dfrac{4+3p}{5} = 5$ **6** $\dfrac{3t+9}{4} = 6$

7 $\dfrac{2m-5}{3} = 1$ **8** $\dfrac{16-2r}{6} = 2$ **9** $\dfrac{8+3k}{2} = 10$

When you have an equation containing more than one fraction, you can simplify either by multiplying both sides by each denominator in turn, or by multiplying by a common multiple of all the denominators.

When you have an equation containing more than one fraction, you can either:

- multiply both sides by each denominator in turn, or
- multiply both sides by a common multiple of all the denominators.

EXAMPLE 4

Solve the equation $\dfrac{3x-4}{5} = \dfrac{2x+1}{7}$.

$$\frac{3x-4}{5} = \frac{2x+1}{7}$$

Multiply both sides by 5

$$5 \times \left(\frac{3x-4}{5}\right) = 5 \times \left(\frac{2x+1}{7}\right)$$

$$3x - 4 = \frac{10x+5}{7}$$

Multiply both sides by 7

$$7 \times (3x-4) = 7 \times \left(\frac{10x+5}{7}\right)$$

$$21x - 28 = 10x + 5$$

Add $(28 - 10x)$ to both sides

$$21x - 28 + (\mathbf{28 - 10x}) = 10x + 5 + (\mathbf{28 - 10x})$$

$$\Rightarrow \quad 11x = 33$$

Divide both sides by 11

$$\Rightarrow \quad x = 3$$

EXAMPLE 5

Solve the equation $\dfrac{x}{2} + \dfrac{x}{3} = 5$.

$$\frac{x}{2} + \frac{x}{3} = 5$$

Multiply both sides by 6

$$\mathbf{6} \times \left(\frac{x}{2} + \frac{x}{3}\right) = \mathbf{6} \times 5$$

$$3x + 2x = 30$$

$$\Rightarrow \quad 5x = 30$$

Divide both sides by 5

$$x = 6$$

EXERCISE A27

Solve the following equations.

1 $\dfrac{x}{2} - \dfrac{x}{5} = 6$ **2** $\dfrac{2x}{3} + \dfrac{x}{4} = 22$ **3** $\dfrac{3x}{2} - \dfrac{x}{4} = 10$

4 $\dfrac{2x}{3} = 1 + \dfrac{3x}{5}$ **5** $\dfrac{5x}{6} = 27 - \dfrac{2x}{3}$ **6** $\dfrac{3x}{4} = \dfrac{2x}{5} + 7$

7 $\dfrac{x-1}{2} = \dfrac{x+3}{3}$ **8** $\dfrac{2x+1}{5} = \dfrac{4x-1}{9}$ **9** $\dfrac{3x-5}{8} = \dfrac{2x-5}{5}$

10 $2 + \dfrac{3x+1}{4} = \dfrac{4x-2}{3}$ **11** $3x - \dfrac{2x+1}{5} = \dfrac{8x-3}{3}$

A 07 Further brackets and transforming formulae

Expanding brackets

A simple way to expand an expression with two pairs of brackets, such as $(2x - 3)(3x + 4)$, is to use a multiplication table.

Step 1
Write the elements of the brackets in a multiplication table. It does not matter which bracket is put across the top and which is put down the side.

Step 2
Fill in the table. There are **four** spaces to complete. Take care with negative signs.

Step 3
Collect together the like terms and simplify the expression.

EXAMPLE 1

Expand $(2x - 3)(3x + 4)$.

First bracket down the side of the table

×	3x	+4
2x		
−3		

Second bracket across the top of the table

×	3x	+4
2x	6x²	+8x
−3	−9x	−12

Fill in the 4 elements in the table

$$6x^2 + (-9x + 8x) - 12 = 6x^2 - x - 12$$

Notice the pattern of the elements in the product table.

In the   top left corner   is a term in x^2
In the   top right   is a term in x
In the   bottom left   is a term in x
In the   bottom right   is a   constant (integer) term.

EXERCISE A28

Expand the following brackets.

1 $(a + 2)(a - 3)$ **2** $(b + 3)(b + 4)$ **3** $(c - 6)(c + 2)$

4 $(d - 8)(d - 3)$ **5** $(2e - 3)(3e - 2)$ **6** $(4f + 3)(2f - 5)$

7 $(g - 4)(3g + 2)$ **8** $(2h + 2)(3h + 8)$ **9** $(4k - 3)(3k + 4)$

Sometimes the brackets contain more than one variable. Treat these in the same way.

EXAMPLE 2

Expand $(2a - 3b)(3a + 4b)$.

Step 1 and *Step 2*

$\times$	$2a$	$-3b$
$3a$	$6a^2$	$-9ab$
$+4b$	$+8ab$	$-12b^2$

Step 3 $6a^2 + (-9ab + 8ab) - 12b^2$
         $= 6a^2 - ab - 12b^2$

EXERCISE A29

Expand the following brackets.

1 $(2a - 3b)(3a - 2b)$ **2** $(3c + 4d)(2c - 5d)$ **3** $(e + 2f)(3e + 4f)$

4 $(3g - 2h)(4g + 3h)$ **5** $(2k - 4m)(3k - 5m)$ **6** $(2p + 5q)(3p - 4q)$

7 $(x + y)(x + y)$ **8** $(x - y)(x - y)$ **9** $(x + y)(x - y)$

Three important results:

- $(x + y)(x + y)$
  $= x^2 + 2xy + y^2$
- $(x - y)(x - y)$
  $= x^2 - 2xy + y^2$
- $(x + y)(x - y)$
  $= x^2 - y^2$

Three special results
Questions 7–9 in Exercise A29 illustrate three important general results. The first two of these relate to **perfect squares** and the third is called the **difference of two squares**.

EXAMPLE 3

Expand the perfect square $(2a - b)^2$.

Using $(x - y)(x - y) = x^2 - 2x\ y + y^2$ $\boxed{\begin{array}{l}\text{Replace} \\ x \text{ by } 2a \\ y \text{ by } b\end{array}}$
            $\updownarrow$ $\updownarrow\ \updownarrow$ $\updownarrow$ $\updownarrow$ $\updownarrow\ \updownarrow$ $\updownarrow$
     $(2a - b)^2 = (2a - b)(2a - b) = (2a)^2 - 2(2a)(b) + (b)^2$

         $\Rightarrow$ $(2a - b)^2 = 4a^2 - 4ab + b^2$ $\boxed{\text{Simplify}}$

EXERCISE A30

Use the three special results to expand the following expressions.

1 $(3a+b)(3a+b)$ **2** $(c-4d)(c-4d)$ **3** $(e+2f)(e+2f)$

4 $(3g+h)(3g-h)$ **5** $(k-4m)(k+4m)$ **6** $(2p+5q)(2p+5q)$

7 $(3r-4s)(3r-4s)$ **8** $(2t+6u)(2t-6u)$ **9** $(5v-3w)(5v+3w)$

Transforming formulae

A formula is an equation with several variables in it. It expresses a relationship between the variables and is often used to represent a general rule governing some physical relationship. For example, the volume of a cylinder is given by

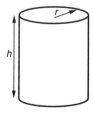

$$V = \pi r^2 h$$

where V represents the volume
        r represents the radius
        h represents the height

We use the formula to find the value of one of the variables when we know the values of the others.

> **EXAMPLE 4**
>
> Find the volume of a baked-bean can whose height is 10 cm and whose radius is 4 cm.
>
> $$V = \pi r^2 h$$
>
> | Substitute the known values into the formula |
>
> $$V = \pi \times 4^2 \times 10$$
>
> | Calculate the result |
>
> $$V = 502.6 \, \text{cm}^3$$

When the formula is written like this, with V by itself on the left-hand side, V is called the **subject** of the formula.

We often want to find one of the other variables. There are two equivalent ways to do this. We can either

- substitute the values we know and then solve the resulting equation, or
- transform the formula to make the required variable the subject. We can then substitute the values and calculate the result.

(Side notes)

A **formula** is an equation with several variables in it. By substituting known values for all variables except one, you can find the appropriate value of the unknown variable.

When a variable is written by itself on one side (usually the left-hand side) of a formula, it is called the **subject** of the formula. That is usually the variable whose value we need

Should you want to find the value of another variable, either

- substitute the known values of the variables and then solve the resulting equation, or
- transform the formula to make the required variable the subject. Then substitute the values and calculate the result.

EXAMPLE 5

Find the height of a cylinder whose volume is $1000\,\text{cm}^3$ and whose radius is $6\,\text{cm}$.

Note Dividing both sides by πr^2 is equivalent to dividing first by π and then by r^2. We have to eliminate both of these and we can do it in one go.

Method 2 is known as **transforming** or **transposing the formula**.

To transform a formula

1 Decide what you want to get rid of.
2 Decide what process gets rid of it.
3 Make a note at the side saying what you are going to do.
4 Do this to **both sides**.
5 Simplify both sides of the formula.

The processes you can use are

- add the same thing to both sides
- subtract the same thing from both sides
- multiply both sides by the same thing, **except zero**
- divide both sides by the same thing, **except zero**

- square (cube, ...) both sides
- square (cube, ...) root both sides

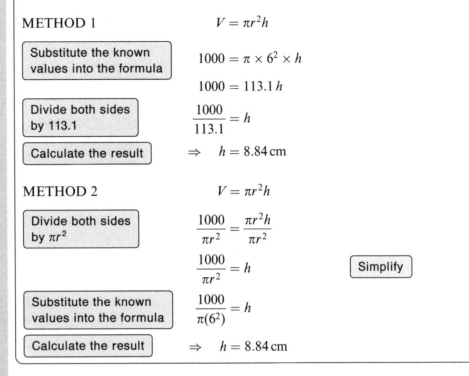

METHOD 1 $\qquad V = \pi r^2 h$

Substitute the known values into the formula
$$1000 = \pi \times 6^2 \times h$$
$$1000 = 113.1\,h$$

Divide both sides by 113.1
$$\frac{1000}{113.1} = h$$

Calculate the result
$$\Rightarrow \quad h = 8.84\,\text{cm}$$

METHOD 2 $\qquad V = \pi r^2 h$

Divide both sides by πr^2
$$\frac{1000}{\pi r^2} = \frac{\pi r^2 h}{\pi r^2}$$
$$\frac{1000}{\pi r^2} = h \qquad \boxed{\text{Simplify}}$$

Substitute the known values into the formula
$$\frac{1000}{\pi(6^2)} = h$$

Calculate the result
$$\Rightarrow \quad h = 8.84\,\text{cm}$$

Notice that the calculation and the result are the same in each method. The only difference is that in Method 1, we divided by $\pi \times 6^2$ and in Method 2, by πr^2. These are equivalent since $r = 6$.

The technique in Method 2 is known as **transforming the formula**. It is exactly the same as solving an equation and the same rules apply. The difference is that you operate with variables and not values.

EXAMPLE 6

Make a the subject of the formula $v = u + at$.

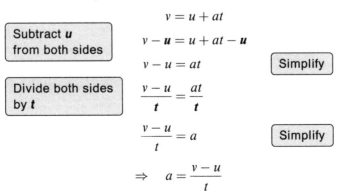

$$v = u + at$$

Subtract u from both sides
$$v - u = u + at - u$$
$$v - u = at \qquad \boxed{\text{Simplify}}$$

Divide both sides by t
$$\frac{v - u}{t} = \frac{at}{t}$$
$$\frac{v - u}{t} = a \qquad \boxed{\text{Simplify}}$$
$$\Rightarrow \quad a = \frac{v - u}{t}$$

EXERCISE A31

Make the variable in square brackets the subject of the formula.

1 $[S]$; $D = ST$ **2** $[D]$; $C = \pi D$ **3** $[\theta]$; $a = r\theta$

4 $[a]$; $F = ma$ **5** $[x]$; $y = mx + c$ **6** $[s]$; $v^2 = u^2 + 2as$

7 $[g]$; $mg - T = ma$ **8** $[h]$; $A = 2\pi r(r + h)$ **9** $[F]$; $C = \frac{5}{9}(F - 32)$

Powers and roots

Some formulae involve powers or roots. You can eliminate a square root by isolating it and then squaring both sides.

EXAMPLE 7

Make c the subject of the formula $a = b + \sqrt{c}$.

$$a = b + \sqrt{c}$$

| Isolate the square root | $a - \boldsymbol{b} = \sqrt{c}$ | Subtract $\boldsymbol{b}$ from both sides |

| Get rid of the square root | $\Rightarrow \quad (a - b)^2 = c$ | Square both sides |

$$c = (a - b)^2$$

EXAMPLE 8

Make r the subject of the formula $V = \pi r^2 h$

$$V = \pi r^2 h$$

| Get rid of $\pi \boldsymbol{h}$ | $\dfrac{V}{\pi h} = r^2$ | Divide both sides by $\pi \boldsymbol{h}$ |

| | $r^2 = \dfrac{V}{\pi h}$ | Rewrite with $\boldsymbol{r}^2$ on the left |

| Get rid of the power | $\Rightarrow \quad r = \sqrt{\dfrac{V}{\pi h}}$ | Take the square root of both sides |

EXERCISE A32

Make the variable in square brackets the subject of the formula.

1 $[p]$; $r = q - \sqrt{2gp}$ **2** $[r]$; $A = \pi r^2$ **3** $[a]$; $h^2 = a^2 + b^2$

4 $[r]$; $V = \frac{4}{3}\pi r^3$ **5** $[t]$; $s = \frac{1}{2}at^2$ **6** $[L]$; $T = 2\pi\sqrt{\dfrac{L}{g}}$

7 $[R]$; $A = P(1 + R)^3$ **8** $[u]$; $v^2 = u^2 + 2as$ **9** $[v]$; $E = \frac{1}{2}mv^2$

Factorisation

If the subject appears more than once, factorise it out.

When the subject appears more than once then, provided that the powers of the subject are all the same, we can factorise and isolate the subject.

EXAMPLE 9

Make m the subject of the formula $I = mv - mu$.

| m appears more than once |

$I = mv - mu$

$I = m(v - u)$ | Factorise |

$\Rightarrow \quad m = \dfrac{I}{v - u}$ | Divide both sides by $(v - u)$ |

EXERCISE A33

Make the variable in square brackets the subject of the formula.

1 $[m]$; $mg - T = ma$ **2** $[r]$; $A = \pi rs + 2\pi rh$ **3** $[c]$; $n = 4c + 2cr$

4 $[a]$; $S = ar^2 + ar^3$ **5** $[u]$; $2gd + e^2 u^2 = u^2$ **6** $[v]$; $uv = fv + fu$

7 $[r]$; $V = \frac{1}{3}\pi r^2 h + \pi r^2 H$ **8** $[m]$; $E = \frac{1}{2}mv^2 + mgh$

A 08 Construction and solving of problems

Solving problems

The stages of problem solving in mathematics are:

1 Express the problem as a mathematical equation.
2 Solve the equation.
3 Check that the solution works.

To solve a problem:

When you choose your letter to represent a variable, **do not choose** *i*, *l*, *o*, or *s*. They look too much like numbers when written by hand.

Expressing a problem in algebraic terms

The first stage is to express the problem as an equation, using algebra. The important question is: 'What is it that you want to know?' This is your starting point.

1 Choose a letter to represent this variable. The letter x is often chosen but any letter would do if it easily identifies what it represents.
2 Express the other quantities in terms of your chosen letter.
3 Identify the relationship between the quantities.
4 Write this relationship as an equation.

You are now in a position to solve the problem.

Ask the question: 'What is it that you want to know?'

Then

1 Choose a letter to represent this variable. The letter x is often chosen but any would do if it easily identifies what it represents.
2 Express the other quantities in terms of your chosen letter.
3 Identify the relationship.
4 Write the equation.
5 Solve the equation.
6 State the solution to the problem.
7 Check that the solution works.

EXAMPLE 1

A pair of compasses costs 25 p more than a pencil. If together they cost 39 p, how much is the pencil?

Step 1 Identify the unknown quantity	Let the cost of the pencil be x pence.
Step 2 Translate the information into expressions	The cost of a pair of compasses is $(x + 25)$ p.
Step 3 Identify the relationship	The total cost is $x + (x + 25)$.
Step 4 Write an equation	So $x + (x + 25) = 39$
Step 5 Solve the equation	$2x + 25 = 39$ $\Rightarrow \quad 2x = 14$ $x = 7$
Step 6 State the solution	The pencil therefore costs 7 p.
Step 7 Check the solution	The compasses cost $7\,p + 25\,p = 32\,p$ Therefore, the total cost $= 7\,p + 32\,p = 39\,p$

EXERCISE A34

1 Three consecutive odd numbers add up to 63. What are they?

2 The longer side of a rectangle is three times its shorter side. If the perimeter is 48 cm, what is the length of the shorter side?

3 A bag contains a number of 10 p coins and twice that number of 20 p coins. If the total amount of money in the bag is £4, how many 10 p coins are there?

4 In a triangle, the longest side is 4 cm more than the length of the mid-length side, which is twice the length of the shortest side. If the perimeter is 29 cm, what is the length of the shortest side?

5 A box and its contents weigh 480 g. The contents weigh three times as much as the box. How heavy is the box?

6 A group of three people win £2 500 000 on the National Lottery. They split it up so that one person received the smallest share, the next person received £100 000 more, and the person who chose the numbers and bought the ticket received twice as much as the smallest share. How much was the smallest share?

Equations containing brackets or fractions

Some problems lead to equations containing brackets and/or fractions. The process of forming the equations is just the same as before. The equations, once formed, may be more difficult to solve.

EXAMPLE 2

The sum of two numbers is 11. Four times the larger number plus three times the smaller number is 40. What is the smaller number?

| **Step 1** Identify the unknown quantity | Let the smaller number be n. |

| **Step 2** Translate the information into expressions | The larger number is therefore $(11 - n)$. |

| **Step 4** Write an equation | $4(11 - n) + 3n = 40$ |

| **Step 5** Solve the equation | $44 - 4n + 3n = 40$
$44 - n = 40$
$-n = 40 - 44$
$\Rightarrow \quad -n = -4$
$\Rightarrow \quad n = 4$ |

| **Step 6** State the solution | The smaller number is 4. |

EXERCISE A35

1 The mean of two consecutive even numbers is 17. What is the smaller of the numbers?

2 A party of 3 adults and 7 children went on a bus trip. The adult fare was £5 more than a child's fare. If the total cost of the trip was £45, how much was each type of ticket?

3 In an isosceles triangle, the equal angles are each 30° more than double the third angle. How large are the angles?

4 The fraction two-fifths has an integer added to its numerator. The same integer is added to its denominator. The new fraction is exactly double the original one. What integer was added?

Sometimes the unknown quantity appears on both sides of the equation. Setting up the equation often involves finding two expressions for the same quantity.

EXERCISE A36

1 In eight years time, John will be half as old again as he is now. How old is he now?

2 Fifteen years ago a man was half his age of two years ago. How old is he now?

3 Potatoes cost 4p per lb more than carrots. Jean bought 9 lb of potatoes and 5 lb of carrots, while Susan bought 4 lb of potatoes and 11 lb of carrots. They were surprised to find that they each paid the same amount of money for their purchases. What was the cost of 1 lb of each vegetable?

4 In his will, Mr Martin left all his money to his three grandchildren to be distributed as follows. Anne was to receive half the total. Bernard was to receive one quarter of the total plus £1000. Charles was to receive one eighth of the total plus £2000. How much did each child receive?

5 The sum of two numbers is 9. Five times the larger number is 12 more than six times the smaller number. What are the numbers?

6 In a number game, a boy thinks of a number, doubles it and adds 3. He then divides it by 5. Starting with the same number, he multiplies it by 3, adds 1 to the result and then divides this by 7. On each occasion his final result was the same. What number did he start with?

A 09 Inequalities

Notation

$=$ means **is equal to**. It is used to show that two quantities are exactly the same size.

When this is not the case, one of them must be larger than the other and we have symbols to represent this situation.

$<$ means **is less than**

$>$ means **is greater than**

$\leqslant$ means **is less than or equal to**

$\geqslant$ means **is greater than or equal to**

In each case, the open (wider) end always faces the larger value

Like an equation, an inequality is either true or false.

So that $3 \leqslant 7$ means   3 **is less than or equal to** 7 and is **true**,
whilst $6 > 12$ means   6 **is greater than** 12 and is **false**.

The number line

We can illustrate inequalities using the number line.

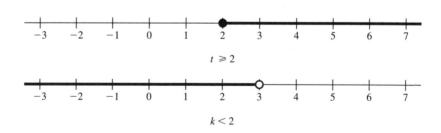

$t \geqslant 2$

$k < 2$

In the first case, t is greater than or **equal to 2**. The value 2 is included and so is represented by a solid circle. In the second case, the value 3 is not included and so is represented by an open circle. Any value on the thick line is a possible solution to the inequality.

Notation

$<$ means **is less than**
$>$ means **is greater than**
$\leqslant$ means **is less than or equal to**
$\geqslant$ means **is greater than or equal to**

Like an equation, an inequality is either **true** or **false**.

A **solid circle** indicates that the value is **included** ●

An **open circle** indicates that the value is **not included**. ○

On the number line
the **greater** the number is the further to the **right** it is
the **smaller** the number is the further to the **left** it is

Some problems can only have solutions that are integers (whole numbers). These would be represented by a series of solid circles on the number line.

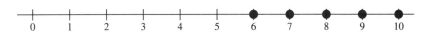

Notice that $h > 5$ and $h \geqslant 6$ would give the same set of solutions if h could only be an integer.

EXERCISE A37

1 Decide whether each of the following statements is true or false.

    a $3 < 9$ **b** $5 \geqslant 7$ **c** $-4 \leqslant 3$

2 Write the following pairs of numbers, putting the correct symbol ($<$ or $>$) between each pair.

    a $2 \quad -5$ **b** $4 \quad 7$ **c** $-2 \quad -7$

3 Use a number line to illustrate each of the following inequalities.

    a $x < 2$ **b** $y \geqslant -1$ **c** $z \leqslant 5$

Solving inequalities

You solve inequalities in exactly the same way that you solve equations. You change the inequality to make a simpler one with the same solutions.

To make an equivalent equation you **do the same thing to both sides**. You can

a add the same thing to both sides
b subtract the same thing from both sides
c multiply both sides by the same thing
d divide both sides by the same thing

except that in **c** and **d** you **cannot** multiply or divide by **zero**. If you multiply or divide by a **negative quantity**, you must **change the direction of the inequality**.

Think about two values on the number line. If you move them both the same distance to the right (adding the same thing) or the same distance to the left (subtracting the same thing), they will not cross over and the inequality will still be true. If you multiply or divide by a negative quantity, they will **change positions** and the inequality is **reversed**.

Warning **Never** multiply or divide by a quantity whose **value you do not know**. You cannot tell whether to reverse the inequality or not.

To solve an inequality:

a Add the same thing to both sides.
b Subtract the same thing from both sides.
c Multiply both sides by the same thing.
d Divide both sides by the same thing.

Except that in **c** and **d**

- **you cannot multiply or divide by zero**
- if you multiply or divide by a negative quantity, you must **change the direction of the inequality**.

Warning **Never** multiply or divide by a quantity whose **value you do not know**. You cannot tell whether to reverse the inequality or not.

EXAMPLE 1

Solve the inequality $4x + 7 \geqslant 31$.

| Subtract 7 from both sides | $4x + 7 \geqslant 31$ |
| | $4x + 7 - 7 \geqslant 31 - 7$ |

$$4x \geqslant 24 \qquad \boxed{\text{Simplify}}$$

| Divide both sides by 4 | $\Rightarrow \quad x \geqslant 6$ |

EXAMPLE 2

Solve the inequality $6 - 7x < 34$.

| Subtract 6 from both sides | $6 - 7x < 34$ |
| | $6 - 7x - 6 < 34 - 6$ |

$$-7x < 28 \qquad \boxed{\text{Simplify}}$$

| Divide both sides by -7 | $\dfrac{-7x}{-7} > \dfrac{28}{-7}$ | Change direction |

$$\Rightarrow \quad x > -4 \qquad \boxed{\text{Simplify}}$$

EXERCISE A38

Solve the following inequalities and represent the solutions on the number line.

1 $a - 3 > -5$ **2** $8 + b < 17$ **3** $c + 5 \leqslant 7$

4 $-3 \geqslant e - 7$ **5** $3 \leqslant 8 + f$ **6** $9 > g + 5$

7 $3h \geqslant 18$ **8** $-5k < 25$ **9** $4m \geqslant 36$

10 $15 > -5n$ **11** $30 \leqslant -6p$ **12** $49 < 7q$

13 $\dfrac{r}{4} > -5$ **14** $\dfrac{s}{6} \geqslant 9$ **15** $\dfrac{t}{7} \leqslant -3$

16 $\dfrac{v}{3} < -6$ **17** $\dfrac{w}{5} \leqslant 8$ **18** $\dfrac{x}{9} > 4$

EXERCISE A39

Solve the following inequalities and represent the solutions on the number line.

1 $2a - 4 < 12$ **2** $5 + 3b \geqslant 17$ **3** $5c + 22 > 7$

4 $15 \leqslant -3e - 9$ **5** $34 > 6 + 4f$ **6** $9 \leqslant 23 - 2g$

7 $3h - 7 < 17$ **8** $9 - 5k > 24$ **9** $7 - 4m \geqslant 31$

10 $18 - 3n < 5n + 2$ **11** $4p + 21 \geqslant 7p - 12$

12 $49 + 7q > 3q + 25$ **13** $5r - 19 \leqslant 8r + 11$

EXERCISE A40

Solve the following inequalities and represent the solutions on the number line.

1 $4(x + 5) > 28$ **2** $3(5 + y) \leqslant 12$ **3** $5(1 - 2z) \geqslant -25$

4 $\dfrac{2x - 3}{7} < 3$ **5** $\dfrac{4 + 3p}{5} \leqslant 5$ **6** $\dfrac{3t + 9}{4} > 6$

7 $\dfrac{x - 1}{2} \geqslant \dfrac{x + 3}{3}$ **8** $\dfrac{2x + 1}{5} > \dfrac{5x + 2}{13}$ **9** $\dfrac{3x - 5}{8} < \dfrac{2x - 5}{5}$

Problem solving

EXAMPLE 3

The cost of sending a parcel is 50 p plus 20 p per 1 kg.

a Write down an expression for the cost of sending a parcel weighing x kg.
b John has a maximum of £2 cash available. What is the largest parcel he can send?

	a
Step 1 Identify the unknown quantity	The weight of the parcel is x kg
Step 2 Translate the information into expressions	The cost of sending the parcel is $(50 + 20x)$ p
	b
Step 3 Identify the relationship	The total cost is **less than or equal to** 200 p.
Step 4 Write an inequality	$50 + 20x \leqslant 200$
Step 5 Solve the inequality	$20x \leqslant 150$ $\Rightarrow \quad x \leqslant 7.5$
Step 6 State the solution	John's largest parcel weighs 7.5 kg.

Problems with two constraints

The inequality $a < b < c$ means that $a < b$ **and** $b < c$.

Say to yourself 'b lies between a and c'.

We can also have $a < b \leqslant c$

$$\circ\!\!-\!\!-\!\!-\!\!-\!\!-\!\!-\!\!-\!\!\bullet$$
$$a \qquad\qquad b$$

But $a < b > c$ is meaningless.

Sometimes a quantity has both a maximum and a minimum value. For example, the temperature in a warehouse might need to be kept between 3 °C and 12 °C. If t is the temperature then

$$t \geqslant 3 \quad \text{and} \quad t \leqslant 12$$

We shorten this to $\quad 3 \leqslant t \leqslant 12$

On the number line, it looks like this.

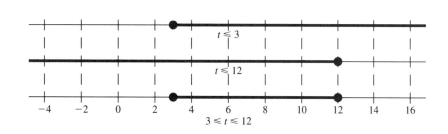

$$3 \leqslant t \leqslant 12$$

The complete solution is where the two solution sets overlap.

Notice that a pair of conditions such as

$$x \geqslant 8 \quad \text{and} \quad x < 3$$

can have no complete solution because the solution sets do not overlap.

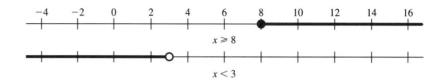

EXERCISE A41

1 A journey took place partly on foot and partly by bus. The total journey time was 3 hours and it is known that the bus journey took less than 2 hours. Form an inequality for the time taken for the walking section of the journey and solve it.

2 The hire agreement for a drinks machine stipulates that, in order to gain a preferential rate of £5 per case, at least 10 cases of soft drinks must be ordered per month. The storage facility allows a maximum of 50 cases per month to be ordered. Form inequalities for the cost of the drinks and show the solutions on the number line.

3 A length of rope 160 m long is used to mark out a rectangular region on a sports field. If the rectangle must have a minimum width of 15 m, write down inequalities for the sides of the region marked out and show them on the number line.

4 Two companies offer car hire services at an airport. How many miles must be driven before Quickhire is cheaper than Hirerite?

5 Draw the rectangle ABCD. The point P moves so that

$$20° \leqslant \theta \leqslant 60°$$

and

$$4 \, \text{cm} \leqslant d \leqslant 9 \, \text{cm}$$

Identify the region in which P must lie.

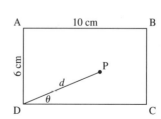

A 10 Plotting points and non-linear graphs

Plotting points

We describe the position of a point by its displacement from a fixed reference point called the **origin** (labelled O), through which pass two perpendicular reference lines called **axes**.

The **x-axis** goes **across** the page, with its **positive direction** to the **right**.
The **y-axis** goes **up and down** the page, with its **positive direction upwards**.
The position of a point is given by **coordinates** (**x**, **y**) showing first the horizontal and then the vertical displacement from the origin.

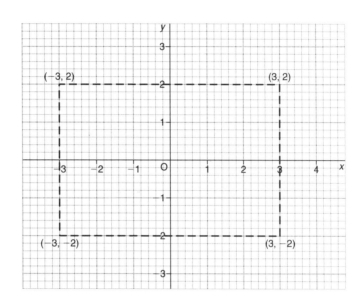

For example, the point with coordinates (3, 2) is 3 in the *x*-direction and 2 in the *y*-direction from the origin.

Memory aid

To get the axes the right way round remember '*x* is across (a cross)'. The directions of the coordinates are then in alphabetical order.

Graphs and mappings

A **mapping** is a rule which takes a set of input values and produces from each a corresponding output value.
The set of **input values** is called the **domain**.
The set of **output values** is called the **range**.
It is usual to label input values **x** and output values **y**.

The mapping $x \rightarrow x + 2$ acts on numbers in the domain to give corresponding values in the range.

We use *x* for values in the domain and *y* for the corresponding values in the range. We then have $y = x + 2$.

From this mapping, we can list pairs of corresponding values (*x*, *y*).

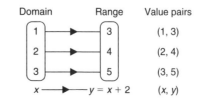

The pairs of values obtained from a mapping can be represented as points on a coordinate diagram and joined up to form a graph.

A **function** is a special kind of mapping in which **each input value** leads to **only one output value**.

In this case, they form a straight line. **All points on this line** are related by the mapping

$$y = x + 2$$

This is called the **graph of the function** $y = x + 2$. (Or the graph of the **equation** $y = x + 2$.)

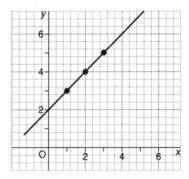

Several notations are used:

$$y = x + 2$$

$$f(x) = x + 2$$

$$f : x \rightarrow x + 2$$

Non-linear graphs

The function $y = x + 2$ is called a **linear function** because its graph is a straight line.

Non-linear functions produce graphs which are **curves**.

EXAMPLE 1

Draw the graph of the function $y = x^2 + 3x - 4$ for $-4 \leqslant x \leqslant 2$.

The set of input values to be used is often described as, for example,

$$-4 \leqslant x \leqslant 2$$

meaning **values of x between -4 and 2**.

x	-4	-3	-2	-1	0	1	2
x^2	16	9	4	1	0	1	4
$3x$	-12	-9	-6	-3	0	3	6
-4	-4	-4	-4	-4	-4	-4	-4
y	0	-4	-6	-6	-4	0	6

Draw the axes between the largest and smallest x and y-values which appear in the table.

Draw the x-axis between -4 and 2 and the y-axis between -6 and 6.

Plot the points
Join them with a **smooth curve**.

Notice that the curve dips below the value $y = -6$. As the curve is symmetrical, we can tell where the lowest point is by finding the value of y when $x = -1.5$:

$$y = (-1.5)^2 + 3 \times (-1.5) - 4$$
$$= -6.25$$

So the curve dips down as far as the point $(-1.5, -6.25)$.

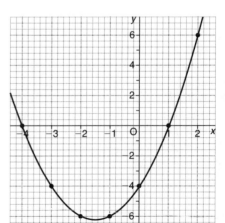

Finding values from a graph

Graphs of some common functions

- Linear functions (highest power of x is x^0 or x^1)

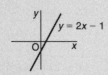

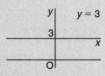

- Quadratic functions (highest power of x is x^2)

- Cubic functions (highest power of x is x^3)

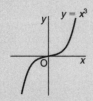

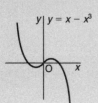

EXAMPLE 2

Use the graph of $y = x^2$ to find the value of **a** 3.4^2, **b** $\sqrt{7}$.

a We need to find y when $x = 3.4$

A vertical line at $x = 3.4$ meets the curve at point P.

The approximate value of y at P is 11.6, giving

$$3.4^2 \approx 11.6$$

b We need to solve the equation $x^2 = 7$, i.e. we need the value(s) of x when $y = 7$.

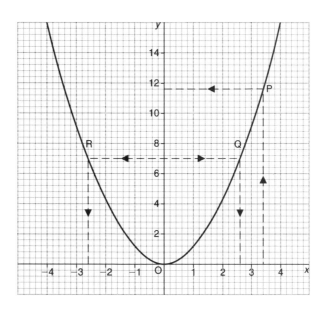

A horizontal line drawn at $y = 7$ meets the curve at two points, Q and R, with x-values of approximately 2.6 and -2.6. These give

$$\sqrt{7} \approx 2.6 \quad \text{or} \quad -2.6$$

EXERCISE A42

1 Draw the graph of $y = 2x^2 + 3x - 6$ for $-4 \leqslant x \leqslant 2$.
 Use your graph to find **a** y when $x = -1.6$, **b** x when $y = 4$.

2 Draw the graph of $y = x^3 - 13x + 4$ for $-4 \leqslant x \leqslant 4$.
 Use your graph to find the values of x for which $y = 0$.

3 Draw the graph of $y = x^2$ for $-4 \leqslant x \leqslant 4$ and use it to find an approximate value for $\sqrt{13}$.

● Reciprocal functions
(x appears in the
denominator of a fraction)

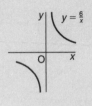

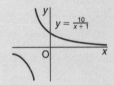

4 For each of the following graphs, choose an appropriate equation from the list below.

a   **b**   **c**

$$y = 5 - 2x \qquad y = x^2 - 3x - 4 \qquad y = x^3 - 9x$$

$$y = 3 + 2x - x^2 \qquad y = -x^3 \qquad y = \frac{4}{(x-2)}$$

A 11 Linear algebraic graphs

Recognising a linear relationship

We can recognise those equations which give straight-line graphs by the form of the equation.

Equations of the form

$$y = c$$

give **horizontal lines**.

Equations of the form

$$x = c$$

give **vertical lines**.
c is just a number in each case.

Horizontal and vertical lines
Some equations give horizontal lines, for example,

$$y = 2$$

This is satisfied by all points which have a y-coordinate of 2, such as $(0, 2)$, $(2, 2)$, $(-1, 2)$. These form a horizontal line as shown.
Some equations give vertical lines, for example,

$$x = 4$$

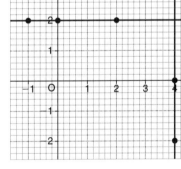

This is satisfied by all points which have an x-coordinate of 4, such as $(4, 0)$, $(4, 3)$, $(4, -2)$. These form a vertical line as shown.

'Sloping' lines
Equations such as $y = 2x$, $y = 3x + 2$ and $y = 1 - 2x$ give straight-line graphs. They always consist of a term with x and a constant term (just a number) which may be zero, as in the first equation.

For any numbers **m** and **c** the equation

$$y = mx + c$$

is a linear relation and gives a straight-line graph.

If we recognise an equation as being linear, we only need to find the coordinates of two points in order to draw the graph, though we should always find three points to act as a check.

$y = 2x$

x	−1	1	2
y	−2	2	4

$y = 3x + 2$

x	−1	0	1
y	−1	2	5

$y = 1 - 2x$

x	−1	0	1
y	3	1	−1

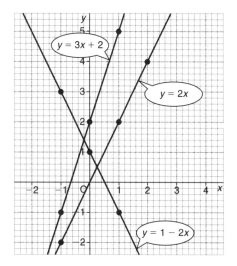

Gradient and rate of change

The **rate of change of y with respect to x** is given by

$$\frac{\textbf{Change in } y}{\textbf{Change in } x}$$

as we move between any two points on the line.

The rate of change of y gives the **gradient** of the line.

If $A(x_1, y_1)$ and $B(x_2, y_2)$ are two points on the line then

$$\textbf{Gradient} = \frac{y_2 - y_1}{x_2 - x_1}$$

If we move between two points on a straight-line graph, the values of x and y both change. The change in y compared with the change in x is called the

rate of change of y with respect to x.

The rate of change is the same between any two points on the line.

EXAMPLE 1

The diagram shows the line $y = 2x$ with points A(0, 0) and B(3, 6). As we move from A to B,

y changes by 6
x changes by 3

The rate of change of y with respect to x is

$6 \div 3 = 2$

That is, y changes twice as fast as x.

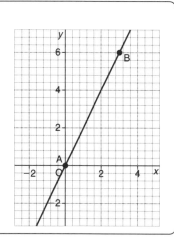

When a graph goes 'uphill'
- the rate of change is **positive**
- the gradient is **positive**
- y is an **increasing function** of x

When a graph goes 'downhill'
- the rate of change is **negative**
- the gradient is **negative**
- y is an **decreasing function** of x

For any number m, the equation

$$y = mx$$

gives a straight line through the origin with **gradient m**.

For any numbers m and c the equation $y = mx + c$ gives a straight line.

The **gradient** of the line is m. The **y-intercept** of the line is c.
That is, it crosses the y-axis at the point $(0, c)$.

EXAMPLE 2

The diagram shows the line $y = -2x$ with points A$(-3, 6)$ and B$(0, 0)$.
As we move from A to B,

    y changes by -6
    x changes by 3

The rate of change of y with respect to x is

    $-6 \div 3 = -2$

That is, y changes twice as fast as x but decreases when x increases.

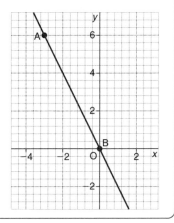

The greater the rate of change, the steeper the line is. So rate of change measures the **gradient** of the line.

The gradient of the line in Example 1 is 2, and that of the line in Example 2 is -2.

The relation between an equation and its gradient

Notice from Examples 1 and 2 that $y = 2x$ has gradient 2 and $y = -2x$ has gradient -2.

It is true, in general, that the number multiplying x (the 'coefficient' of x) in such an equation is the gradient of the line. For example,

    $y = 5x$ is a straight line through the origin with gradient 5
    $y = -4x$ is a straight line through the origin with gradient -4

The equation $y = mx + c$

The diagram shows the lines

    $y = 2x$
    $y = 2x + 1$
    $y = 2x + 3$

The lines are **parallel**.

The gradient of all these lines is 2.

    $y = 2x$ crosses the y-axis at $(0, 0)$
    $y = 2x + 1$ crosses the y-axis at $(0, 1)$
    $y = 2x + 3$ crosses the y-axis at $(0, 3)$

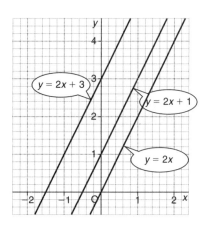

In each case, the number on its own (the 'constant' term) in the equation gives the y-value at the point where the line crosses the y-axis. This is called the **y-intercept**.

EXAMPLE 3

Find the equation of the line through the points A(1, 4) and B(3, 10).
Moving from A to B,

> y changes by 6
> x changes by 2

The gradient is $6 \div 2 = 3$

So, in the equation, $m = 3$

The line crosses the y-axis at (0, 1).
So, in the equation, $c = 1$.

The equation of the line is therefore $y = 3x + 1$.

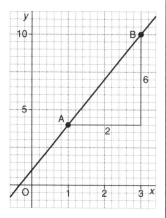

Sometimes we cannot easily find the value of c from a graph but we can still calculate it.

EXAMPLE 4

Find the equation of the line through A(19, 26) and B(23, 18).
Moving from A to B, y changes by -8 and x changes by 4. So the gradient is

$$-8 \div 4 = -2$$

Therefore, in the equation, $m = -2$, and so the equation must be
$$y = -2x + c.$$

The line passes through A(19, 26), so the values $x = 19$ and $y = 26$ should satisfy the equation. Substituting them gives

$$26 = -2 \times 19 + c$$
$$\Rightarrow \quad 26 = -38 + c$$
$$c = 64$$

The equation of the line is therefore $y = -2x + 64$.

EXERCISE A43

1 State whether the following relations are linear. For those which are, state
i the gradient of the line, **ii** the coordinates of the point at which the line crosses the y-axis, and **iii** whether y is an increasing or decreasing function of x.

    a $y = 3x^3 - 5$ **b** $y = 5x + 3$ **c** $y = 7 - 2x$ **d** $3x - y + 4 = 0$

2 Identify the two pairs of parallel lines in the following list.

    A $y = x + 2$ **B** $y = 2x - 1$ **C** $y = 8 - x$ **D** $x - y = 3$ **E** $y = 11 + 2x$

3 Find the equation of the lines illustrated.

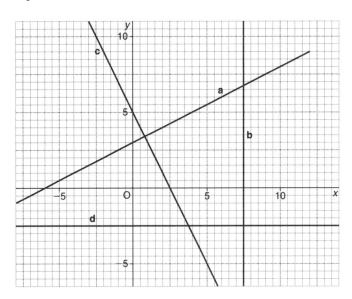

4 Find the equation of the line joining the points A(14, 69) and B(19, 99).

5 The table shows the results of an experiment in which various masses were suspended from a spring and the length of the spring was measured.

Mass in kg (x)	4	5.5	7	9	12	14
Length in cm (y)	73	79	85	93	105	113

   a Plot these results on a graph and join the points with a straight line.

   b Find the equation of the line.

   c Use your equation to find   **i** the unstretched length of the spring,
      ii the length of the spring when a mass of 20 kg is suspended from it.

A 12 Linear algebraic inequalities

Graphs of linear inequalities

When we draw the graph of a linear equation, such as $y = 2x + 1$, it divides the diagram into two regions. In one of these regions $y < 2x + 1$, and in the other $y > 2x + 1$.

To graph an inequality, we follow these steps:

1 Draw the graph of the corresponding equation. When the points on the line are part of the required region (i.e. when the sign is $\leqslant$ or $\geqslant$), we draw a solid (continuous) line. When the points on the line are not to be included (i.e. when the sign is $<$ or $>$), we draw a broken (dashed) line.

A **solid line** means that the points are **included** in the region required (use for $\leqslant$ or $\geqslant$).

A **broken line** means that points on the line are **not included** in the region required (use $<$ or $>$).

Check which region to shade by testing whether the inequality is satisfied by a chosen point which is not on the line.
(The origin (0, 0) is the easiest test point to use, unless it is on the line).

2 Decide which of the two regions to shade. To do this we choose any point not on the line and test whether it satisfies the required condition. If it does, we shade the region containing that point. If it does not, we shade the other region.

3 Shade the required region.

EXAMPLE 1

Shade the region $y > x - 1$.

First we draw the line $y = x - 1$, as shown. The points on the line are not to be included, so we use a broken line.

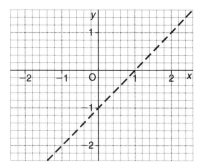

We then test a point. In this case, the easiest point to test is the origin (0, 0). Putting $y = 0$ and $x = 0$, the inequality would read $0 > 0 - 1$. This is true, so the origin is in the required region.

We then shaded the required region, as shown.

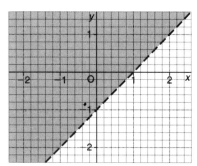

Inequalities can be illustrated by either shading the region required or by shading the unwanted region. Always **a** check what the question wants and **b** where you have a choice state clearly which method you are using.

More than one inequality

When we wish to illustrate those points which satisfy two or more inequalities, there are two approaches:

- Shade those points which **do satisfy** all the inequalities.
- Shade those points which **do not satisfy** all the inequalities (i.e. the **unwanted region**).

It is important that you use the method required by the question.
If no method is specified, you should state clearly what you are doing.

EXAMPLE 2

Shade the region for which $y < x - 1$, $y \leqslant 2x - 1$ and $x < 1$.

First draw the three lines, as shown. We use a broken line for $y = x - 1$ and $x = 1$ and a solid line for $y = 2x - 1$.

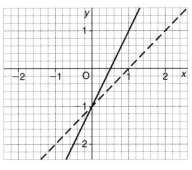

We then choose a test point. The origin is not on any of the lines, so this is the easiest test point.
For $y = 0$ and $x = 0$

   $y < x - 1$ is **not true**

   $y \leqslant 2x - 1$ is **not true**

   $x < 1$ is **true**.

The region to be shaded is on the same side of the line $x = 1$ as the origin and on the opposite side of the other two lines from the origin, as shown.

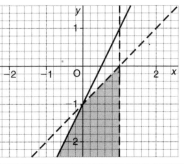

Shading the **unwanted region** has two advantages:

- When we have several inequalities to consider, we can shade out the unwanted regions one by one.
- When we want to read solutions from the graph, it is easier to do so if they occupy an unshaded region.

Example 2 would then look like this.

First shade the region where $y < x - 1$ is **not true**.

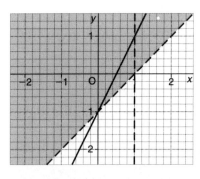

Next, shade the region where $y \leqslant 2x - 1$ is **not true**.

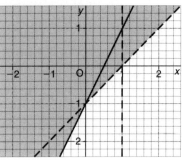

Shading the unwanted region is usually the better method when there are several inequalities involved.

Finally, shade the region where $x < 1$ is **not** true.

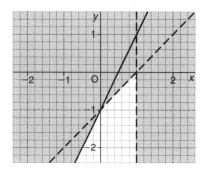

The region left unshaded is the region we want.

Problems involving inequalities

EXAMPLE 3

A truck can carry 3 tonnes. It is to be loaded with one large and three small girders. A large girder must weigh more than a small girder but must weigh less than twice as much as a small girder. Find the possible masses of the girders.

Let the mass of a small girder be x tonnes and of a large girder be y tonnes. The conditions to be satisfied are

$$3x + y \leqslant 3 \qquad (1)$$

$$y > x \qquad (2)$$

$$y < 2x \qquad (3)$$

The diagram shows the lines $3x + y = 3$, $y = 2x$ and $y = x$.

If we use the point A(0, 1) to test the three conditions above, we find that conditions (1) and (2) are true and (3) is false.

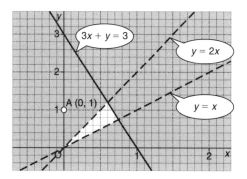

We can use this to shade the unwanted regions, as shown.

The unshaded region gives all the possible masses for the girders. So, for example, a small girder of 0.6 tonnes and a large girder of 0.8 tonnes will satisfy all the conditions.

Sometimes the solution to a problem can take only whole-number (integer) values.

EXAMPLE 4

There is room in my garden for 8 apple or pear trees. I wish to grow at least 2 pear trees, but decide that I want more apple trees than pear trees. What are the possible numbers of trees?

If x is the number of apples trees and y the number of pear trees, the conditions to be satisfied are

$$x + y \leqslant 8$$

$$y \geqslant 2$$

$$y < x$$

As before, we draw the lines for the three conditions and shade the unwanted regions, as shown.

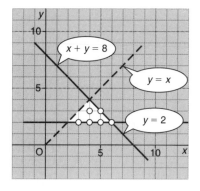

x and y have to be whole numbers, so the points marked with circles on the diagram correspond to the possible solutions to the problem.

I can have 2 pear trees with 3, 4, 5 or 6 apple trees, or 3 pear trees with 4 or 5 apple trees.

EXERCISE A44

1 On separate graphs shade the regions corresponding to the following inequalities.

    a $y \leqslant x + 3$ **b** $x + 2y < 6$ **c** $y > -2$ **d** $y \geqslant \frac{1}{2}x - 1$

2 For each case draw a graph and by shading the unwanted area illustrate the region satisfying

    a $x > 2, y \leqslant 5$ and $x + y < 10$

    b $y > 1, y > -x$ and $y \leqslant -\frac{1}{2}x + 2$

3 Manfred is diluting orange squash in a bowl which will hold at most 5 litres. He has an unlimited supply of water but has only 2 litres of squash. He wants to end up with more than 2 litres of the mixture. The squash will be too strong if there is more squash than water in it and too weak if there is more than three times more water than squash.

If the amount of water used is x and the amount of squash is y

    a write down the five inequalities which describe the problem and

    b by shading the unwanted regions illustrate on a graph the possible amounts of squash and water that Manfred could use.

4 A sweet shop sells bags containing a mix of jelly beans and wine gums. The shopkeeper states that there are at least 10 sweets in the bag and that more than half of them are wine gums. The bags are sold for 18 p each. The jelly beans cost the shopkeeper 1 p each and the wine gums 2 p each.

Taking x to be the number of jelly beans and y the number of wine gums in the bag, illustrate on a graph, and list, the possible contents of the bag for which the shopkeeper will make a profit.

A 13 Linear simultaneous equations

If we have two equations connecting the unknown quantities x and y, there will be one pair of values (x, y) for which both equations are satisfied.

The equations are called **simultaneous equations** and the pair of values is the solution of the equations (both equations are satisfied **simultaneously**).

Graphical solution

EXAMPLE 1

$$x + y = 6 \ldots\ldots\ldots(1)$$
$$y = 3x \ldots\ldots (2)$$

Values for equation (1)

x	0	2	4
y	6	4	2

Values for equation (2)

x	0	1	2
y	0	3	6

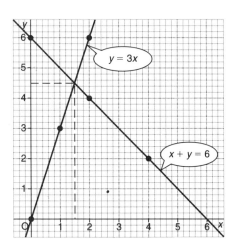

The solution is $x = 1.5$, $y = 4.5$ (Check this in the equations.)

The solution of the equations is given by the x- and y-coordinates of the point where the lines intersect.

If the lines cross at (a, b), then the solution of the equations is $x = a$ and $y = b$.

EXERCISE A45

Use graphical methods to solve the following pairs of equations giving answers where necessary to one decimal place.

1 $x - y = 2$
   $y = 3x - 5$

2 $y = 2x + 1$
   $y = 4 - x$

3 $x + 2y = 7$
   $3x + 4y = 12$

4 $4x - 6y = 13$
   $x + y = 2$

5 $x - 2y = 2$
   $3x - y = -2$

6 $2x - 3y = 4$
   $2x + 3y = -10$

When solving by substitution:

Step 1
Rearrange one of the equations to obtain one unknown in terms of the other.

Step 2
Substitute the expression obtained into the other equation.

Step 3
Solve for the other unknown.

Step 4
Substitute the value obtained into one of the equations to find the remaining unknown.

Step 5
Check that the solution satisfies both equations.

When solving by elimination:

Step 1
Decide which unknown to eliminate.

Step 2
If necessary, multiply throughout one or both equations to make the coefficient (number in front) of the chosen unknown the same in both equations (except perhaps for a different sign).

Step 3
Combine the equations to eliminate this unknown. When the terms have the same sign, we subtract; when they have opposite signs, we add.

Step 4
Solve for the other unknown.

Step 5
Substitute into one of the equations to find the remaining unknown.

Step 6
Check that the solution satisfies both equations.

Solution by substitution

EXAMPLE 2

Solve $\quad x - y = 4 \ldots\ldots\ldots(1)$

$\qquad\quad 5x + y = 8 \ldots\ldots\ldots(2)$

From (1) $\quad y = x - 4 \ldots\ldots(3)$

Substitute (3) into (2): $\quad 5x + (x - 4) = 8$

$\Rightarrow \quad 6x - 4 = 8$

$\Rightarrow \quad 6x = 12$

$\Rightarrow \quad x = 2 \ldots\ldots(4)$

Substitute (4) into (3): $\quad y = 2 - 4$

$\Rightarrow \quad y = -2$

The solution of the equations is $x = 2$, $y = -2$.

Check that the solution satisfies the other equation.

In equation (2) $\quad 5x + y = 5 \times 2 + (-2)$

$\qquad\qquad\qquad\quad = 8$

So the equation is satisfied.

EXERCISE A46

Use substitution to solve the following pairs of equations.

1 $\ y = 5x - 1$
$\quad\ y = 2x + 11$

2 $\qquad x = 10 - 2y$
$\qquad\ x - y = 5$

3 $\ 3a + b = 5$
$\quad\ 4a - b = 9$

4 $\ 7m - 6n = -3$
$\quad\ 5m - n = 11$

5 $\ x = 4 - 3y$
$\quad\ y = 5x - 4$

6 $\ 2y - 3 = x$
$\quad\ 3x + 4y = -4$

Solution by elimination

EXAMPLE 3

Solve $\quad 3x + 4y = 26 \ldots\ldots(1)$

$\qquad\quad 4x - 3y = 18 \ldots\ldots(2)$

Multiply (1) by 3: $\quad 9x + 12y = 78 \ldots\ldots(3)$

Multiply (2) by 4: $\quad 16x - 12y = 72 \ldots\ldots(4)$

Add (3) and (4): $\qquad\qquad 25x = 150$

$\Rightarrow \quad x = 6 \ldots\ldots\ldots(5)$

Substitute (5) into (1): $\quad 18 + 4y = 26$

$\Rightarrow \quad 4y = 8$

$\Rightarrow \quad y = 2$

The solution of the equations is $x = 2$, $y = -2$.

Check that the solution satisfies the other equation.

In equation (2) $\quad 4x - 3y = 4 \times 6 - 3 \times 2$

So the equation is satisfied.

EXERCISE A47

Use elimination to solve the following pairs of equations.

1 $x + y = 8$
$x - y = 2$

2 $x + 5y = 11$
$x + 2y = 2$

3 $3x + 5y = 19$
$4x - y = 10$

4 $3x + 4y = 7$
$x + 3y = -1$

5 $6x - 5y = 11$
$4x + 3y = 1$

6 $7x - 2y = -9$
$6x - 4y = -10$

Steps in solving a problem:

Step 1
Assign a letter to each unknown.

Step 2
Use the given information to write two equations connecting these unknowns.

Step 3
Use substitution or elimination to solve the equations.

Step 4
Relate these solutions back to the original problem.

Solving problems

EXAMPLE

A pen and a pencil cost 34 p. Three pens and two pencils cost 92 p. Find the cost of a pen and the cost of a pencil.

Let a pen cost x pence and a pencil cost y pence. Then

$$x + y = 34 \ldots\ldots (1)$$
$$3x + 2y = 92 \ldots\ldots (2)$$

Multiply (1) by 2: $2x + 2y = 68 \ldots\ldots (3)$

Subtract (3) from (2): $x = 24 \ldots\ldots (4)$

Substitute (4) into (1): $24 + y = 34$
$$\Rightarrow \quad y = 10$$

The solution of the equations is $x = 24$, $y = 10$

Check in equation (2): $3 \times 24 + 2 \times 10 = 72 + 20$
$$= 92$$

The cost of a pen is 24 pence and the cost of a pencil is 10 pence.

EXERCISE A48

1 Five oranges and three lemons cost £1.05, while four oranges and five lemons cost £1.23. Letting x be the cost of an orange and y be the cost of a lemon, write down two equations. Solve your equations to find the cost of an orange and the cost of a lemon.

2 If I run for one hour and walk for a further two hours, I travel 22 km. If I run for 90 minutes and walk for a further 4 hours, I travel 39 km. Write down two equations and solve them to find my running speed and my walking speed (assuming that these are constant throughout).

3 Nirmal is four times as old as his son Naresh. Two years ago he was five times as old as Naresh. Write down two equations and solve them to find the ages of Nirmal and Naresh.

4 One small and one large can of chick peas contain a total of 500 grams. Seven small cans plus six large cans contain the same as ten small cans plus four large cans. Find the contents of a small can and those of a large can.

5 Angela is out for a Sunday drive. She travels from Angelton to Bluesville at 48 km/h and from there to Charleston at 50 km/h. The journey takes 4 hours. She then realises she has an appointment and hurries back to Bluesville at 90 km/h and on to Angelton at 108 km/h. The return journey takes 2 hours. Find the distances between the towns.

A 14 Variation

Variation covers situations where two quantities are related so that a change in one causes a change in the other. The two types of variation are **direct proportion** and **inverse proportion**.

Direct proportion

y is **directly proportional** to *x* if an **increase** in *x* causes an **increase** in *y* in the **same ratio**.

We write $y \propto x$

In the table *x* is the number of colas purchased and *y* is the cost in pence.

x	1	2	3	4	5	6	7
y	23	46	69	92	115	138	161

When the value of *x* changes, the value of *y* changes in the **same ratio**. We say that *y* is **directly proportional** to *x* (sometimes just 'proportional to') or that *y* **varies directly as** *x*. This is written as

$$y \propto x.$$

There is an obvious relationship between *x* and *y*, namely

$$y = 23x$$

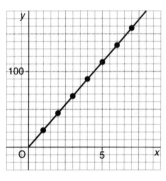

When $y \propto x$, there is a relationship of the form $y = kx$, where *k* is called the **constant of proportionality**.

The relationship can be represented as a straight-line graph with gradient *k* passing through the origin.

This can be illustrated by a straight line through the origin with gradient 23, as shown.

All direct proportions can be represented by a straight-line graph in this way.

Inverse proportion

In the following table *x* represents the speed in m/s of an object travelling a certain distance and *y* represents the time taken in seconds.

x	5	10	20	30	40	60	80
y	24	12	6	4	3	2	1.5

y is **inversely proportional** to *x* when an **increase** in *x* causes a **decrease** in *y* in the **same ratio**.

We write $y \propto \dfrac{1}{x}$

There is then a relationship of the form $y = \dfrac{k}{x}$

When the value of *x* **increases**, the value of *y* **decreases in the same ratio**. We say that *y* is **inversely proportional to** *x*, or that *y* **varies inversely as** *x*. This is written as

$$y \propto \frac{1}{x}$$

The relationship in this case is

$$y = \frac{120}{x}$$

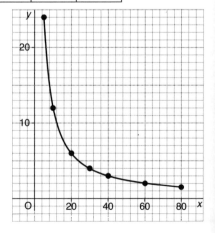

For an inverse proportion, the graph of *y* against *x* is not a straight line but has the shape shown.

This curve is called a **hyperbola**.

x	5	10	20	30	40	60	80
$\frac{1}{x}$	0.2	0.1	0.05	0.033	0.025	0.0167	0.0125
y	24	12	6	4	3	2	1.5

When y and x are related by $y = \frac{k}{x}$, we can obtain a straight line graph with gradient k by plotting values of y against values of $\frac{1}{x}$.

We can show the relationship

$$y = \frac{120}{x}$$

as a straight-line graph if we draw the graph using values of y and against values of $\frac{1}{x}$.

We then get a straight line with gradient 120 passing through the origin.

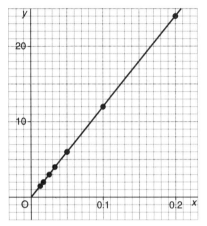

In any proportional relationship, we can find an exact formula connecting the variables provided we know a set of corresponding values. The steps are:
1 Write the formula using a constant of proportionality k.
2 Find the value of k by substituting the given values of the variables.

Finding the value of k

EXAMPLE 1

y is directly proportional to x and $y = 6$ when $x = 24$. Find the relationship between x and y and hence find the value of y when $x = 14$.

$$y \propto x \quad \Rightarrow \quad y = kx$$

Substituting $x = 2.4$ and $y = 6$ gives $\quad 6 = 2.4k$

$$\Rightarrow \quad k = 2.5$$

So the relationship is $y = 2.5x$.

When $x = 14 \quad y = 2.5 \times 14$

$$\Rightarrow \quad y = 35$$

EXAMPLE 2

If y is inversely proportional to x and $y = 4$ when $x = 6$, find the relationship between x and y and hence find the value of y when $x = 18$.

$$y \propto \frac{1}{x} \quad \Rightarrow \quad y = \frac{k}{x}$$

Substituting $x = 6$ and $y = 4$ gives $\quad 4 = \frac{k}{6}$

$$\Rightarrow \quad k = 24$$

So the relationship is $y = \frac{24}{x}$.

When $x = 18 \quad y = \frac{24}{18}$

$$\Rightarrow \quad y = 1\frac{1}{3}$$

Other relationships

Sometimes a proportion may involve a function of the variable.

EXAMPLE 3

y is proportional to the square of x and $y = 54$ when $x = 3$. Find the relationship between x and y and hence find the value of y when $x = 5$.

$$y \propto x^2 \quad \Rightarrow \quad y = kx^2$$

Substituting $x = 3$ and $y = 54$ gives $\quad 54 = 9k$

$$\Rightarrow \quad k = 6$$

So the relationship is $y = 6x^2$.

When $x = 5 \quad y = 6 \times 25$

$$\Rightarrow \quad y = 150$$

The inverse square law

When an effect such as light or magnetic attraction originates from a single, point source, its intensity at any point varies inversely as the square of the distance of the point from the source.

Because this relationship applies in so many different situations it is singled out for special notice and is called the **inverse square law**.

A physical effect obeys the **inverse square law** if its intensity at any point is inversely proportional to the square of the distance of the point from the source of the effect.

EXAMPLE 4

The intensity of light from a certain source is 6 candelas/m^2 at a distance of 4 m from the source. Find the intensity at a distance of 10 m.

Call the intensity I and the distance d. Then

$$I \propto \frac{1}{d^2} \quad \Rightarrow \quad I = \frac{k}{d^2}$$

Substituting $I = 6$ and $d = 4$ gives $\quad 6 = \frac{k}{16}$

$$\Rightarrow \quad k = 96$$

So the relationship is $I = \frac{96}{d^2}$

When $d = 10 \quad I = \frac{96}{100}$

$$\Rightarrow \quad I = 0.96 \text{ candela/m}^2$$

Joint variation

A proportion may involve more than two variables. For example, y may be related to both x and z in such a way that, for a fixed value of x, y is directly proportional to z and for a fixed value of z, y is directly proportional to x.

We say that y **varies jointly** as x and z and write $y \propto xz$.
This leads to the relationship $y = kxz$.

Inverse variation may also be involved. For example, y may vary directly as x and inversely as z.

We would write $y \propto \dfrac{x}{z}$.

This leads to the relationship $y = \dfrac{kx}{z}$.

EXAMPLE 5

The time taken for an ice cube to melt varies directly as the cube of the length of its side and inversely as the temperature of the surrounding air. An ice cube with sides of length 3 cm took 45 minutes to melt in a temperature of 20°C. How long would an ice cube of side length 5 cm take in a temperature of 30°C?

Call the side length L, the temperature T, and the melting time t. Then

$$t \propto L^3 \quad \Rightarrow \quad t = \frac{kL^3}{T}$$

Substituting $t = 45$, $L = 3$, $T = 20$ gives $\quad 45 = \dfrac{27k}{20}$

$$\Rightarrow \quad k = \frac{100}{3}$$

So the relationship is $\quad t = \dfrac{100L^3}{3T}$

When $L = 5$ and $T = 30$ $\quad t = \dfrac{12\,500}{90}$

$$\Rightarrow \quad t = 138\tfrac{8}{9} \text{ minutes}$$

EXERCISE A49

1 If y is directly proportional to x and $y = 24$ when $x = 16$, find the relationship connecting x and y and hence find **a** the value of y when $x = 30$, **b** the value of x when $y = 78$.

2 The air resistance acting on a vehicle is proportional to the cross-sectional area of the vehicle and to the square of its speed. A vehicle whose cross-sectional area is 4.5 m² suffers air resistance of 1107 newtons when travelling at 20 m/s. Find the air resistance acting on a vehicle of cross-sectional area 6 m² when it is travelling at 30 m/s.

3 The frequency with which an object bounces up and down on the end of a certain spring is inversely proportional to the square root of the mass of the object. An object of mass 64 grams makes 25 oscillations in 1 minute. How many oscillations will a mass of 100 grams make in 1 minute?

4 p is directly proportional to the square of q and inversely proportional to r and to the cube of s. Given that $p = 50$ when $q = 2$, $r = 10$ and $s = 3$, find the value of p when $q = 5$, $r = 4$ and $s = 6$.

5 The gravitational force acting on a certain object is 540 newtons when it is 12 000 km from the centre of the earth. Assuming the inverse square law, find the gravitational force acting on the same object when it is 72 000 km from the centre of the earth.

A 15 Indices

Rules for indices

The rules used for powers of numbers also apply to algebraic expressions.

$$a^2 = 1 \times a \times a \qquad a^3 = 1 \times a \times a \times a$$

and so on.

Zero index rule

$a^0 = 1$

Product rule
$a^m \times a^n = a^{m+n}$

Zero index rule

$a^0 \times 1$

Product rule
When multiplying two powers of the **same** number, add the powers:

$$a^m \times a^n = a^{m+n}$$

Quotient rule

$a^m \div a^n = a^{m-n}$

Quotient rule
When dividing one power of a number by another power of the **same** number, subtract the second power from the first:

$$a^m \div a^n = a^{m-n}$$

Powers rule

$(a^m)^n = a^{mn}$

Powers rule
When a power of a number is raised to another power, multiply the powers:

$$(a^m)^n = a^{m \times n} = a^{mn}$$

Negative index (reciprocal) rule

$a^{-n} = \dfrac{1}{a^n}$

Negative index (reciprocal) rule
A negative index indicates a reciprocal of the number:

$$a^{-n} = \frac{1}{a^n}$$

Fractional index rule

$a^{\frac{1}{n}} = \sqrt[n]{a}$

Fractional index rule
A fractional index indicates a root of the number:

$$a^{\frac{1}{n}} = \sqrt[n]{a}$$

EXAMPLE 1

Simplify $\dfrac{a^3 \times a^4}{a^5}$.

$$\frac{a^3 \times a^4}{a^5} = a^{3+4-5}$$

$$= a^2$$

> Using the product rule and the quotient rule

EXAMPLE 2

Simplify $\dfrac{3a^3b^2 \times 6a^4b^3}{12a^5b^8}$.

| Treat each variable and the numbers separately | $\dfrac{3a^3b^2 \times 6a^4b^3}{12a^5b^8} = \dfrac{3 \times 6}{12} \times a^{3+4-5} \times b^{2+3-8}$ | Using the product and quotient rules |

$$= \dfrac{3a^2b^{-3}}{2}$$

$$= \dfrac{3a^2}{2b^3}$$

Using the reciprocal rule

EXERCISE A50

Simplify the following

1 $a \times a \times a \times a$ **2** $b^4 \times b^5$ **3** $c^3 \times c^2 \times c^4$

4 $d^2 \times e^3 \times e \times d^3$ **5** $3f^2 \times 5f^3$ **6** $(6g^2h^3) \times (4g^3h^4)$

EXERCISE A51

Simplify the following

1 $k^5 \div k^3$ **2** $m^5 \div m^2$ **3** $n^4 \div n^9$

4 $p^3 \times p^5 \div p^4$ **5** $q^2 \div q^6 \times q^2$ **6** $(6r^3s^4) \div (2rs^2)$

EXERCISE A52

Simplify the following.

1 $\dfrac{2t^2u^5 \times 6t^3}{3tu^2 \times 2u^2}$ **2** $\dfrac{8v^2w^2}{6vw^2} \times \dfrac{9v^3w}{6v^2}$

3 $\dfrac{2a^3}{b^2} \div \dfrac{4a^2}{b^4}$ **4** $\dfrac{x^3y^2z^2 - x^2y^3z^2 + x^2y^2z^3}{xyz^2}$

Hint: separate this into three fractions

EXERCISE A53

Simplify the following and express them as a single power.

1 $(x^3)^4$ **2** $(2y^4)^2$ **3** $(z^2)^3$

4 $\sqrt{(a^6)}$ **5** $(\sqrt[3]{b})^9$ **6** $(\sqrt{c})^{-4}$

7 $\dfrac{(2x^2)^3 \times (3x^3)^2}{(6x^3)^4}$ **8** $\dfrac{(8a^3b^2)^2 \times (2ab)^3}{(4a^2b^3)^4}$

A 16 Trial and improvement

Solving equations

Many equations and inequalities cannot be solved exactly by algebraic means. We then have to use numerical methods to find an approximate solution to the problem.

The words **root** and **solution** mean the same thing. However, the word **root** is usually applied only to equations rather than to problems in general.

The trial-and-improvement method involves:

Step 1 Estimate a solution.

Step 2 Keep fine tuning the solution to improve its accuracy, as required.

Step 3 State the degree of accuracy (significant figures) of the solution.

When we want to indicate 'between 3 and 4' we use the notation

$[3, 4]$ for $3 \leqslant x \leqslant 4$

and $]3, 4[$ for $3 < x < 4$

We also use

$]3, 4]$ for $3 < x \leqslant 4$

and $[3, 4[$ for $3 \leqslant x < 4$

EXAMPLE 1

Solve the equation $x^3 - 40 = 0$.

Step 1 Estimate a solution

x	0	1	2	3	4	5
$x^3 - 40$	-40	-39	-32	-13	24	85

A quick check shows that the solution is somewhere between 3 and 4.

Step 2 Improve the solution

x	3.3	3.4	3.5	3.6
$x^3 - 40$	-4.063	-0.696	2.875	6.656

So the solution lies in the interval [3.4, 3.5]

Step 3 Repeat

x	3.41	3.42	3.43	3.44
$x^3 - 40$	$-0.348\,179$	$0.001\,688$	$0.353\,607$	$0.707\,584$

So the solution lies in the interval [3.41, 3.42].

So we know the solution is 3.4, correct to 1 decimal place.

This process is continued until the solution is as accurate as required.

Where the graph of $y = f(x)$ cuts the line $\quad y = a$

the x-values are solutions of the equation $f(x) = a$.

Similarly when the graph of $y = f(x)$ cuts the graph of $y = g(x)$

the x-values are solutions of the equation $f(x) = g(x)$

Another way to find a first approximation to the root is to draw a graph of the function and find where it cuts the x-axis.

The graph of $y = $ (some function of x) cuts the x-axis when the y-value is 0. So the corresponding x-values are solutions of the equation

$\quad 0 = $ (some function of x)

A graph may also show us where any other roots might lie. We can then investigate them further.

EXAMPLE 2

Solve the equation $x^3 + x - 5 = 0$.

We can rewrite this equation to give $x^3 = 5 - x$

Then we draw the graphs $y = x^3$
and $y = 5 - x$

The solution is the x-coordinate where these two graphs cross.

We can see that this occurs when $x \approx 1.6$.

We can use this x-value as a starting point and then proceed as before to obtain a more accurate solution.

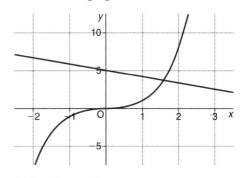

The result is $x = 1.51598$, correct to 6 significant figures.

EXERCISE A54

1 The equation $x^3 - x - 5 = 0$ has only one solution. Find this solution correct to 3 sf.

2 The graphs of the equations $y = \cos x$ and $y = \tan x$ cross once only in the interval $0° \leqslant \theta \leqslant 90°$.

   a What equation has its root given by the coordinate of intersection of these graphs?

   b Find this value of x correct to 2 decimal places.

3 Sketch the graphs of $y = x^3$ and $y = x^2 - 5$. Your sketch should show that they cross once only. Starting with the approximate solution, improve its accuracy to 3 significant figures.

Inequalities

In Example 2, the graph of $y = 5 - x$ is above the graph of $y = x^3$ for values of x less than 1.51598 and below it for values of x greater than 1.51598.

We can use this fact to solve the inequality $x^3 > 5 - x$. The solution set is $x > 1.51598$.

EXERCISE A55

From your results to question 3 in Exercise A54, solve the inequality $x^3 > x^2 - 5$.

Iterative methods

1 Choose a number less than 1000.
2 Write down this number in **words**.
3 Count the number of **letters** you have written down.
4 Go to instruction 2.

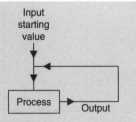

Input
starting
value

Process   Output

Sometimes processes take a long time to converge. Sometimes they never get to the final point but keep getting closer and closer to it. We stop the process when we are close enough.

When you feel that you are not going to make any further progress, start again with a different number.

This is an example of an iterative procedure.

1 We have a starting value.
2 This is put into a process.
3 The value that results is then fed back into the process.

Sometimes, as in the example above, you get to the point where the output value is the same as the input value. When this happens, the process is said to have **converged**. In other cases, the process does not converge. Sometimes it diverges and eventually reaches infinity, and sometmes it oscillates between two or more values or jumps about chaotically.

Iterative processes are very important for solving problems, especially when using a computer. Only those processes that converge are useful and their study is an important branch of mathematics.

x_1 is the starting value.

x_n is the current value.

x_{n+1} is the next value.

An iterative formula is a rule showing how to obtain the next value from the current value.

When it has converged, x_{n+1} and x_n are the same thing, so we can ignore the ns.

EXAMPLE 3

a With $x_1 = 1$, use the iterative formula

$$x_{n+1} = \frac{2x_n^3 + 5}{3x_n^2 + 1}$$

to investigate whether it converges.

b What equation would this formula solve?

a $x_2 = 1.75$
$x_3 = 1.542\,9448$
$x_4 = 1.516\,3912$
$x_5 = 1.515\,9803$
$x_6 = 1.515\,9802$
$x_7 = 1.515\,9802$ Converged

b Ignoring the ns and rearranging the formula gives
$$x(3x^2 + 1) = 2x^3 + 5$$
$$3x^3 + x = 2x^3 + 5$$
$$x^3 + x - 5 = 0$$

EXERCISE A56

a Investigate the convergence of each of the following iterative procedures.

b What equation were they an attempt to solve?

1 $x_{n+1} = 2.5x_n(1 - x_n)$ with $x_1 = 0.1$

2 $x_{n+1} = 2.5x_n(1 - x_n)$ with $x_1 = 2$

3 $x_{n+1} = 3.3x_n(1 - x_n)$ with $x_1 = 0.1$

4 $x_{n+1} = \frac{1}{2}\left(x_n + \frac{2}{x_n}\right)$ with $x_1 = 1$

A 17 Quadratic functions and equations

A quadratic function has the form

$$ax^2 + bx + c$$

A quadratic function of x is one in which the highest power of x occurring is x^2. For example,

$$2x^2 - 3x + 4, \; x^2 - 7, \; 5x - 3x^2$$

are all quadratic functions.

A quadratic expression may arise as a result of multiplying two linear functions. For example,

$$(2x + 3)(x - 2) = 2x^2 - 4x + 3x - 6$$
$$= 2x^2 - x - 6 \quad \text{which is a quadratic function.}$$

Factorising quadratics

Some quadratic functions can be factorised and in general give the product of two linear brackets.

Factorising expressions like $x^2 + px + q$

The expression $x^2 + px + q$ can be factorised as $(x + a)(x + b)$ if we can find numbers a and b so that

$$ab = p$$
and $$a + b = q$$

EXAMPLE 1

Factorise $x^2 + 8x + 15$.

If this factorises as $(x + a)(x + b) = x^2 + (a + b)x + ab$

then $a + b = 8$ and $ab = 15$

The pairs of numbers which multiply to give 15 are

$$1 \times 15, \; -1 \times -15, \; 3 \times 5 \text{ and } -3 \times -5$$

The pair which add up to 8 are 3 and 5, so the required factorisation is

$$(x + 3)(x + 5)$$

Special case (difference of squares):

$$x^2 - a^2 = (x + a)(x - a)$$

EXERCISE A57

Factorise the following quadratic functions.

1 $x^2 + 7x + 12$ **2** $x^2 + 9x + 14$ **3** $x^2 + x - 12$

4 $x^2 - 5x - 14$ **5** $x^2 - 8x + 15$ **6** $x^2 - 11x + 30$

7 $x^2 + 2x - 15$ **8** $x^2 - 11x + 28$ **9** $x^2 + 21x + 20$

10 $x^2 - 49$ **11** $x^2 - 7x - 18$ **12** $x^2 + 13x + 42$

Factorising expressions like $ax^2 + bx + c$

There are two likely methods.

The expression $ax^2 + bx + c$ can be factorised as $(px + q)(rx + s)$ if we can find numbers p, q, r and s so that

$$pr = a, \quad qs = c$$

and $\quad ps + qr = b$

EXAMPLE 2

Factorise $5x^2 - 6x - 8$.

METHOD 1

If this factorises as $(px + q)(rx + s) = prx^2 + (ps + qr)x + qs$

then $\quad pr = 5, \quad qs = -8 \quad$ and $\quad ps + qr = -6$

The pairs of numbers which multiply to give 5 are

$$1 \times 5 \quad \text{and} \quad -1 \times -5$$

The pairs of numbers which multiply to give -8 are

$$-1 \times 8, \ 1 \times -8, \ -2 \times 4 \text{ and } 2 \times -4$$

We just try all the possible combinations until we get the required expression:

$(x - 1)(5x + 8) = 5x^2 + 3x - 8 \qquad$ (not the one we need)
$(x + 2)(5x - 4) = 5x^2 + 6x - 8 \qquad$ (not the one we need)
$(x - 2)(5x + 4) = 5x^2 - 6x - 8 \qquad$ which is the required factorisation

METHOD 2

Again factorising $5x^2 - 6x - 8$:

Multiply the 5 and the -8: $\qquad\qquad 5 \times -8 = -40$
List the factors of -40: $\quad -1 \times 40, \ 1 \times -40, \ -2 \times 20, \ 2 \times -20$
$\qquad\qquad\qquad\qquad\qquad -4 \times 10, \ 4 \times -10, \ -5 \times 8, \ 5 \times -8$

Choose the pair which add up to -6: $\qquad$ choose $4, -10$

Rewrite the quadratic using these numbers and factorise:

$$\begin{aligned} 5x^2 - 6x - 8 &= 5x^2 + 4x - 10x - 8 \\ &= x(5x + 4) - 2(5x + 4) \\ &= (5x + 4)(x - 2) \end{aligned}$$

Method 2 is best when the number of combinations to try is large.

For this alternative method of factorising $ax^2 + bx + c$

Step 1 Multiply a and c

Step 2 List the factors of the result

Step 3 Choose the pair which add up to b

Step 4 Use these numbers to split up the middle term of the quadratic

Step 5 Factorise in two stages.

Again look out for the special case of a difference of squares:

$$a^2x^2 - b^2 = (ax + b)(ax - b)$$

EXERCISE A58

Factorise the following quadratic functions.

1 $2x^2 + 5x + 2$ **2** $2x^2 - 3x - 2$ **3** $3x^2 + 13x + 14$

4 $7x^2 - 19x - 6$ **5** $6x^2 - 11x + 4$ **6** $10x^2 - 11x - 6$

7 $6x^2 - 5x - 4$ **8** $4x^2 - 25$ **9** $14x^2 + 19x + 6$

10 $9x^2 + 12x + 4$ **11** $5x^2 + 21x + 4$ **12** $21x^2 - 22x - 8$

A quadratic equation should be written in the form

$$ax^2 + bx + c = 0$$

Quadratic equations

A quadratic equation is one which is presented or can be rearranged as

$$ax^2 + bx + c = 0$$

Graphical solution

To solve the equation

$$ax^2 + bx + c = 0$$

draw the graph of $y = ax^2 + bx + c$ and find the values of x where the curve cuts the x-axis (the line $y = 0$)

The roots of the equation

$$ax^2 + bx + c = d$$

can be found where the graph of $y = ax^2 + bx + c$ cuts the line $y = d$.

EXAMPLE 1

Draw the graph of $y = x^2 - 2x - 4$ and use it to solve
a $x^2 - 2x - 4 = 0$ **b** $x^2 - 2x - 7 = 0$

Step 1
Make a table of values for the function.

x	−3	−2	−1	0	1	2	3	4	5
x^2	9	4	1	0	1	4	9	16	25
$-2x$	6	4	2	0	−2	−4	−6	−8	−10
-4	−4	−4	−4	−4	−4	−4	−4	−4	−4
y	11	4	−1	−4	−5	−4	−1	4	11

Step 2 Draw the graph

Step 3 Read off the solution

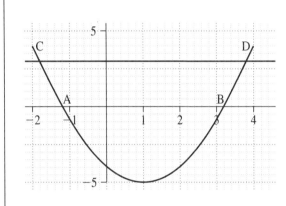

a The roots occur at A and B on the graph, where $y = 0$.
The roots are
$x = -1.24$ and $x = 3.24$

b This equation is the same as

$$x^2 - 2x - 4 = 3$$

The roots occur at C and D on the graph, where $y = 3$.
The roots are
$x = -1.83$ and $x = 3.83$

A quadratic equation has two roots (which may be equal) or no real roots.

Notice that if a quadratic equation has roots it always has two.

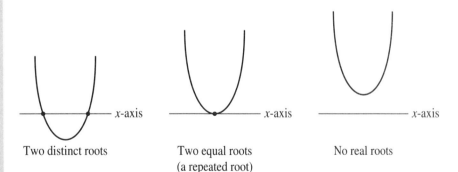

Two distinct roots

Two equal roots
(a repeated root)

No real roots

If the product of two quantities is zero, one of the quantities must be zero, so

$$(px + q)(rx + s) = 0$$
$\Rightarrow$ either $px + q = 0$
    or $rx + s = 0$

Solution by factorisation

As an example, $x^2 - 2x - 8 = 0$ factorises to $(x - 4)(x + 2) = 0$

$\Rightarrow$ **either** $x - 4 = 0$ **or** $x + 2 = 0$
$\Rightarrow$ $x = 4$ or $x = -2$

EXERCISE A59

1 Draw the graph of $y = x^2 + x - 8$ and hence find the roots of
   a $x^2 + x - 8 = 0$ **b** $x^2 + x - 10 = 0$

2 Write down the roots of the following factorised quadratic equations.
   a $(x + 3)(x + 5) = 0$ **b** $(x - 1)(x + 2) = 0$
   c $x(x + 7) = 0$ **d** $(2x - 1)(3x + 2) = 0$

3 Solve the following by factorisation (remember it must be in the form
$ax^2 + bx + c = 0$ before you factorise).
   a $x^2 - 4x + 3 = 0$ **b** $x^2 - 11x + 28 = 0$
   c $x^2 + 5x + 6 = 0$ **d** $x^2 - 12x + 27 = 0$
   e $x^2 - 5x = 24$ **f** $x^2 - 63 = 2x$
   g $x^2 - 3x = 18$ **h** $2x^2 - 3x + 1 = 0$
   i $8x^2 + 10x = 3$ **j** $4x^2 - 4x + 1 = 0$

The quadratic formula:

$$ax^2 + bx + c = 0$$

$$\Rightarrow x = \frac{-b \pm \sqrt{(b^2 - 4ac)}}{2a}$$

Solution using the quadratic formula

If the left-hand side of your equation does not factorise or you cannot easily factorise it, the equation may be solved using the quadratic formula.

Take particular care if the value of c is negative.

EXAMPLE 2

Solve the equation $2x^2 + 5x + 1 = 0$

In this case we have $a = 2$, $b = 5$ and $c = 1$

Substitute in the formula $x = \dfrac{-5 \pm \sqrt{25 - 8}}{4}$

Taking the plus sign gives $x = (-5 + \sqrt{17})/4 = -0.219$ (3 dp)

Taking the minus sign gives $x = (-5 - \sqrt{17})/4 = -2.281$ (3 dp)

If the number to be square-rooted is negative, the equation has no real roots.

EXERCISE A60

Find the roots, if any, of the following equations (answers to 3 dp).

1 $x^2 + 4x + 2 = 0$ **2** $3x^2 - 4x - 2 = 0$ **3** $2x^2 + 4x + 3 = 0$

4 $5x^2 + 7x - 1 = 0$ **5** $x^2 + 6x + 2 = 0$ **6** $2x^2 - 6x = 3$

7 $2x^2 + 4 = 5x$ **8** $3x - 4x^2 = -1$ **9** $x(2x + 7) = 4$

The steps in solving a problem are:

1 Decide which quantity to call *x*

2 Express all other quantities in terms of *x*

3 Identify a relationship between the quantities

4 Write the relationship as an equation

5 Solve the equation

6 State the solution to the problem and check that it is correct.

Problems leading to quadratic equations

EXAMPLE 3

The length of a rectangle is 5 cm more than its width. Its area is 104 cm². Find its width.

| **Step 1** Label the unknown quantity *x*. | Let the width be *x* cm. |

| **Step 2** Express other quantities in terms of *x*. | The length is $(x + 5)$ cm The area is $x(x + 5)$ cm² |

| **Step 3** Identify the relationship. | The area is 104 cm² |

Step 4 Write an equation.

$x(x + 5) = 104$

$\Rightarrow \quad x^2 + 5x - 104 = 0$

Step 5 Solve the equation for *x*.

$\Rightarrow \quad (x + 13)(x - 8) = 0$

$\Rightarrow \quad x = -13 \quad \text{or} \quad x = 8$

Step 6 State the solution to the problem.

Width cannot be negative, so width $= 8$ cm

You should check that this satisfies the original problem.

EXERCISE A61

1 Two numbers differ by 4. The sum of their squares is 170. Find them.

2 A piece of wire is bent into three sections. The second is 3 cm longer than the first and the third is 3 cm longer than the second. The sections are found to form a right angled triangle. Find the length of the wire.

3 A train travels a distance of 360 km at a steady speed. If it had gone 30 km/h faster, it would have taken one hour less to complete the journey. How fast did it travel?

4 The diagram shows part of a section of stepped sea defences. AE is a straight line. BC is 2 m less than AB. CD is 3 m more than AB. The total length ABCDE is 25 m. Find the length of AB (hint: use similar triangles).

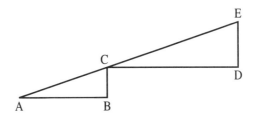

S 01 Two-dimensional geometry: introduction

Lines and angles

EXERCISE S1

We use the notation

∠**ABC** or **AB̂C**

to indicate the angle ABC.
B is at the vertex of the angle.

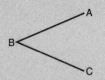

1 revolution is 360°

A **straight line** (a **half turn**) has an angle of **180°**.

A **right angle** is **90°**.

An **acute angle** is **less than 90°**.

An **obtuse angle** is **greater than 90° but less than 180°**.

A **reflex angle** is **greater than 180° but less than 360°**.

Lines that are at right angles are called **perpendicular**.

1 In the diagrams, state whether the following angles are acute or obtuse.

  a ∠ABC   **b** ∠RPQ   **c** ∠PQR   **d** ∠HEF   **e** ∠AOB

2 Draw the triangle ABC in which AB = 10 cm, ∠ABC = 40° and BC = 8 cm.

  a What is the length of AC?

  b What is ∠CAB?

  c What is ∠ACB?

  d What is the **reflex** ∠ACB?

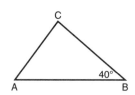

3 Draw the triangle PQR in which PQ = 12 cm, ∠PQR = 125° and QR = 6 cm.

  a What is the length of PR?

  b What is ∠QPR?

  c What is ∠PRQ?

  d What is the **reflex** ∠RPQ?

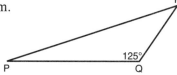

4 Draw a line EG 12 cm long. Another line FH, 16 cm long, is perpendicular to EG, and both lines cross at their mid-points. Join the ends of the lines in the order EFGH.

  a How long is EF?

  b What is ∠FGH?

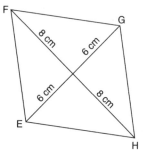

5 Draw a triangle whose sides are of lengths 7 cm, 10 cm and 15 cm. Measure the angles of the triangle.

6 In the diagram, estimate the size of each of the following angles.

  a ∠AOB

  b ∠BOC

  c ∠AOD

  d Reflex ∠BOD

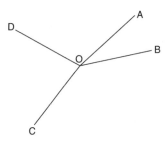

Angles on a **straight line**
add up to 180°.
$$p + q + r = 180°$$

Angles at a **point** add up to
360°.
$$a + b + c + d = 360°$$

Vertically opposite angles
are equal.
$$a = c \quad b = d$$

Parallel lines are indicated
by arrowheads.

Corresponding angles are
equal.
$$b = d$$

Alternate angles are equal.
$$c = f$$
Look for the **Z** shape
(sometimes reversed).

EXERCISE S2

Find the angles labelled with letters.

1

2

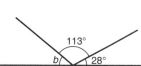

3

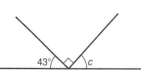

4

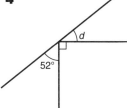

5

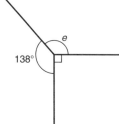

6

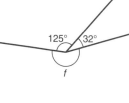

7

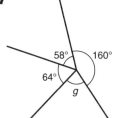

8

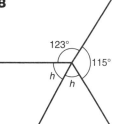

9

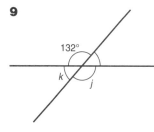

10

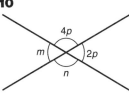

11

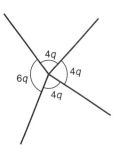

12

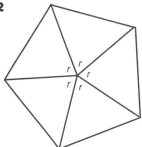

EXERCISE S3

Find the angles labelled with letters.

1

2

3

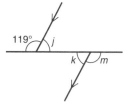

Interior angles add up to 180°.

$$c + d = 180°$$

4
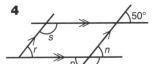

5
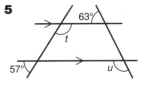

6
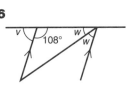

7
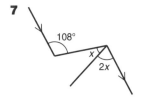

8
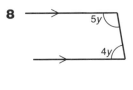

9
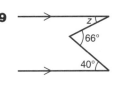

Symmetry

There are two types of symmetry:

line (reflection) symmetry   and   **rotational symmetry**

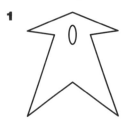

Line (reflection) symmetry

The figure can be folded along the line so that both halves fit together.

Rotational symmetry

The figure can be rotated about the point (**centre of rotation**) so that it fits exactly on the space where it was.

We count
- the number of lines of symmetry
- the number of different ways the figure will fit its own shape (the **order**)

1 line of symmetry rotational symmetry of order **1**

no lines of symmetry rotational symmetry of order **3**

8 lines of symmetry rotational symmetry of order **8**.

1 line
of symmetry

8 lines
of symmetry

rotational
symmetry
order **3**

rotational
symmetry
order **8**

Some figures have only one type of symmetry; some have both types.

Some figures have no lines of symmetry.

All figures have rotational symmetry of order 1 or more.

EXERCISE S4

Describe the symmetries of the following shapes.

1

2
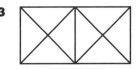

3

4

5

6

On squared paper, copy and complete each diagram using the broken lines as lines of symmetry and the points as centres of rotational symmetry.

7   **8**   **9**   **10**

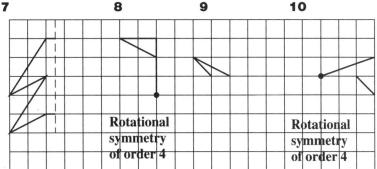

Rotational symmetry of order 4

Rotational symmetry of order 4

The **interior angles** of a triangle add up to 180°.

A **scalene triangle** has sides of different lengths and angles of different sizes.

An **acute-angled** triangle is a triangle with all its angles acute.

An **obtuse-angled** triangle is one whose largest angle is obtuse.

A **right-angled** triangle contains an angle of 90°.

The longest side of a right-angled triangle is called the **hypotenuse**.

An **isosceles** triangle has two equal sides and two equal angles.

S 02 Triangles and symmetry

EXERCISE S5

Identify these triangles as right-angled, isosceles, equilateral or scalene.

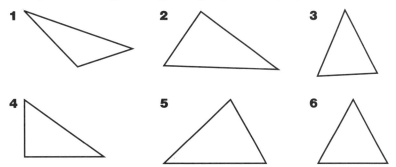

EXERCISE S6

Find the angles labelled with letters.

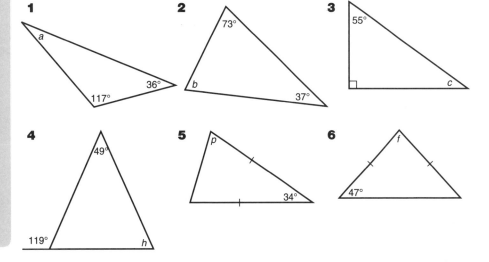

An **equilateral triangle** has all sides equal and all angles equal.

Each angle of an equilateral triangle is 60°.

Equal sides are usually marked

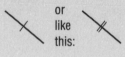

or like this:

7

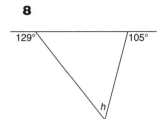

8

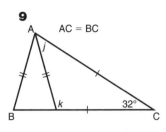

9   AC = BC

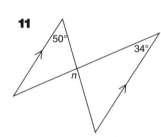

10

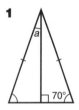

11

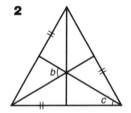

12

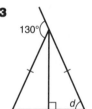

EXERCISE S7

Find the angles *a*, *b*, *c* and *d*.

1

2

3

An **isosceles triangle** has **1** line of symmetry and rotation symmetry of order **1**.

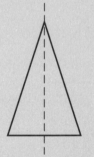

An **equilateral triangle** has **3** lines of symmetry and rotational symmetry of order **3**.

Equilateral triangles are also isosceles.

4 The figure shown has rotational symmetry of order 4. The triangles are either equilateral or isosceles.

   a Find the angles *e*.

   b How many lines of symmetry does the figure have?

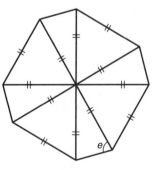

5 The figure shows a regular hexagon (a six-sided figure whose sides are all equal and whose angles are all equal) with some internal lines drawn. The internal angle of a regular hexagon is 120°.

   a Find the angles *f* and *g*.

   b Describe the symmetries of the figure.

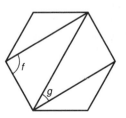

6 An isosceles triangle has one line of symmetry. This means that

① ∠ADB = 90°   ② BD = DC

③ AB = AC   ④ ∠ABD = ∠ACD

Is it possible to draw a figure other than that shown with the following combinations of information?

a ① and ②   **b** ① and ③   **c** ① and ④

d ② and ③   **e** ② and ④   **f** ③ and ④

S 03 Quadrilaterals

A quadrilateral has **four** *sides and* **four** *angles.*

The sum of the **interior angles** *of a quadrilateral is* 360°.

A **trapezium** *has one pair of opposite sides parallel.*

An **isosceles trapezium** *has its non-parallel sides equal in length and pairs of equal angles.*

A **parallelogram** *has its opposite sides parallel and equal in length. Opposite angles are equal.*

A **rhombus** *is a parallelogram with all of its sides equal.*

A **kite** *has pairs of adjacent sides equal.*

A **rectangle** *is a parallelogram with right-angled corners.*

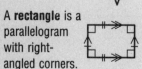

EXERCISE S8

Find the angles labelled with letters.

1

2

3

4

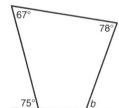

5

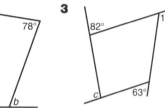

6

7

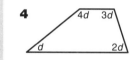

8

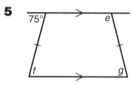

9

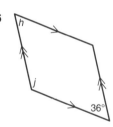

10

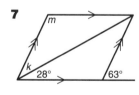

11

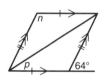

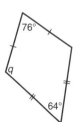

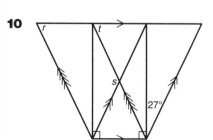

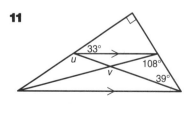

A square is:

a **rectangle** with all of its sides equal or

a **rhombus** with right-angled corners

A trapezium has rotational symmetry of order **1** and **no** lines of symmetry.

An isosceles trapezium has rotational symmetry of order **1** and **1 line** of symmetry.

A parallelogram has rotational symmetry of order **2** and **no** lines of symmetry.

A rhombus has rotational symmetry of order **2 and 2 lines of symmetry.**

A kite has rotational symmetry of order **1** and **1 line of symmetry.**

A rectangle has rotational symmetry of order **2** and **2 lines of symmetry.**

A square has rotational symmetry of order **4** and **4 lines of symmetry.**

12

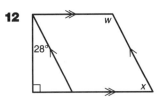

13

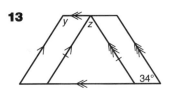

EXERCISE S9

1 In the figure, ABDE and BCDE are parallelograms. Show that

  a AB = BC

  b ∠AEB = ∠BDC

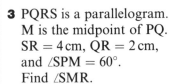

2 ABCD is a rhombus. Show that AC is perpendicular to BD.

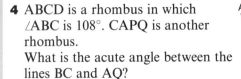

3 PQRS is a parallelogram. M is the midpoint of PQ. SR = 4 cm, QR = 2 cm, and ∠SPM = 60°. Find ∠SMR.

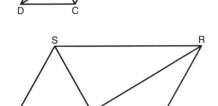

4 ABCD is a rhombus in which ∠ABC is 108°. CAPQ is another rhombus. What is the acute angle between the lines BC and AQ?

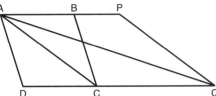

5 ABCD is a square and DAPQ is a rhombus. CAP is a straight line. Find the angles of triangle DRQ.

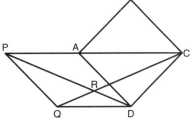

6 ABCD is a rectangle and KAP is an equilateral triangle. ∠ACD = 25°.

  a What is ∠AKB?

  b Show that PK = KB.

  c What is ∠PBK?

  d Find the angles of the triangle APB.

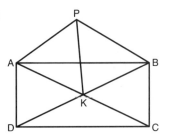

S 04 Polygons and tesselations

A **polygon** is a plane figure with any number of straight sides (poly = many).

No. of sides	Name
3	Triangle
4	Quadrilateral
5	Pentagon
6	Hexagon
7	Heptagon
8	Octagon
9	Nonagon
10	Decagon

The **exterior angles** of any polygon add up to 360°.

$$a + b + c + d = 360$$

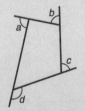

For a polygon of n sides, the sum of the **interior angles** is

$$(180n - 360)° \quad \text{or}$$
$$180(n - 2)°$$

A **regular polygon** has all of its sides and all of its interior angles equal.

A **regular triangle** is **equilateral**.

A **regular quadrilateral** is a **square**.

A regular polygon with n sides has n lines of symmetry and rotational symmetry of order n.

Polygons

EXERCISE S10

Find the angles labelled a, b, c.

1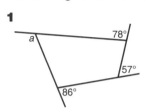

2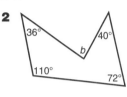

3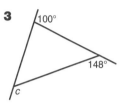

4 What is the internal angle of a regular
   a pentagon,   **b** hexagon,   **c** octagon?

5 How many sides does a regular polygon have if its exterior angles are
   a 30°,   **b** 45°,   **c** 18°?

6 How many sides does a regular polygon have if its interior angles are
   a 135°,   **b** 160°,   **c** 165°?

7 The figure shows a regular stellated pentagon. Find the angle at a vertex of the star.

8 Use compasses to draw a circle of radius 5 cm. Use your protractor to draw lines from the centre of the circle, every 45°, all the way round.
Finally, join the points where these radii meet the circle.
The figure you have drawn is a regular octagon.

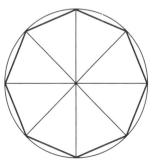

9 Use the technique of question 8 to draw a regular decagon.

10 The figure is a regular octagon.
Find the size of the angles marked x and y.

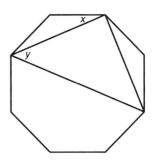

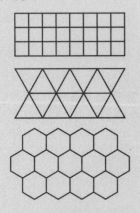
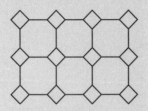

Tesselations

EXERCISE S11

Use squared paper to test whether the following shapes tesselate.

1   **2**   **3**

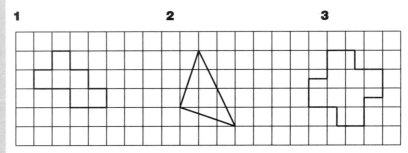

4 The figure shows an irregular tesselation formed from regular pentagons and rhombuses.

a Why is it not possible to tesselate regular pentagons by themselves?

b What are the angles of the rhombus?

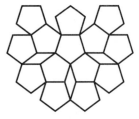

5 Is it possible to make a tesselation with the following combinations of regular polygons at each vertex?

a 3 equilateral triangles and 2 squares

b 1 square, 1 hexagon and 1 duodecagon (12 sides)

c 1 square and 2 octagons

d 2 pentagons and 1 decagon

6 Which of the quadrilaterals will tesselate?

7 The diagram shows two possible arrangements of 1 triangle, 2 squares and 1 hexagon around a vertex. Is it possible to continue the tesselation so that every vertex has the same arrangement?

a

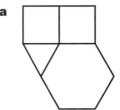

b

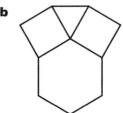

S 05 Perimeters

> The **perimeter** of a figure is the **total distance round its edge**

A flat, two-dimensional shape is called a **plane shape** or **plane figure**. The total distance around the boundary or edge of such a figure is called its **perimeter**.

As perimeter is a distance it is measured in length units such as centimetres or inches.

Figures with straight sides

To find the perimeter of a simple figure, we add up the lengths of its sides. For example, a quadrilateral has sides of 3.2, 5.7, 6.4 and 7 cm. Find its perimeter.

$$\text{Perimeter} = 3.2 + 5.7 + 6.4 + 7$$
$$= 22.3 \, \text{cm}$$

For some shapes there is a simple formula for the perimeter. For example, a square with sides of length x cm has a perimeter of $4x$ cm.

Circles

> **Radius (r)** is the **distance** from the **centre** of a circle to its **edge**.
> **Diameter (d)** is the distance across a circle **through its centre**.
> **Circumference (c)** is the perimeter of a circle.
>
> $d = 2r$
> $c = \pi d$ or $c = 2\pi r$
> where $\pi = 3.141\,59\ldots$

There are special names for the dimensions associated with a circle.

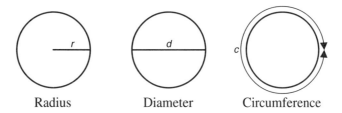

Radius   Diameter   Circumference

The diameter is twice the radius.

The circumference is approximately three times the radius. The actual ratio involved, $3.141\,59\ldots$, cannot be written down exactly as the decimal digits continue for ever without recurring. To refer to this ratio easily we represent it by the Greek letter π (pronounced 'pie' but spelt 'pi').

When using π in a calculation you should use either 3.14 or the π key on your calculator. For example, find the diameter and circumference of a circle of radius 4 cm.

$$\text{Diameter} = 2 \times 4 = 8 \, \text{cm}$$
$$\text{Circumference} = \pi \times 8 = 25.1 \, \text{cm}$$

Perimeters of composite shapes

We sometimes need the perimeter of a shape made up partly of straight lines and parts of circles.

Notice that although the lengths of the curved edges have been written to 2 dp in the example, you should always calculate the total perimeter using the full values on your calculator and then round the final answer.

EXAMPLE 1

Calculate the perimeter of the shape shown correct to 2 decimal places.

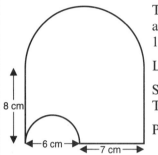

The shape consists of straight sides of 8 cm, 8 cm and 7 cm plus semicircles of diameter 6 cm and 13 cm.

Large curved edge $= \frac{1}{2}(\pi \times 13) = 20.42$ cm

Small curved edge $= \frac{1}{2}(\pi \times 6) = 9.42$ cm
Total length of straight edges $= 8 + 8 + 7 = 23$ cm

Perimeter $23 + 20.42 + 9.42 = 52.8$ cm (3 sf)

Problems using circumferences

EXAMPLE 2

A bicycle has wheels of diameter 60 cm. How far will it travel if the wheels turn 10 complete revolutions?

   Distance travelled in one revolution = circumference of wheel

   Circumference $= \pi \times 60 = 188.5$ cm

So,   distance travelled $= 10 \times 188.5 = 1885$ cm   or   18.85 m

---

EXERCISE S12

1 Find

  a The circumference of a circle of radius 8.2 cm.

  b The diameter of a circle with circumference 67 cm.

2 Find the perimeter of each of the shapes shown.

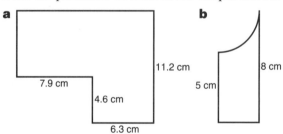
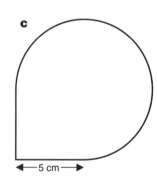

3 The minute hand of a clock is 20 cm long and the hour hand is 13 cm long. Find the distance travelled by the tip of   **a** the minute hand and   **b** the hour hand between 9.00 a.m. and midday.

4 A bicycle has wheels of diameter 50 cm. The cyclist rides one complete circuit of a circular track of radius 25 metres.

  a How far does she travel?

  b How many revolutions do the wheels make?

S 06 Area

Area is the measure of the size of a surface.

Area is two-dimensional – the position of any point on a surface can be described by combining moves in only two directions (for example, across the page and up and down the page).

When we are working in centimetres, the unit of area is a **square centimetre** (written **cm^2**). The size of the surface is measured by the number of 1 cm squares it would take to cover it.
In the same way, area might be measured in **square metres (m^2), square inches (in^2)** etc.

Area of a rectangle

The rectangle shown has length 4 cm and width 3 cm.
It can be covered by three rows of four 1 cm squares.

Its area is $4 \times 3 = 12\,\text{cm}^2$.

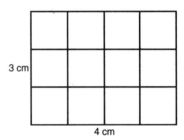

In general, the number of unit squares in a row is the length and the number of rows is the width, so the area is the length multiplied by the width.

Area of a parallelogram

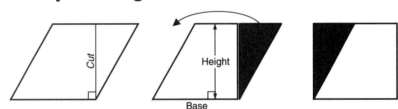

The diagram shows how a parallelogram can be cut and reassembled into a rectangle with the same area.

The length of the rectangle is the same as the **base** of the parallelogram. The width of the rectangle is the same as the **height** of the parallelogram. (**Height** is the **perpendicular distance** between the **base** and the **opposite parallel side**.)

This means that the area of the parallelogram is found by multiplying its base by its height

Area of a triangle

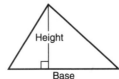
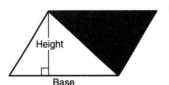

The diagram shows that we can construct a parallelogram from a given triangle by adding a rotated copy of the triangle.

Area is two-dimensional.

Area is measured in square units. For example
square centimetres (cm^2)
square metres (m^2)
square inches (in^2)

For a **rectangle**:
Area = Length × Width

For a **parallelogram**:
Area = Base × Height

The parallelogram has the **same base** and **same height** as the triangle. (The height of a triangle is the **perpendicular distance from its base to the opposite corner.**) The parallelogram has **twice the area** of the triangle.

As the area of the parallelogram is base × height, the area of the triangle will be half of this.

For a triangle:
Area = $\frac{1}{2}$ Base × Height

Area of a trapezium

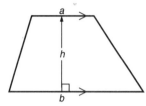 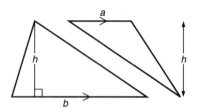

The diagram shows a trapezium with parallel sides a and b, and height h. (Height is the **perpendicular distance between the parallel sides**). The trapezium can be cut along its diagonal, as shown, to form two triangles. The bases of the triangles have lengths a and b and they both have height h.

The triangles have area $\frac{1}{2}ah$ and $\frac{1}{2}bh$, respectively

The area of the trapezium is therefore $\frac{1}{2}ah + \frac{1}{2}bh$ or $\frac{1}{2}(a+b)h$.

For a trapezium with parallel sides a and b and height h:
Area = $\frac{1}{2}(a+b)h$
or in words:
Area = Half the sum of the parallel sides times the height

Area of kite and rhombus

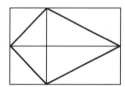 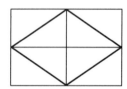

The diagram shows that a kite or a rhombus has half the area of a rectangle drawn as shown.
The length and width of the rectangle are equal to the lengths of the diagonals of the kite or rhombus.
The area of a kite or a rhombus is therefore half of the product of its diagonals.

For a kite or rhombus:
Area = $\frac{1}{2}$ (Product of diagonals)

Area of a circle

Finding the area of a circle involves – like its circumference – the use of $\pi = 3.141\,59\ldots$ (Use 3.14 or the π key on your calculator.)

For a circle with radius r, its area = πr^2. (Remember that this means you **first** square the radius and **then** multiply by π.)

You can remember which circle formula is which because, as area is two dimensional, all area formulae will involve a length × a length – in this case, radius × radius.

For a circle: Area = πr^2

All formulae for area involve multiplying a length by a length.

EXERCISE S13

Find the area of each of these figures.

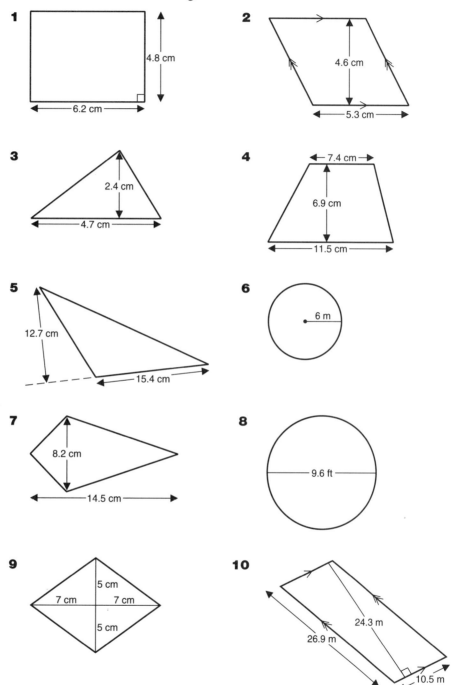

Area of composite shapes

Composite shapes are made by combining two or more simple shapes. The area can be found by adding (or in some cases subtracting) the areas of the separate shapes.

EXAMPLE 1

The shape shown can be thought of as two rectangles and a triangle minus a semicircle.

The rectangles have areas

$$3 \times 2 = 6 \, cm^2$$

and

$$4 \times 3 = 12 \, cm^2$$

The triangle has a base of 5 cm and a height of 4 cm, so

$$area \ of \ triangle = \tfrac{1}{2} \times 5 \times 4$$

$$= 10 \, cm^2$$

The semicircle has a radius of 1 cm, so

$$area \ of \ semicircle = \tfrac{1}{2} \times \pi \times 1^2$$

$$= 1.57 \, cm^2$$

Area of composite shape is $6 + 12 + 10 - 1.57 = 26.43 \, cm^2$

EXERCISE S14

1 Find the area of each of the following composite shapes.

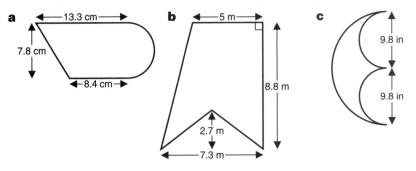

2 A rectangular lawn, 4.6 metres by 6.9 metres, has a path 1 metre wide all the way round it. Find the area of the path.

S 07 Pythagoras' theorem

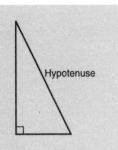

Pythagoras' theorem applies **only to right-angled triangles**.

A right-angled triangle is a triangle in which one of its angles is a right angle. This may be shown in a diagram as

The longest side of a right-angled triangle is always the side opposite the right angle. It is called the **hypotenuse**.

Pythagoras' theorem

In any right-angled triangle with sides a and b and hypotenuse h,

$$a^2 + b^2 = h^2$$

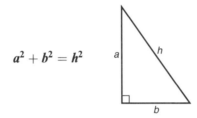

> It doesn't matter which of the other two sides of the triangle you decide is **a** or **b** as long as you **identify the hypotenuse correctly**.

This can be seen to be true by considering the two diagrams below.

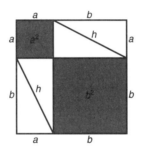 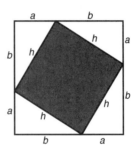

> Each of these squares has area $(a+b)^2$

Both of the big squares have the same area, which is made up of a shaded area and four unshaded triangles. The four unshaded triangles are the same in both big squares, so the shaded areas must be equal. Therefore

$$a^2 + b^2 = h^2$$

EXAMPLE 1

Find the length of the side marked x in the right-angled triangle below.

> Since Pythagoras' theorem applies to the **squared** length of the sides of a right-angled triangle, we must use the **square root** when calculating the lengths of the sides.

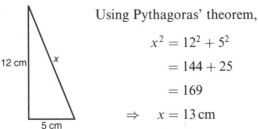

Using Pythagoras' theorem,

$$x^2 = 12^2 + 5^2$$
$$= 144 + 25$$
$$= 169$$
$$\Rightarrow \quad x = 13\,\text{cm}$$

The lengths must have the same units of measurement.

EXAMPLE 2

Find the length of the side AC in the triangle ABC.

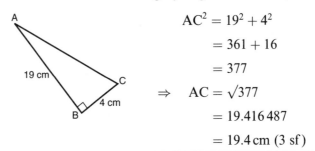

Using Pythagoras' theorem,

$$AC^2 = 19^2 + 4^2$$
$$= 361 + 16$$
$$= 377$$
$$\Rightarrow \quad AC = \sqrt{377}$$
$$= 19.416\,487$$
$$= 19.4\,cm \ (3\ sf)$$

When we are given the hypotenuse and are asked to find one of the shorter sides, we rearrange the formula to make a^2 (or b^2) the subject of the formula. For example

$$h^2 = a^2 + b^2 \text{ becomes}$$
$$h^2 - b^2 = a^2$$

EXAMPLE 3

Find the length of the side marked a in the triangle below.

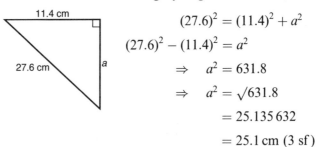

Using Pythagoras' theorem,

$$(27.6)^2 = (11.4)^2 + a^2$$
$$(27.6)^2 - (11.4)^2 = a^2$$
$$\Rightarrow \quad a^2 = 631.8$$
$$\Rightarrow \quad a^2 = \sqrt{631.8}$$
$$= 25.135\,632$$
$$= 25.1\,cm \ (3\ sf)$$

EXERCISE S15

Calculate, to 3 significant figures, the length of the side marked with a letter in each of the following triangles.

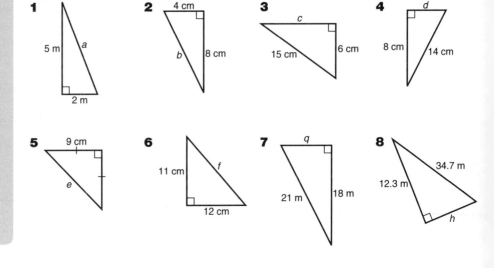

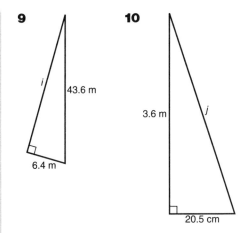

9

i

43.6 m

6.4 m

10

3.6 m

j

20.5 cm

Recognising and using right-angled triangles

In some cases, a right-angled triangle can form part of a diagram which depicts a problem being investigated. Here are several examples.

● *Working with equilateral and isosceles triangles*

Because of the symmetry of these triangles, we can use Pythagoras' theorem to find their height, AD.

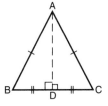

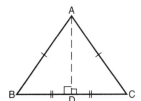

OA = OB = OC (all radii of the circle)
Triangle AOC is isosceles with equal angles $x°$, and triangle BOC is isosceles with equal angles $y°$. In triangle ABC,

$$x + x + y + y = 180°$$

so $x + y = 90°$

● *Angle at the circumference of a semicircle*

A triangle drawn using the diameter AB and any point on the circumference of the circle will be a right-angled triangle.

$$\angle APB = \angle AP_1B = \angle AP_2B = 90°$$

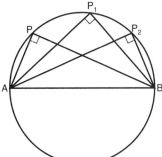

● *Bisecting a chord of a circle*

A line drawn from the centre of a circle to the mid-point of a chord is perpendicular to the chord.

$$\angle APO = \angle BPO = 90°$$

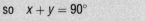

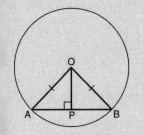

Because OA and OB are radii of the circle, triangle AOB is isosceles, so the axis of symmetry through O bisects AB at 90°.

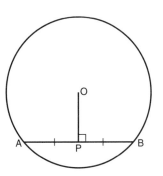

● *Triangles within triangles*

In this diagram, there are two right-angled triangles, OMP and OMN.

OM is a common side as it is part of both triangles.

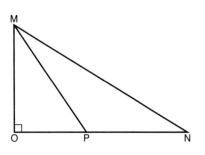

EXAMPLE 4

Find the height of an equilateral triangle of side 8 cm.

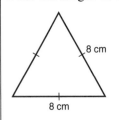

Drawing the vertical line of symmetry gives two identical right-angled triangles.

Applying Pythagoras' theorem, to one then gives

$$8^2 = x^2 + 4^2$$
$$\Rightarrow \quad 8^2 - 4^2 = x^2$$
$$\Rightarrow \quad x^2 = 48$$
$$x = 6.93\,\text{cm (3 sf)}$$

Remember to take **half** of the base as part of the new triangle when you use a line of symmetry.

EXAMPLE 5

Find the length of the side CD in the diagram.

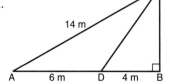

Using Pythagoras' theorem in triangle BCD,

$$CD^2 = BC^2 + BD^2$$

We need to find the value of BC^2.

In triangle ABC,

$$14^2 = 10^2 + BC^2$$
$$\Rightarrow \quad 14^2 - 10^2 = BC^2$$
$$\Rightarrow \quad BC^2 = 44$$

Now in triangle BCD,

$$CD^2 = 44 + 16$$
$$= 60$$
$$\Rightarrow \quad CD = 7.75\,\text{m (3 sf)}$$

It is helpful to draw the two triangles as separate diagrams.

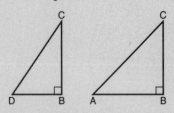

Note that we do not need to find the length of BC – just BC^2.

EXERCISE S16

1

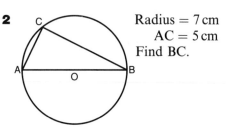

AC = 10 cm
BC = 8 cm
Find AD.

2

Radius = 7 cm
AC = 5 cm
Find BC.

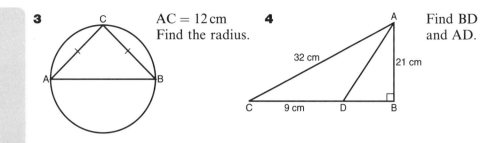

3 AC = 12 cm
Find the radius.

4 Find BD and AD.

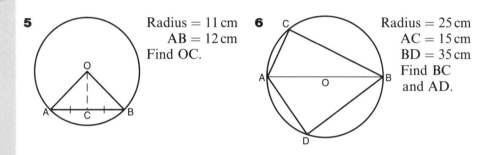

5 Radius = 11 cm
AB = 12 cm
Find OC.

6 Radius = 25 cm
AC = 15 cm
BD = 35 cm
Find BC and AD.

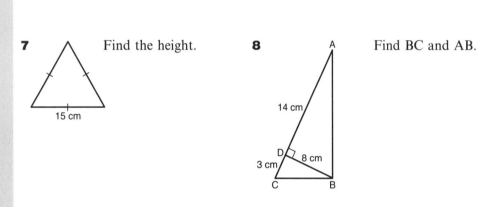

7 Find the height.

8 Find BC and AB.

S 08 Transformations and congruence

Location of points in a plane

To describe the position of a point P in a plane, we choose a fixed reference point called the **origin** (labelled O), and through it we draw two perpendicular reference lines called the **x-axis** and the **y-axis**. The x-axis is usually horizontal (across the page) and the y-axis vertical (up and down the page). The position of point P is specified by its displacement from the origin in the x-direction (its x-coordinate) and in the y-direction (its y-coordinate). The coordinates of P are given as (x, y)

The + sign is not normally included.

The origin always has coordinates (0, 0). Distances to the right or above the origin are positive (+). Distances to the left or down are negative (−).

The coordinates are given as an ordered pair in brackets separated by a comma (*x*, *y*)

In the diagram below, A is located at (3, −2), B has coordinates (5, 1), C has coordinates (−4, −2) and D has coordinates (−2, 1).

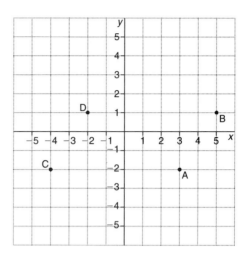

EXERCISE S17

1 Give the coordinates of the points plotted below.

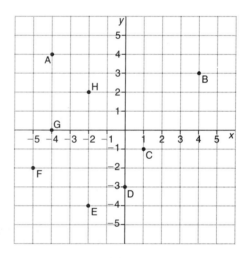

2 On your own copy of the diagram above, plot these points.

   a M (2, 5)   **b** N (−4, 4)   **c** P (−1, 0)   **d** Q (−3, 4)
   e R (0, −4)   **f** S (−2, −3)   **g** T (5, −2)   **h** U (−2, 5)

Transformations

Transformations involve a change in the location of a point.

The original location is called the **object**, and the 'new' location is called the **image**.

The usual notation uses a capital letter, say A, for an object and the same letter with a dash A′, for its image. We call this image 'A dash'

A whole set of points may follow the same 'rule' to change their positions. We can see the effect of moving plane figures, such as a triangle, by examining the transformation of their vertices.

We can check this by examining any point on the object ABC and its corresponding point on the image A′B′C′, e.g. the mid-point of BC. But it is much easier to check the transformation of the vertices A, B and C themselves.

In the diagram below, the triangle ABC has changed position to A′B′C′. This change in position has occurred by 'sliding' the triangle 5 units to the right and 4 units up.

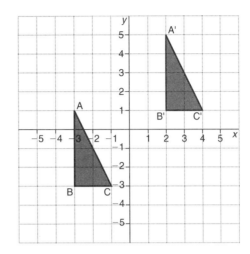

A transformation is often described as a **mapping** of a figure on to its image.

A change in position which is brought about by 'sliding' a point or set of points is called a **translation**.

Notice that the image is the **same size and shape** as the object and that all the **corresponding sides are parallel**.

A translation can be described by stating how far the image is horizontally and vertically from the object, using positive and negative numbers appropriately, or by using **vector notation**.

Vector notation describes a translation by a column of two numbers in brackets. The top number gives the horizontal displacement and the number underneath gives the vertical displacement, using + and − signs in the usual way.

In the example above, the translation can be described by the vector $\begin{pmatrix} 5 \\ 4 \end{pmatrix}$.

A translation of 2 units to the left and 3 units down would be described by the vector $\begin{pmatrix} -2 \\ -3 \end{pmatrix}$.

EXERCISE S18

1 Find the image of the point $(-3, 6)$ after the translations described by these vectors.

a $\begin{pmatrix} 4 \\ -2 \end{pmatrix}$ **b** $\begin{pmatrix} -2 \\ -4 \end{pmatrix}$ **c** $\begin{pmatrix} 0 \\ 1 \end{pmatrix}$

2 Triangle ABC has points A(2, 3), B(−1, −2) and C(4, −2). A translation takes A to A′(0, 1).

a Describe the translation as a vector.
b Draw the triangles ABC and A′B′C′.
c Write down the coordinates of B′ and C′.

3 In the diagram opposite, describe the translation which maps

  a R1 on to R2

  b R4 on to R3

  c R3 on to R1

  d R4 on to R2.

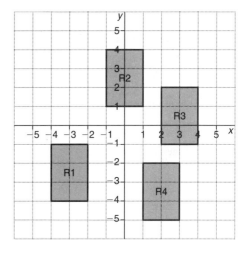

Reflection

The transformation of ABC on to A′B′C′ is an example of a **reflection**.

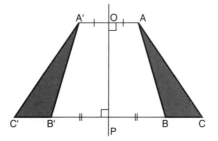

The line OP is called the **mirror line**. The line joining point A to its image A′ cuts the mirror line at 90° and this is true for all lines which are drawn from an object point to an image point after a reflection. It is also important to note that each object point is the same distance from the mirror line as its image point.

It is as though triangle ABC has been 'flipped over' on to A′B′C′

The image is both the same size and shape as the object but 'back-to-front'

OP is an axis of symmetry of the two figures.

In the previous case, the mirror line was outside of the object altogether but it is possible for the mirror line to be along the edge of a shape (Figure 1) or even within the shape itself (Figure 2).

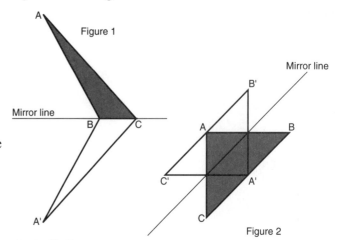

In each of these diagrams, the triangle ABC has been reflected in the mirror line as shown.

You can relate this to your own experience of looking in a mirror.

Your reflection appears to be the same distance behind the mirror as you are in front of it.

You can check a reflection by tracing it onto tracing paper and then folding along the mirror line. The object should fold exactly on top of the image.

EXAMPLE 1

Trapezium ABCD has vertices A(1, 1), B(5, 1), C(3, 3) and D(1, 3). Plot these points and on separate diagrams show A'B'C'D', a reflection in the line

a $x = 1$ **b** $y = 2$ **c** $y = x$ **d** $x = 0$

a

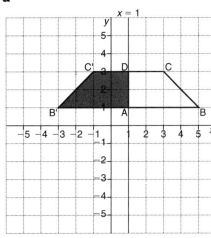

c

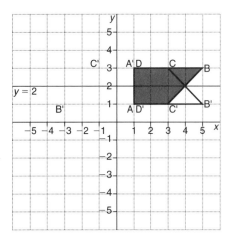

b

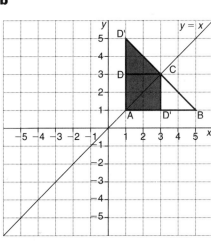

d

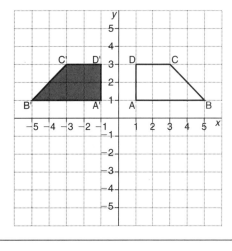

EXERCISE S19

Triangle ABC has vertices A(2, 1), B(3, 4) and C(−1, 3). On separate diagrams show ABC and its image A′B′C′ after a reflection in the line **a** $y = 1$, **b** $x = -1$, **c** $x = 2$.

Rotation

The point around which the rotation takes place is called the **centre of rotation**.

The centre of rotation can be inside, outside or even on an edge or vertex of a shape.

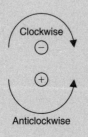

The diagram below shows the transformation of the point A(2, 1) to A′ (−1, 2).

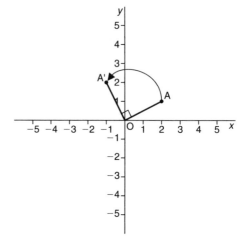

This type of transformation is called a **rotation**. It is as though A were moving on the circumference of a circle with centre (0, 0) and radius OA. The angle moved through in this case is 90° in an anticlockwise direction or +90°.

This diagram shows the result of the same rotation on triangle ABC.

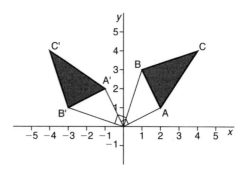

Notice that   OA = OA′
              OB = OB′
              OC = OC′

and $\angle$AOA′ = $\angle$BOB′ = $\angle$COC′ = 90°

It is very helpful to use tracing paper to carry out rotations.

- Trace the original (object) and the axes.
- Prepare to rotate the tracing paper by putting your pencil point on the centre of rotation.
- Rotate the **axes** through the required angle and in the required direction (+ or −).
- Press through the tracing paper at each of the corners of the image.
- Draw the image.

EXAMPLE 2

Rectangle ABCD has A(1, −1), B(4, −1), C(4, −3) and D(1, −3). Draw ABCD and its image A′B′C′D′ after a rotation of −90° about the point P(−1, 1) and write down the coordinates of A′, B′, C′ and D′.

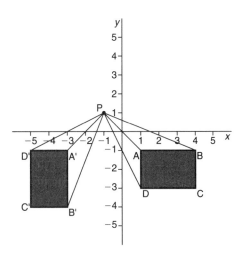

In order to fully describe a rotation you must always give

- the centre of rotation
- the angle of rotation
- the sense (direction) of rotation.

EXERCISE S20

1 Plot the points P(1, 1), Q(3, 2) and R(2, 4) and join them to make triangle PQR. On separate diagrams, draw the image of PQR after a rotation of

    a −90° about the origin (0, 0)
    b 180° about the point P(1, 1)
    c +90° about the point Q(3, 2)
    d 180° about the point C(−1, −1).

In each case, write down the coordinates of P′Q′R′.

2 Plot the trapezium KLMN with K(1, 1), L(1, 4), M(2, 4) and N(3, 1) and its image K′(−1, −1), L′(−1, −4), M′(−2, −4) and N′(−3, −1). Describe fully the transformation which maps KLMN onto K′L′M′N′.

Congruence

Congruent figures are exactly the **same size and shape**.

The image produced by a translation, a reflection or a rotation is exactly the same size and shape as the original object. When two or more figures are **exactly the same size and shape** they are said to be **congruent**.

S 09 Transformations and similarity

Enlargement

In the diagram below, the lengths of the sides of triangle A′B′C′ are twice those of the sides of triangle ABC. This is an example of a transformation which changes both the location and size of the object but not its shape. Such a transformation is called an **enlargement**.

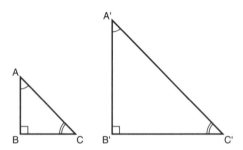

Because enlargements do not alter the shape of the image, the **angles remain the same** as they were in the original.

The change of size is given as a **scale factor**, where

$$\text{Scale factor} = \frac{\text{Any length in the image shape}}{\text{Corresponding length in the original (object) shape}}$$

Corresponding sides can be recognised because they face angles which are equal in the original and its image.

In the above example,

$$\frac{A'B'}{AB} = \frac{A'C'}{AC} = \frac{B'C'}{BC} = 2$$

Centre of enlargement

The scale factor and centre of enlargement are related. The scale factor not only tells us by how much the size of the image has changed but also how much further the image is from the centre of enlargement.

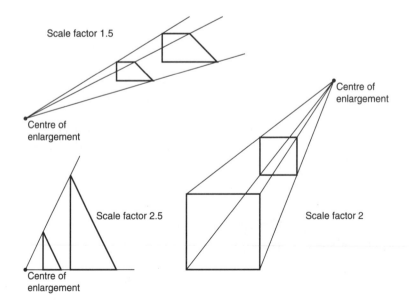

The **centre of enlargement** can be found after an enlargement by drawing lines from the points in the image back through the corresponding points in the original. These lines will all meet at a single point – the centre of enlargement.

Figures can be enlarged using this method when the centre of enlargement and the scale factor are given.

EXAMPLE 1

All measuring must be done from the centre of enlargement when locating the image points.

Draw the image of triangle ABC with A(1, 1), B(2, 1) and C(1, −1) after an enlargement at scale factor 3 with centre of enlargement P(2, 2).

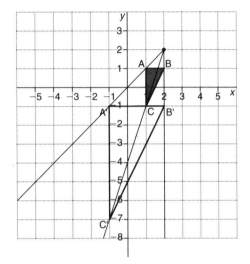

The diagram below shows the enlargement of trapezium ABCD, using a scale factor of 3 from the point P(−5, −4).

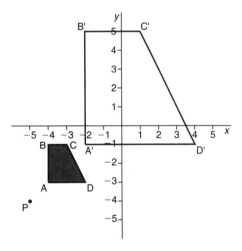

We are using the fact that the scale factor determines not only the size of the image but also how much further the image is from the centre of enlargement.

Instead of drawing lines from the centre of enlargement through the vertices of ABCD and measuring from P to locate A′B′C′D′ three times further away, we can use vector displacements.

The vector displacement of A from P is $\begin{pmatrix} 1 \\ 1 \end{pmatrix}$.

This applies to the horizontal and vertical displacements as well as to the straight-line distances we would use by drawing the lines from P.

In each case, the vector displacement **from the centre of enlargement** of the object vertex is multiplied by 3 to get the vector displacement of the image vertex **from the centre of enlargement**.

So the vector displacement of A′ will be $\begin{pmatrix} 3 \\ 3 \end{pmatrix}$, putting A′ at $(-2, -1)$.

Similarly, the vector displacement of B from P is $\begin{pmatrix} 1 \\ 3 \end{pmatrix}$.

So the vector displacement of B′ will be $\begin{pmatrix} 3 \\ 9 \end{pmatrix}$, putting B′ at $(-2, 5)$.

The vector displacement of C from P is $\begin{pmatrix} 2 \\ 3 \end{pmatrix}$.

So the vector displacement of C′ will be $\begin{pmatrix} 6 \\ 9 \end{pmatrix}$, putting C′ at $(1, 5)$.

The vector displacement of D from P is $\begin{pmatrix} 3 \\ 1 \end{pmatrix}$.

So the vector displacement of D′ will be $\begin{pmatrix} 9 \\ 3 \end{pmatrix}$, putting D′ at $(4, -1)$.

EXERCISE S21

1 Plot triangle XYZ with X(1, 1), Y(3, 2) and Z(2, 4). On separate diagrams, enlarge XYZ at

  a scale factor 1.5 from centre of enlargement (0, 0)
  b scale factor 3 from centre of enlargement (3, 5)
  c scale factor 2 from centre of enlargement (2, 2).

2 For each of the following, find the scale factor and the coordinates of the centre of enlargement.

  a P(1, 1), Q(2, 1), R(2, 3) mapped on to P′(0, −1), Q′(2, −1), R′(2, 3).
  b A(−1, 1), B(−1, −1), C(1, −1), D(1, 1) mapped on to A′(−3, 3), B′(−3, −3), C′(3, −3), D′(3, 3).
  c K(−3, 1), L(−3, 2), M(−1, 2), N(−1, 1) mapped on to K′(−1, −3), L′(−1, 0), M′(5, 0), N′(5, −3).

Fractional scale factors

We can still use the vector displacement **from the centre of enlargement** to an object vertex and multiply it by the scale factor to get the vector displacement of the corresponding image vertex **from the centre of enlargement**.

The diagram below shows A′B′C′D′, the image of ABCD, after an enlargement from (0, 0) with scale factor $\frac{1}{4}$. Although the image is **smaller** than the original, it is still called an **enlargement** but the scale factor is a **fraction**.

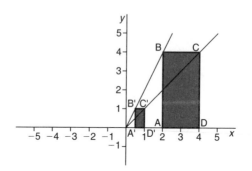

Negative scale factors

After a negative enlargement the image will be the same shape as the object but a different size and 'upside down' or 'back to front'.

A negative scale factor indicates the change in size of the image after enlargement in the same way as a positive scale factor does. The negative sign means that the image is located on the opposite side from the centre of enlargement to the object.

The diagram shows the enlargement of trapezium EFGH with centre (2, 0) and scale factor −2.

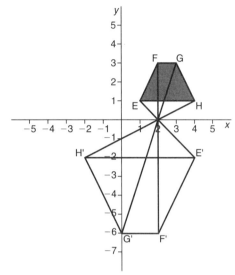

Measurement must **always** be from the centre of enlargement. For a negative enlargement, the image is located on the opposite side of the centre from the object.

Vector displacements can be used in the usual way instead of drawing lines. For example, the vector displacement of E from (2, 0) is $\begin{pmatrix} -1 \\ 1 \end{pmatrix}$

Multiply this by the scale factor −2 to get $\begin{pmatrix} +2 \\ -2 \end{pmatrix}$ which is the displacement of E′ from (2, 0).

EXERCISE S22

1 Plot rectangle ABCD with A(−6, 4), B(−2, 4), C(−2, 2) and D(−6, 2). Draw its image after the following enlargements and write down the co-ordinates of A′B′C′D′.

   a scale factor $\frac{1}{2}$ from (0, 0)   **b** scale factor $-\frac{1}{2}$ from (0, 0)

2 Plot triangle PQR with P(0, 1), Q(3, 4) and R(3, 1). Draw the image P′Q′R′ after the following enlargements and write down the coordinates of P′Q′R′.

   a scale factor $\frac{1}{3}$ from (0, 1)   **b** scale factor −2 from (−1, 0)

3 Triangle ABC with A(0, 0), B(0, 4) and C(2, 0) maps on to triangle A′B′C′ with A′(−2, −2), B′(−2, 0) and C′(−1, −2). Find the centre of enlargement and the scale factor.

4 Trapezium DEFG with D(−1, 3), E(−1, 4), F(−2, 4) and G(−3, 3) maps on to trapezium D′E′F′G′ with D′(−1, −5), E′(−1, −8), F′(2, −8) and G′(5, −5). Find the centre of enlargement and the scale factor.

Similarity

Similar figures have exactly the **same shape** but are a **different size**.

When using similar figures, we do not need to be concerned about the centre of enlargement.

Translations, reflections and rotations are transformations which produce an image which is the same size and shape as the original but in a different location and, in the case of reflections and rotations, a different orientation. The original figures and their images are **congruent** figures. In the case of enlargement, the image is the same shape as the original, but is a different size. Such figures are described as **similar** figures. In mathematics the term 'similar' means more than it does in everyday use where it means 'alike in some way'. It tells us that one figure is an **enlargement** of the other and consequently the lengths of the corresponding sides have all been **increased by the same scale factor**.

In this diagram, triangle XYZ is an enlargement of triangle ABC at scale factor 2. The two triangles are **similar**.

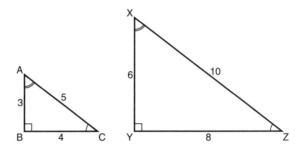

Since the enlargement preserves shape, we can identify corresponding sides as those which face an angle which is the same both in the original and in its image. In the above example, AC corresponds to XZ, BC corresponds to YZ and AB corresponds to XY. Checking the ratios

$$\frac{AC}{XZ} = \frac{BC}{YZ} = \frac{AB}{XY} = \frac{1}{2}$$

We can use this property of similarity to find unknown lengths when we have similar figures.

EXAMPLE 2

The quadrilaterals in the diagram are similar. Find the length of **a** PQ, **b** AB.

Checking the vertices:

> A corresponds to R
> B corresponds to Q
> C corresponds to P
> D corresponds to O

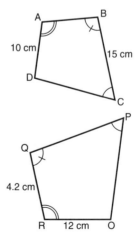

Scale factor $= \dfrac{OR}{AD} = 1.2$

a $\dfrac{PQ}{BC} = 1.2$

$\Rightarrow$ $PQ = 1.2 \times 15$
            $= 18\,cm$

b $\dfrac{QR}{AB} = 1.2$

$\Rightarrow$ $AB = \dfrac{4.2}{1.2} = 3.5\,cm$

Similar triangles

When the angles of one
triangle are the **same** as
those of another triangle,
the triangles are **always**
similar.

**This is true only for
triangles**.

Warning All pairs of similar
figures have a set of equal
angles **but** not all pairs of
figures with a set of equal
angles are similar.

For example, a square and a
rectangle both have a set of
equal angles (all right
angles) but they are not
similar figures.

When the angles of one triangle are the same as those of another triangle, the triangles are **always similar**.

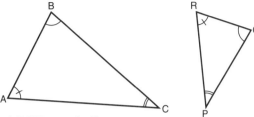

Triangles ABC and PQR are **similar**.

EXAMPLE 3

In the diagram below, find the length of **a** KL, **b** YZ.

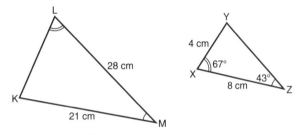

LM and XZ are corresponding sides whose lengths are given.

$$\text{Scale factor} = \frac{LM}{XZ}$$

$$= \frac{28}{8} = 3.5$$

a $\frac{KL}{XY} = 3.5$, so $KL = 4 \times 3.5$

$$= 14\,cm$$

b $\frac{KM}{YZ} = 3.5$, so $YZ = \frac{21}{3.5}$

$$= 6\,cm$$

EXAMPLE 4

In the diagram below,
calculate the value of x.

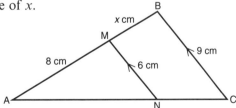

This will always happen
when a triangle is divided by
a line drawn inside the
triangle, and parallel to one
of its sides.

Since MN is parallel to BC, $\angle AMN = \angle ABC$ and $\angle ANM = \angle ACB$
(corresponding angles). We also see that $\angle MAN$ is in both triangles, so the
triangles ABC and AMN are similar.

It is a good idea to sketch the two triangles on separate diagrams.

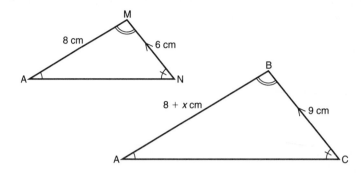

The scale factor is found from the given lengths of the two corresponding sides, BC and MN:

$$\text{Scale factor} = \frac{BC}{MN} = 1.5$$

So $\dfrac{AB}{AM} = 1.5$ and $\dfrac{8+x}{8} = 1.5$

$$\Rightarrow \quad 8 + x = 8 \times 1.5$$
$$\Rightarrow \quad x = 4\,\text{cm}$$

EXERCISE S23

1 Calculate the length of BC.

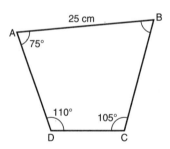
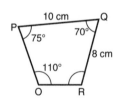

2 Calculate the length of RS.

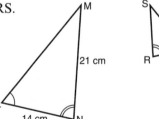

3 Calculate the length of AB.

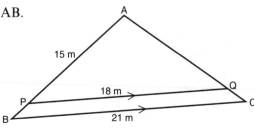

4 Sketch the two similar triangles on separate diagrams. Calculate the length of **a** WX, **b** WZ.

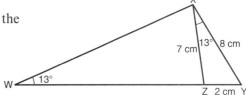

5 Sketch the two similar triangles on separate diagrams. Calculate the length of **a** CD, **b** BC.

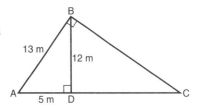

S 10 Trigonometry: introduction

The sides of a right angled triangle are named **according to the angle you are concerned with,** whether it is one, whose size is given or one whose size you have to calculate.

Elementary trigonometry is about the relationship between the lengths of the sides of a right-angled triangle and the size of its angles.

The longest side of a right-angled triangle is the side facing the right angle. It is called the **hypotenuse**.

The other two sides are named in relation to the angle we are concerned with. One side is **opposite** (facing) that angle and the other will be **adjacent to** (next to) it.

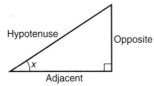
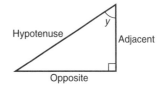

EXERCISE S24

Sketch these right angled triangles and label the sides relative to angle x.

1 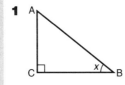 **2** 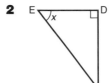 **3**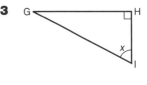

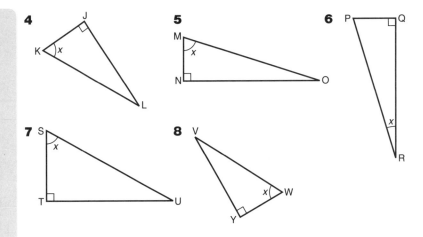

Trigonometric ratios

For **any** right-angled triangle, the following ratios apply:

The **sine** of angle $x = \dfrac{\text{opposite}}{\text{hypotenuse}}$

The **cosine** of angle $x = \dfrac{\text{adjacent}}{\text{hypotenuse}}$

The **tangent** of angle $x = \dfrac{\text{opposite}}{\text{adjacent}}$

These are usually abbreviated to

$$\sin x = \frac{\text{opp}}{\text{hyp}}$$

$$\cos x = \frac{\text{adj}}{\text{hyp}}$$

$$\tan x = \frac{\text{opp}}{\text{adj}}$$

Note: we still say 'sine' here, **not** 'sin'.

These can be remembered using the initials

SOH CAH TOA

(which can be pronounced like 'soccer tour').

SOH   sine $= \dfrac{\text{opp}}{\text{hyp}}$

CAH   cosine $= \dfrac{\text{adj}}{\text{hyp}}$

TOA   tangent $= \dfrac{\text{opp}}{\text{adj}}$

The value you will get when dividing the length of one side of a right-angled triangle by the length of another can be obtained from your calculator.

Trigonometric ratios and your calculator
You should be able to use your calculator to find $\sin x$, $\cos x$ and $\tan x$, for any angle x. Make sure you can obtain the following on **your** calculator.

$$\sin 35° = 0.573\,576\,436$$
$$\cos 18° = 0.951\,056\,516$$
$$\tan 53° = 1.327\,044\,822$$

Check that your calculator is in degrees (DEG) mode

To find the **value of the angle,** you need to use the **inverse ratio** of what is on the calculator display.

Inverse trigonometric operations
Using your calculator you should also be able to find the associated angle of a trigonometric ratio. This requires using the inverse trigonometric ratios $\sin^{-1}$, $\cos^{-1}$ and $\tan^{-1}$. With most calculators this operation involves **first** pressing the key marked

You may need to consult your calculator handbook or get further help if you have difficulty with these.

| INVERSE | | SHIFT | or | 2ND FN |

and **then** pressing the sin, cos or tan key.

EXAMPLE 1

Find x when **a** $\cos x = 0.5$, **b** $\sin x = 0.835\,42$, **c** $\tan x = 2.3$.

a $\cos^{-1} 0.5 = 60°$

b $\sin^{-1} 0.83542 = 56.659\,596\,82°$

c $\tan^{-1} 2.3 = 66.501\,434\,32°$

EXERCISE S25

1 Use your calculator to find the value of

a $\cos 23°$	**b** $\tan 85°$	**c** $\cos 5°$	**d** $\sin 34°$
e $\sin 75°$	**f** $\tan 15°$	**g** $\sin 30°$	**h** $\tan 45°$

2 Use the inverse trigonometric operations on your calculator to find x when

a $\sin x = 0.25$	**b** $\cos x = 0.666$	**c** $\sin x = 0.975$
d $\tan x = 4$	**e** $\tan x = 0.345$	**f** $\cos x = 0.123$

Finding an unknown angle in a right-angled triangle

Hyp **always** faces the right angle.

Opp is **always** the side facing the angle we want to find.

When we know the lengths of any two sides of a right-angled triangle we can find the size of a particular angle by following this procedure:

1 Label the sides in relation to the angle you want to find.
2 Select the appropriate ratio using SOH CAH TOA.
3 Carry out the division.
4 Convert the number you get into an angle using the inverse trigonometric operation.

EXAMPLES 2

Find the value of x in each of these triangles.

a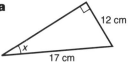

b

c

a

We have:
  the hypotenuse $= 17\,$cm
  the opposite $= 12\,$cm

so we use the **sine** ratio $\sin x = \dfrac{12}{17} = 0.705\,882\,352$

$\Rightarrow$ $x = \sin^{-1} 0.705\,882\,352 = 44.9°$ (1dp)

b

We have:
  the opposite $= 15\,$cm
  the adjacent $= 21\,$cm
so we use the **tangent** ratio $\tan x = \dfrac{15}{21} = 0.714\,285\,714$

$\Rightarrow$ $x = \tan^{-1} 0.714\,285\,714 = 35.5°$ (1dp)

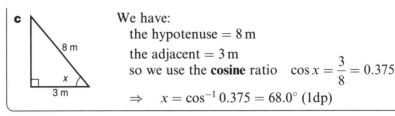

We have:
  the hypotenuse $= 8\,\text{m}$
  the adjacent $= 3\,\text{m}$
  so we use the **cosine** ratio $\cos x = \dfrac{3}{8} = 0.375$

$$\Rightarrow \quad x = \cos^{-1} 0.375 = 68.0°\ (1\text{dp})$$

EXERCISE S26

Calculate the size of the angles marked with a letter in these triangles.

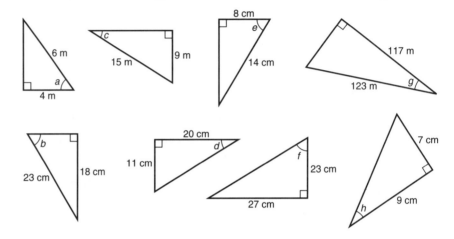

Finding the length of a side

In order to calculate the length of a side of a right-angled triangle using trigonometric ratios, you must:

- know the length of one side and the size of one of the acute angles
- select the appropriate trigonometric ratio.

In general, when we rearrange a formula of the form

$$a = \frac{b}{c}$$

to make b the subject, we multiply both sides by the bottom term:

$$a \times c = \frac{b}{c} \times c$$

Cancelling c on the right-hand side we get

$$b = ac$$

To find the opposite side given the hypotenuse, we use

$$\sin x = \frac{\text{opp}}{\text{hyp}} \text{ and rearrange this to get opp} = \text{hyp} \times \sin x$$

To find the adjacent side given the hypotenuse, we use

$$\cos x = \frac{\text{adj}}{\text{hyp}} \text{ and rearrange this to get adj} = \text{hyp} \times \cos x$$

To find the opposite side given the adjacent side, we use

$$\tan x = \frac{\text{opp}}{\text{adj}} \text{ and rearrange this to get opp} = \text{adj} \times \tan x$$

EXAMPLES 3

Find the length of the side AB in each of the following triangles.

a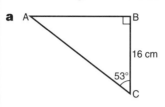

AB is opposite 53°.
BC is adjacent to 53°.
The tangent ratio
involves opp and adj, so
rearranging TOA as above,

AB = 16 × tan 53°

     = 16 × 1.327 044 822

     = 21.233 cm (3dp)

b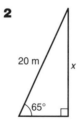

AC is the hypotenuse.
AB is the adjacent side.
The cosine ratio involves
adj and hyp, so rearranging
CAH as above,

AB = 17 × cos 32°

     = 17 × 0.848 048 096

     = 14.417 cm (3dp)

EXERCISE S27

Find the length of the side marked x in these triangles.

1 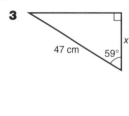   **2**   **3**

4 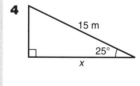   **5** 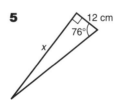   **6**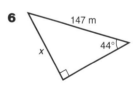

In general, when we rearrange a formula of the form

$$a = \frac{b}{c}$$

to make c the subject, we multiply both sides by the bottom term:

$$a \times c = \frac{b}{c} \times c$$

$$ac = b$$

Then we divide both sides by a:

$$c = \frac{b}{a}$$

In some cases we need to **divide** by a trigonometric ratio in order to find the length of a side of a right-angled triangle.

After further rearrangement of SOH CAH TOA, we obtain

$$\text{opp} = \text{hyp} \times \sin x \quad \text{gives} \quad \text{hyp} = \frac{\text{opp}}{\sin x}$$

$$\text{adj} = \text{hyp} \times \cos x \quad \text{gives} \quad \text{hyp} = \frac{\text{adj}}{\cos x}$$

$$\text{opp} = \text{adj} \times \tan x \quad \text{gives} \quad \text{adj} = \frac{\text{opp}}{\tan x}$$

EXAMPLE 4

Find the length of PQ in each of the triangles below.

a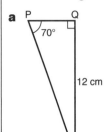

The adjacent side is PQ.
The opposite side = 12 cm.
Rearranging TOA,

$$12 = PQ \times \tan 70°$$

$$\Rightarrow \quad PQ = \frac{12}{\tan 70°}$$

$$= 4.368 \text{ cm (3dp)}$$

b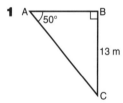

The hypotenuse is PQ.
The adjacent side = 47 m.
Rearranging CAH,

$$47 = PQ \times \cos 50°$$

$$\Rightarrow \quad PQ = \frac{47}{\cos 50°}$$

$$= 73.119 \text{ m (3dp)}$$

EXERCISE S28

Find the length of the side AB in each of these triangles.

1 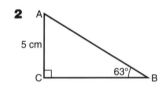 **2** 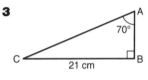 **3**

4 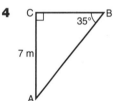 **5** 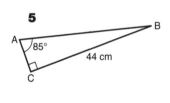 **6**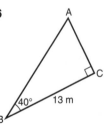

The following exercise involves all the aspects of trigonometry covered in the previous exercises.

EXERCISE S29

Calculate the size of the angle or the length of the side marked with an *x*.

1 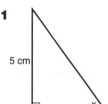 **2** 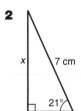 **3**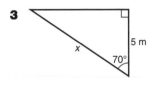

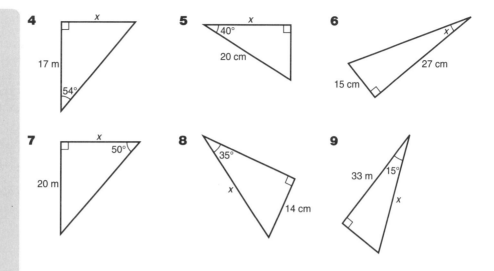

S 11 Applying trigonometry: angles of elevation and depression

Angles of elevation and depression

Figure 1 shows a person raising his line of sight from the horizontal to look at an object. The angle through which his line of sight is raised is called the **angle of elevation** of the object.

Angles of elevation and depression are **always** measured from the **horizontal**.

Figure 2 shows a person lowering her line of sight from the horizontal to look at an object. The angle through which her line of sight is lowered is called the **angle of depression** of the object.

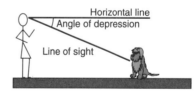

Because the horizontal lines are parallel, the angle of elevation of point B from a point A is equal to the angle of depression of point A from point B. They are **alternate angles**.

Angle of elevation = Angle of depression (alternate angles)

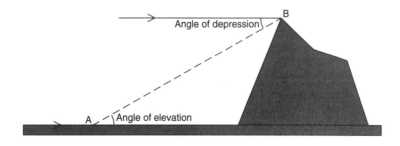

Draw a diagram of the situation as a simple right angled triangle

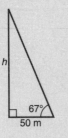

EXAMPLE 1

The angle of elevation of the top of a fir tree is $67°$ from a point $50\,m$ away from its base. Calculate the height of the tree.

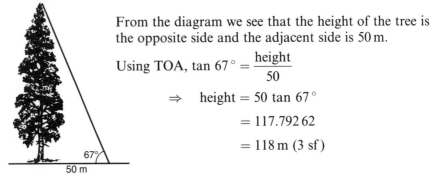

From the diagram we see that the height of the tree is the opposite side and the adjacent side is $50\,m$.

Using TOA, $\tan 67° = \dfrac{\text{height}}{50}$

$\Rightarrow \quad \text{height} = 50 \tan 67°$

$\qquad\qquad\quad = 117.792\,62$

$\qquad\qquad\quad = 118\,m \text{ (3 sf)}$

EXAMPLE 2

The angle of depression of a farmhouse from the top of a $75\,ft$ tower is $25°$. Calculate the distance of the farmhouse from the foot of the tower to the nearest $10\,ft$.

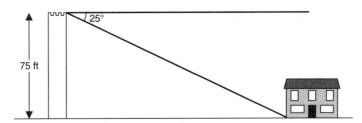

Simplifying the diagram, we see that the opposite side is $75\,ft$ and that we have to find the adjacent side.

From $\tan x = \dfrac{\text{opp}}{\text{adj}}$

$\text{adj} = \dfrac{\text{opp}}{\tan x}$

Using TOA, $\tan 25° = \dfrac{75}{\text{adj}}$

$\Rightarrow \quad \text{adj} = \dfrac{75}{\tan 25°} = 160.838\,019$

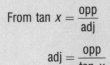

The house is $160\,ft$ from the tower, to the nearest $10\,ft$.

EXERCISE S30

1 The angle of depression of a boat from the top of a cliff is $56°$. The cliff is $150\,m$ high. How far is the boat from the foot of the cliff?

2 A hot-air balloonist radios that she is directly above a lake which is $3500\,m$ from where her friend is following by car. The friend sees the balloon and the angle of elevation is $33°$. How high is the balloon?

3 A rambler notes that the angle of elevation of the top of a crag is $26°$ from where he is standing. He knows that the height of the crag is $576\,m$. Calculate his horizontal distance from the crag.

4 A tourist looks down from the top of the steeple of an historic church and sees his car in the car park. The angle of depression of his car is $38°$ and it is parked at a distance of 235 m from the foot of the steeple. Calculate the height of the steeple.

Sometimes problems about angles of depression and angles of elevation involve more than one right-angled triangle.

EXAMPLE 3

From a height of 3000 m a helicopter sees a ship sailing due north and the angle of depression is 15°. At the same time, the helicopter notices another ship sailing due south and the angle of depression of this ship is 20°. Calculate how far apart the ships are, to the nearest 10 m.

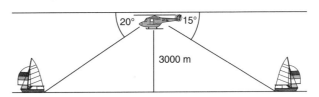

To calculate the horizontal distance of the first ship from the helicopter, we use TOA.

$$\tan 15° = \frac{3000}{\text{adj}}$$

$$\Rightarrow \quad \text{adj} = \frac{3000}{\tan 15°} = 11\,196 \text{ m}$$

Similarly, the distance of the other ship from the helicopter is

$$\text{adj} = \frac{3000}{\tan 20°} = 8242 \text{ m}$$

Therefore, the ships are $11\,196 + 8242 = 19\,438$ m apart, to the nearest 10 m.

EXAMPLE 4

From a point 300 m from the bottom of a vertical cliff, the angle of elevation of a climber on the cliff face is 29°. From the same point, the angle of elevation of the top of the cliff is 34°. Calculate how far the climber is from the top of the cliff.

We need to use triangle ABD to find BD, and triangle ACD to find CD, in order to find BC = BD − CD.

$$BD = 300 \tan 34° \qquad CD = 300 \tan 29°$$
$$= 202.4 \text{ m} \qquad\qquad = 166.3 \text{ m}$$

Therefore, the distance, BC, the climber is from the top
$$= 202.4 - 166.3 = 36.1 \text{ m}$$

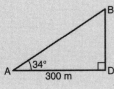

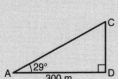

We can include 'rounded off' results in the working, which should be shown.

But ... you **must** use the **full values** given on your calculator in the next stage of the working.

EXERCISE S31

1 From a point 2 km due west of a hill, the angle of elevation of the top of the hill is 26°. From a point due east of the hill, the angle of elevation of the top of the hill is 31°.

  a Calculate the height of the hill, to the nearest metre.

  b Calculate the distance of the second point from the hill, in km and m.

2 The angle of elevation of the top of a tower is 20° from a point 200 m from its base. There is a flagpole on the top of the tower and the angle of elevation of the top of the flagpole is 23° from the same point.

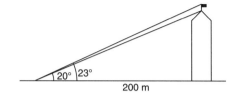

  a Calculate the height of the tower.

  b Calculate the length of the flagpole.

3 From a point A 35 km away, the angle of elevation of the summit of mountain B is 12°. The angle of depression of the same summit from mountain C is 16°. The mountain summits are known to be 14 km apart. Calculate the height of each mountain.

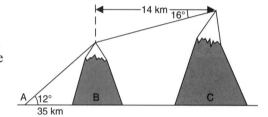

4 From the top of a cliff, 75 m high, two buoys can be seen in line with each other. The angle of depression of the buoy nearer to the cliff is 21°, and the angle of depression of the other buoy is 16°. Calculate the distance between the two buoys.

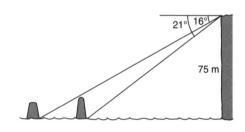

5 A hot air balloon is vertically above the centre of Bath. It can be seen from the centre of Bristol 16 km away at an angle of elevation of 5.1°.

  a Calculate the height of the balloon.

  b Calculate the angle of elevation of the balloon from Corsham which is 11 km from Bath.

6 The diagram shows two boats A and B, at anchor in line with a lighthouse. The distance between A and B is 600 m. The angle of elevation of the top of the lighthouse from boat A is 6° and from boat B is 9°.

  a Calculate how far boat B is from the foot of the lighthouse.

  b Calculate the height of the lighthouse above sea level.

S 12 Bearings and trigonometry

A **bearing** is a way of describing **direction**.

Bearings are described in two ways:

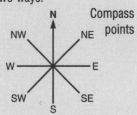

Compass points

Three-figure bearings

144°

Always measured from **North**, in a **clockwise** direction.

Note: **067**° not 67°.

To measure a bearing:
1 Identify the point **from** which the bearing is to be measured.
2 Draw the **North** line through this point.
3 Draw a line **from** this first point to the **point whose bearing is required**.
4 Measure the angle **clockwise** from **North**.

Three-figure bearings

Bearings are always measured **from** some point. This point becomes the centre of the diagram.

To find a bearing, imagine that you are standing at the point **from** which the bearing is required, facing **North**.
You then turn **clockwise** until you are facing the point whose bearing is required. The bearing is the angle you turned through. It is always written as three figures and all bearings are between 000° and 359°.

EXAMPLE 1

Find the bearing of **B from A**.

Step 1 Identify point **A**. We need to measure the bearing **from** here.

B•
•A

Step 2 Draw a **North** line through **A**.

Step 3 Draw a line **from A to B**

Step 4 Measure the bearing **clockwise** from **North**.

The bearing is 290°.

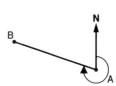

EXERCISE S32

1 What are the three-figure bearings corresponding to the directions
  a North-east, **b** North, **c** North-west?

2 Write the following directions as three-figure bearings.

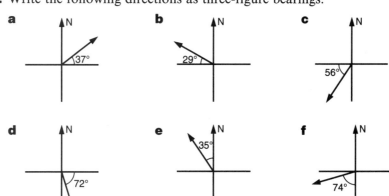

EXERCISE S33

The map shows some principal cities in Italy. Trace the map and find the following bearings.

1 Venice **from** Rome   **2** Taranto **from** Milan   **3** Florence **from** Rome

4 Rome **from** Naples   **5** Milan **from** Genoa   **6** Palermo **from** Venice

7 Milan **from** Taranto   **8** Genoa **from** Venice   **9** Naples **from** Palermo

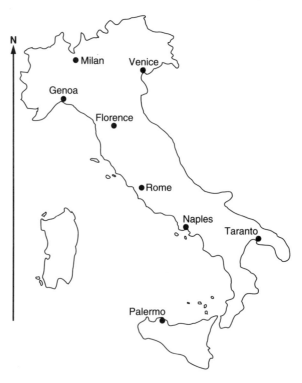

Bearings and right-angled triangles

Bearings can be calculated by drawing appropriate right-angled triangles.

It will help to draw the four cardinal points on your diagram to establish where the right-angled triangle is and which angle should be used.

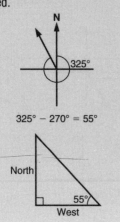

$325° − 270° = 55°$

EXAMPLE 2

A ship sails from a port on a bearing of 325° and travels 200 km. Calculate how far the ship now is to **a** the north, **b** the west of the port.

- Sketch the situation.   • Sketch the appropriate right-angled triangle.

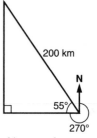

- Use trigonometry to find the required lengths and/or angles.

a Distance north is the opposite side, 200 km is the hypotenuse, so we use the sine ratio.

$$\sin 55° = \frac{\text{opp}}{200}$$

$$\Rightarrow \quad \text{opp} = 200 \sin 55°$$

$$= 163.830 \text{ km N}$$

b Distance west is the adjacent side, so we use the cosine ratio

$$\cos 55° = \frac{\text{adj}}{200}$$

$$\Rightarrow \quad \text{adj} = 200 \cos 55°$$

$$= 114.715 \text{ km W}$$

EXAMPLE 3

An aircraft flies on a bearing of 215°. After 2 hours its position is 300 km further south than its starting point. Calculate how far it has flown.

From the sketch, the distance south is the adjacent side and we want to find the hypotenuse.

Using $\cos 35° = \dfrac{300}{\text{hyp}}$

$$\Rightarrow \quad \text{hyp} = \frac{300}{\cos 35°}$$

$$= 366 \text{ km (3 sf)}$$

EXERCISE S34

1 A ship sails 470 km on a bearing of 300°. Calculate how far **a** north, **b** west it is from its starting point.

2 An aircraft flies 245 miles on a bearing of 123°. Calculate how far **a** south, **b** east it is of its starting point.

3 A ship sails on a bearing of 165° until it is 200 miles east of its starting point. Calculate how far it has travelled and how far south of its original position it now is.

4 After flying on a bearing of 220° a helicopter is 70 km south of its original position. Calculate how far it has travelled and how far west of its original position it now is.

5 A ship sails from port A to port B, which is 340 km west and 125 km north of port A. Calculate **a** the bearing the ship should sail on, and **b** the total distance travelled, giving both answers to 3 sf.

6 A man and his camel are crossing the desert. They need to get to a watering hole which is 11 miles to the east and 7 miles to the south of their present position. Calculate   **a** to the nearest degree, the bearing they should take, and   **b** how far they will have to go to reach the watering hole.

Sometimes journeys involving bearings can be in two or more stages.

EXAMPLE 4

A hiker walks 7 miles on a bearing of 145°, then for 11 miles on a bearing of 255°. Calculate   **a** the bearing which will take her back to her starting point,   **b** the distance she will have to travel on this bearing to return to her starting point.

Take the two relevant right-angled triangles from the sketch.

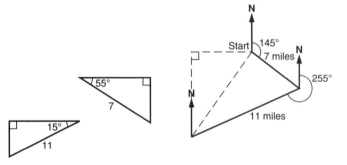

The total distance travelled south of her original position is the sum of the opposite sides of the two triangles:

$$7 \sin 55° + 11 \sin 15° = 8.581 \text{ km}$$

The total distance west is the difference between the two adjacent sides (since the first part of the journey takes her east):

$$11 \cos 15° - 7 \cos 55° = 6.610 \text{ km}$$

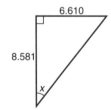

Drawing this as a single 'summary' triangle, we use Pythagoras' theorem to get the required distance of 10.832 km. Let the bearing be x, where

$$\tan x = \frac{6.610}{8.581}$$

$$\Rightarrow \quad x = 038° \text{ (to the nearest degree.)}$$

EXERCISE S35

1 A ship sails on a bearing of 234° for a distance of 87 miles, then changes course to 157° for a further 42 miles. Calculate how far **a** west, **b** south it now is from its original position.

2 An aircraft flies 350 miles on a bearing of 076°, and then flies 500 miles on a bearing of 176°. Calculate how far **a** east, **b** south it is now from its original position.

3 A walker travels 17 km on a bearing of 305° and then a further 12 km on a bearing of 025°. Calculate **a** the distance the walker now is from his starting point and **b** the bearing he must take to return to this point.

4

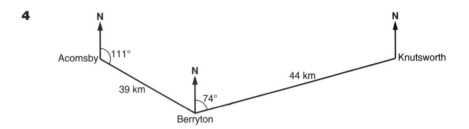

Berryton is 39 km from Acornsby on a bearing of 111°. Knutsworth is 44 km from Berryton on a bearing of 074°. Calculate **a** the bearing of Acornsby from Knutsworth and **b** the distance you would travel on this bearing between the two towns.

5

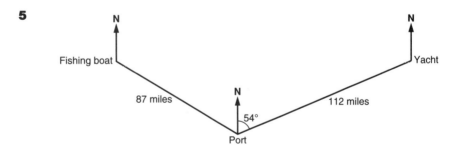

A yacht leaves a port and travels 112 miles on a bearing of 054°. A fishing boat leaves the same port and travels 87 miles on a bearing of 323°. Calculate

a how far north the fishing boat has travelled from the port

b how far north the yacht has travelled from the port

c how far west the fishing boat has travelled from the port

d how far east the yacht has travelled from the port.

S 13 Scale drawings and loci

Scale drawing

Scales

In a scale drawing:

- the **lengths** are **proportional** to those in the real object.
- the **angles** are **exactly the same** as the corresponding angles in the real object.

Scales can be represented by, for example

1 cm : 1 m

or

1 : 100 if the units are the same

or

$\frac{1}{100}$

Map scales are usually of the form 1 : 50 000, 1 : 100 000, etc

A **scale drawing** is a two-dimensional representation of a real object, in which corresponding shapes in the drawing and the object are the same but the original lengths are multiplied by a common **scale factor** to obtain the corresponding lengths in the drawing. A **scale model** is three-dimensional representation of a real object. Because corresponding shapes are the same, all the **angles** are **exactly the same** as the original angles. To calculate the lengths in the drawing, we use the formula

$$\text{Scale factor} = \frac{\text{Model length}}{\text{Original length}}$$

as in, for example,

$$\frac{1\,\text{cm}}{1\,\text{m}} \quad \text{or} \quad \frac{1\,\text{cm}}{100\,\text{cm}}$$

The scale factor is often represented by a ratio: 1 cm : 1 m.

When the units are the same, they are usually not stated, for example   1 : 100.

Map scales are usually of the form 1 : 50 000 or 1 : 100 000, etc. The principle is exactly the same. In the first case, 1 cm represents 50 000 cm or 500 m. In the second, 1 cm represents 100 000 cm or 1 km.

You may find road maps in Imperial units, e.g. 1 inch : 3 miles. This is sometimes more convenient than the equivalent ratio 1 : 190 080.

EXERCISE S36

1 A rectangular garden measures 15 m by 45 m. A scale drawing is to be made of this using a scale of 1 cm : 3 m. What are the dimensions of the drawing?

2 On a map whose scale is 1 : 50 000, the distance between two towns is 20 cm. What is the actual distance, in km, between them?

3 A model Ferrari 512BB is made to a scale of 1 : 43. The length of the model is 10 cm. How long is the real car?

4 A yacht's sail is a triangle, whose sides are 15 m, 10 m and 18 m and whose angles are 56°, 90°, and 34°. A model yacht is made to a scale of 1 cm : 1 m. What are the lengths of the sides and the angles of the model sail?

5 On a map whose scale is 1 : 50 000 a reservoir measures 0.4 cm by 0.2 cm.

   a What are the dimensions of the real reservoir?

   b What is the area of the reservoir on the map?

   c What is the area of the real reservoir?

   d What is the scale factor for area?

Scale drawing

To make and use a scale drawing:

1 Make a sketch of the drawing so that you can see how it will fit on your paper.
2 Use the scale factor to convert all the real lengths to scaled lengths in your drawing.
3 Take any measurements you require from your drawing.
4 Scale these up, if necessary, to obtain real distances.
5 Take care to express all measurements in the correct units.

To make and use a scale drawing:
1 Make a sketch of the drawing so that you can see how it will fit on your paper.
2 Use the scale factor to convert all the real measurements to lengths in your drawing.
3 Take any measurements you require from your drawing.
4 Scale these up, if necessary, to obtain real distances.
5 Take care to express all measurements in the correct units.

EXERCISE S37

1 The diagram shows three hill tops used as signalling points.

Using a scale of 1 cm : 2 km, make an accurate scale drawing and use it to find:

   a the distance from P to R

   b the bearing of R from P

   c the bearing of P from R.

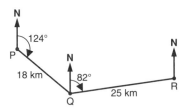

2 A ship (S) leaves a port (P) and travels 20 miles on a bearing of 078 °. It then receives a distress call from a yacht (Y) which reports its position as 15 miles from the port on a bearing of 125 ° (from the port). What course must the ship take to go to the assistance of the yacht, assuming that it remains fixed in its position?

3 Two towns, A and B, are connected by a straight road, 10 miles long.
The bearing of B from A is 075 °.

A chemical factor, F, 6 miles due north of A has a leak of fumes.

The wind is blowing **from** 320 ° and the fumes spread out 5 ° on each side of its direction.

Using a scale of 2 cm to represent 1 mile, determine which section of the road is unsafe and should be cleared of people.

4 A man, setting an orienteering course on a moor, leaves the start control and travels 500 m on a bearing of 325 °, where he leaves the next control flag.

He then travels 650 m on a bearing of 248 ° to a knoll, where he leaves another flag.

The next section of the route is 350 m on a bearing of 123 °.

The final section of the route takes him back to the start point.

How far is this final section and what bearing should he take in order to complete the route?

5 A submarine receives a message saying that an enemy cargo ship is 300 miles east of its position, travelling at 15 miles per hour on a bearing of 205 °. It sets off on a bearing of 125 ° at a speed of 20 miles per hour until it cuts across the route of the cargo ship.

Will the submarine reach this point in time to attack the cargo ship or will the cargo ship already have passed this point?

EXERCISE S38

1 A game requires a board shaped as shown. The board will be surrounded by a wooden barrier to contain the balls used to play the game.

The holes in the board are 8 cm in diameter and a diagonal line of holes makes an angle of 60° with a horizontal line of holes.

The line of centres is 9 cm from each side and 12 cm from the bottom.

Make an accurate scale drawing of the board using a scale of 1 : 5.

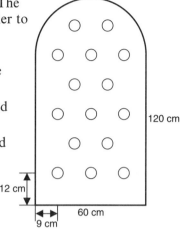

2 The diagram shows a garden, 30 m by 30 m. It contains two ponds, one circular, of diameter 10 m, and the other rectangular. The lawn is formed from two offset rectangles. The rest is gravel paths of width 2 m, with extra gravel around the circular pond.

Make a scale drawing of the garden using a scale of 2 cm : 1 m.

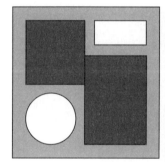

A **locus** is a set of points which obey some rule or set of rules.

The plural of locus is **loci**.

Common loci
• A point moves so that it is always the same distance from a fixed point: This is a circle.

In 3 dimensions, this would be a sphere.

• A point moves so that it is equidistant from two fixed points. This is the perpendicular bisector of the line AB.

In 3 dimensions, this would be a plane perpendicular to the page.

Locus

A **locus** is a set of points which obey some rule or set of rules.

Often the set of points form a path, which may be a closed curve, an open curve, a combination of lines or parts of lines.

Sometimes the locus is a region.

EXAMPLE 3

A goat is tethered to a post P. What grass is it possible for the goat to eat if

a the tether is a rigid pole, 3 m long, free to slip around the post;

b the tether is a rope, 3 m long, free to slip around the post.

a If the tether is rigid, the goat can only eat the grass in a circle of radius 3 m around the pole.

b If the tether is a rope, the goat can also eat the grass within the circle.

- A point moves so that it is always the same distance from a fixed line (L).

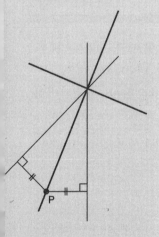

If the line is infinitely long, we get a pair of parallel lines. If not, we get an oblong with straight sides and semicircular ends.

In 3 dimensions, we would get cylinders.

- A point moves so that it is equidistant from two straight lines which intersect. This is the bisector of the angle between the lines.

- A point moves so that the sum of its distances from two fixed points is always the same. This is an ellipse.

$x + y$ = constant

EXAMPLE 4

A chain, 2 m long, has one end fastened to a pole, 6 m long and 30 cm above the ground so that it can slip along the pole. The other end is attached to a dog. Where is the dog able to walk?

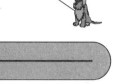

The dog can walk anywhere within the shaded region.

EXAMPLE 5

Two straight lines cross at a point, Q. Another point, P, is able to move in such a way that it must always be the same distance from each of the two lines. What is the locus of P?

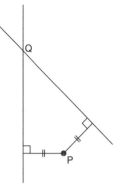

P can move anywhere along the lines bisecting the angles between the two original lines.

These two lines are perpendicular.

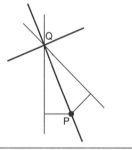

EXERCISE S39

1 The treasure lies 30 paces from the rock and 20 paces from the tree. The bearing of the rock from the tree is 025°.
Draw the map to a scale of 1 cm : 2 paces and find the possible hiding places.

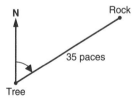

2 The diagram shows a garden measuring 24 m by 17.5 m. The pond is 7.5 m in diameter and the patio is a square of side 12.5 m.

The owners wish to plant a tree in the lawn which will grow to cover a circular area of diameter 8 m. This must partly overhang the patio but not the garden wall, or the pond. Also it must not make contact with the house.

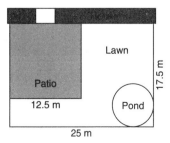

Using a scale of 1 cm : 1 m, draw a scale diagram and shade the region where the tree can be planted.

• A point P moves so that the ∠APB is always 90°, where A and B are two fixed points.
This is a circle.

3 The diagram shows a field of size 50 m by 30 m. In the centre of the field stands a barn, 16 m by 8 m.

A goat is tethered to corner A of the barn by a rope whose length is 20 m.

Draw a scale diagram of the field and use it to shade the region that the goat can graze.

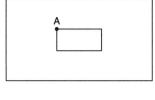

4 A ladder, 5 m long, leans against a wall.

If the ladder slips down the wall starting from vertical, what is the locus of the midpoint M of the ladder?

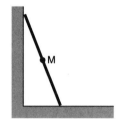

EXERCISE S40

1 What is the locus of the axle of a bicycle wheel as it travels along the road?

2 The diagram shows the cross-section of a cube. What is the locus of the corner P as the cube rolls along the table?

3 What is the locus of a point on the edge of a 10 p coin as it rolls along a table?

4 What is the locus of the tip of the hour hand of a clock between 1600 and 2000?

5 What is the locus of a point on the edge of a 10 p coin as it rolls around another 10 p coin?

EXERCISE S41

1 ABCD is a square of side 10 cm. The position of a point P is restricted by the following conditions:

a P lies within the square, **b** AP < PC, and **c** PB > PD.

Draw the square and shade the region where P must lie.

2 ABC is an equilateral triangle of side 10 cm. The position of a point P is restricted by the following conditions:

a PB > 7 cm, **b** AP < CP, and **c** ∠PCB > ∠PBC.

Draw the triangle and shade the region where P must lie.

3 XY is a horizontal line, 15 cm long. A point Z moves such that
a ∠ZXY > 40°, and **b** ZY = 12 cm.

Draw the diagram and indicate the possible positions of Z.

Geometrical (ruler and compass) constructions

(a) The perpendicular bisector of a line AB

With radius a bit larger than $\frac{1}{2}$ AB and with centres A and B, draw two arcs which cross at X and Y, as shown. The line XY is the perpendicular bisector of AB.

(b) The bisector of an angle BAC

With centre A and any radius, draw an arc cutting AB and AC at X and Y, as shown. Then with radius a bit larger than $\frac{1}{2}$ XY and with centres X and Y, draw two arcs crossing at P, as shown. AP is the bisector of angle BAC.

(c) The perpendicular at a given point P on a line

With centre P and any radius, draw two arcs cutting the line at X and Y as shown. Then with radius a bit larger than XP and with centres X and Y, draw two arcs crossing at Q, as shown. PQ is the required perpendicular.

(d) The perpendicular to a given line from point P

With centre P and any radius, draw arcs cutting the line at X and Y, as shown. Then with radius larger than $\frac{1}{2}$ XY and with centres X and Y, draw arcs crossing at Q on the opposite side of the line from P. PQ is the required perpendicular.

(e) An angle of 60°

Draw a line AB. With centre A, draw a large arc cutting AB at P, as shown. Then with centre P and **the same radius** draw an arc cutting the first arc at Q. Angle PAQ is 60°. **Note.** We construct 30° by bisecting 60°. Similarly we get 45° by bisecting a right angle.

(f) A triangle with side lengths *p*, *q* and *r*.

Draw a line AB of length *p*. With radius *q* and centre A, draw an arc, as shown. Then with centre B and radius *r*, draw an arc cutting the first arc at C. ABC is the required triangle.

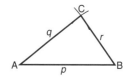

EXERCISE S42

(Make sure you show all construction lines clearly.)

1 Construct a rectangle with sides 12.4 cm and 8.3 cm. Measure and state the length of its diagonal.

2 Construct triangle PQR with PR = 12 cm, angle PQR = 90° and angle QPR = 60°. Measure and state the length of PQ.

3 Construct an isosceles triangle ABC with AB = AC = 10.5 cm and angle BAC = 45°. Measure and state the length of BC.

4 Construct a triangle ABC with AB = 11.5 cm, BC = 9 cm and AC = 7 cm. Construct the perpendicular from C to AB, and measure and state its length.

S 14 Nets and surface area of solids

Solids

A flat surface on a solid is a **face**. Two faces meet along an **edge**. Three or more edges meet at a **vertex** (plural **vertices**).

A solid with **six rectangular faces** is a **cuboid**.
A solid with **six square faces** is a **cube**.

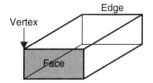

Common solids

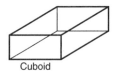

Cuboid   Cube

If we cut perpendicularly through a cuboid at any point along its length, the cut face or **cross-section** is identical to the rectangular end faces. The cuboid has a **uniform cross-section**. Solids with this property are called **prisms**. Here are some examples of prisms.

A **prism** is a solid with a **uniform cross-section**. The cross-section can be any shape, regular or irregular, with straight or curved sides.

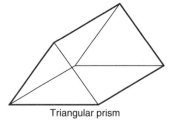 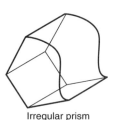

Triangular prism   Irregular prism

A prism with a circular cross-section is called a **cylinder**.

A **cylinder** is a prism with a circular cross-section.

A **pyramid** has a multi-edged flat base and triangular faces with a common vertex.
A **tetrahedron** is a pyramid with a triangular base.
A **cone** is like a pyramid but has a flat circular base and a sloping curved surface which terminates in a single vertex.

A **sphere** is a ball shape.
A **hemisphere** is half a sphere.

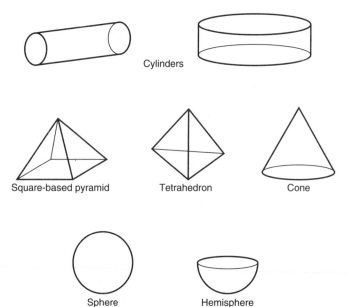

Cylinders

Square-based pyramid   Tetrahedron   Cone

Sphere   Hemisphere

Nets

To make a model of a solid from card, we draw a shape which can be cut out and folded to make the solid. The shape is called a **net** of the solid. The net of a particular solid is **not unique**. Here are some possible nets for a cube.

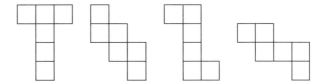

Hints for drawing nets

1 Decide on the sizes and shapes of the faces you must draw.
2 Call one face the 'base' and decide how the other faces will **fold up** from it.
3 Make sure the upper faces are drawn so that they will fold down in the right places.
4 Make sure that the sides of any faces which meet as edges of the solid are the **same length**.

For example, here is a possible net for a cuboid 8 cm long, 5 cm wide and 3 cm high, showing how it would be folded to make the cuboid.

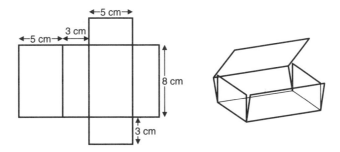

For a cylinder, the curved surface is formed by a rectangle whose length equals the circumference of the circular ends.
The diagram shows the net for a cylinder of radius 5 cm and height 8 cm.

The circumference of the end is $2\pi \times 5 = 31.4$ cm.

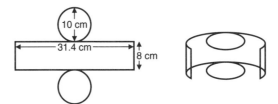

For most solids, to find their surface area **add up the areas of the faces** (the shapes making up the net).

Surface area of a solid

The surface area of a solid can usually be found as the total of the areas of its faces, i.e. of all the shapes which together make up its net.

For a **sphere** of radius r.

Surface area $= 4\pi r^2$

For a **cone**:

Curved surface area $= \pi rs$

where r is the radius of the base and s is the slant height, as shown.

EXAMPLE 1

Find the total surface area of a cuboid which is 6 cm long, 5 cm wide and 3 cm high.

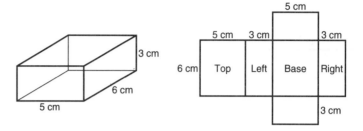

The base and top are both 6 cm by 5 cm, with area $= 6 \times 5 = 30\,\text{cm}^2$
The left and right are both 6 cm by 3 cm, with area $= 6 \times 3 = 18\,\text{cm}^2$
The back and front are both 5 cm by 3 cm, with area $= 5 \times 3 = 15\,\text{cm}^2$
The total surface area $= 2 \times 30 + 2 \times 18 + 2 \times 15 = 126\,\text{cm}^2$

EXERCISE S43

1 A prism has a cross-section as shown and has a length of 18 cm.

   a Draw a net of the prism.

   b Calculate its surface area.

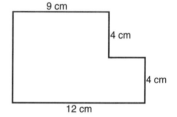

2 Calculate the surface area of a cylinder of radius 8 cm and height 30 cm.

3 The diagram shows a pyramid. Its base is a square with sides of length 10 in and its vertical height is 12 in.

   a Use Pythagoras' theorem to find the length AB.

   b Draw a net of the pyramid.

   c Calculate the surface area of the pyramid.

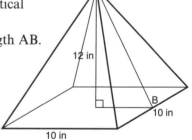

4 The solid shown comprises a cone, a cylinder and a hemisphere. Calculate its surface area.

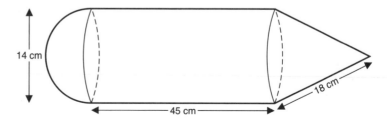

S 15 Volume

Volume

Volume is **three-dimensional**.

Volume refers to the space occupied by a solid object. It can also refer to the space inside a hollow object (this is also called **capacity**).
Volume is three-dimensional.

Volume is measured in **cubic units**. For example,
cubic centimetres (cm³)
cubic metres (m³)
cubic inches (in³)

When we are working in centimetres, the unit of volume if a cubic centimetre (written cm^3). We measure the volume by the number of one-centimetre cubes it would take to fill the whole space.
Volume can also be measured in cubic inches (in^3), cubic metres (m^3) etc.

Volume of a cuboid
A cuboid is a box shape whose faces are rectangles.

The diagram shows a cuboid 4 cm long, 3 cm wide and 5 cm high being filled with one-centimetre cubes.

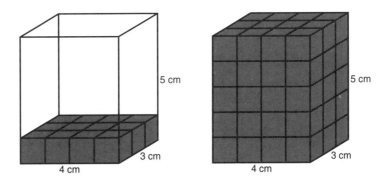

For a **cuboid**:

Volume =
Length × Width × Height

The number of cubes in each layer equals the area of the base (that is, length × width. In this case, the area $= 4 \times 3 = 12\,cm^2$.
The number of layers equals the height. In this case, there are 5 layers so the volume $= 12 \times 5 = 60\,cm^3$.

Volume of a prism
A prism is a solid which when cut perpendicularly at any point along its length produces a cut face of exactly the same shape and size. This shape is called the **constant cross-section** and its area is the **cross-sectional area**.

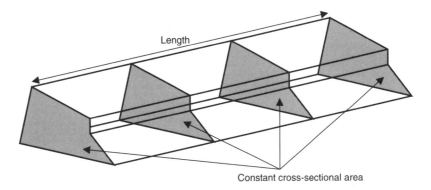

Length

Constant cross-sectional area

We can think of the volume of a prism as being built up of layers 1 cm thick, as shown in the example below.

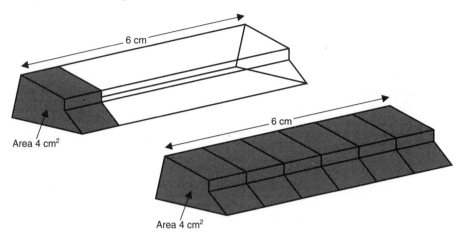

For a **prism**:

Volume = Cross-sectional area × Length

Here the cross-sectional area is $4\,\text{cm}^2$, so the volume of each layer is $4\,\text{cm}^3$.

There are 6 layers (given by the length) so the volume $= 4 \times 6 = 24\,\text{cm}^3$.

Volume of a cylinder
A cylinder is a prism whose cross-section is a circle.

For a **cylinder** with radius r and height h:

Volume $= \pi r^2 h$

The diagram shows a cylinder with radius 3 cm and height 8 cm.

The area of a circle is πr^2, so the cross-sectional area $= \pi \times 3^2 = 28.27\,\text{cm}^2$

This gives the volume as

$$28.27 \times 8 = 226.2\,\text{cm}^3 \text{ (to 4 sf)}$$

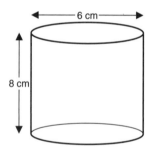

Volume of a pyramid

For a **pyramid**:

Volume $= \frac{1}{3} \times$ Base area $\times$ Perpendicular height

The volume of a pyramid is $\frac{1}{3} \times$ **base area $\times$ perpendicular height**.

(The proof of this is outside the scope of the course.)

EXAMPLE 1

Find the volume of a pyramid having a square base with sides of length 6 cm and height 7 cm.

Base area $= 6 \times 6 = 36\,\text{cm}^2$

$$\text{Volume} = \frac{1}{3} \times 36 \times 7$$
$$= 84\,\text{cm}^3$$

Volume of a cone

The volume of a cone is also $\frac{1}{3} \times$ base area $\times$ perpendicular height

For a **cone** with base radius *r* and height *h*:

$$\text{Volume} = \frac{1}{3}\pi r^2 h$$

EXAMPLE 2

Find the volume of a cone of radius 5 cm and height 8 cm.

Base area is $\pi \times 5^2 = 78.54\,\text{cm}^2$

$$\text{Volume} = \frac{1}{3} \times 78.54 \times 8$$
$$= 209.44\,\text{cm}^3$$

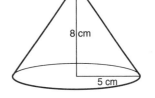

Volume of a sphere

The volume of a sphere is $\frac{4}{3} \times \pi \times (\text{radius})^3$

For a **sphere** of radius *r*:

$$\text{Volume} = \frac{4}{3}\pi r^3$$

EXAMPLE 3

Find the volume of a sphere of radius 4 cm.

$$\text{Volume} = \frac{4}{3} \times \pi \times 4^3$$
$$= 268.08\,\text{cm}^3$$

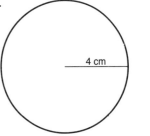

EXERCISE S44

1 Find the volume of each of the following solids.

a
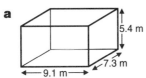

b
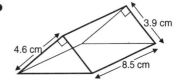

c
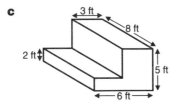

d
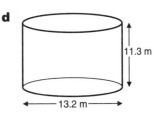

e
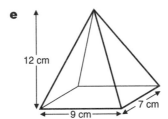

f

2 A solid consists of a cylinder attached to half a sphere as shown. Find its volume.

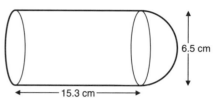

6.5 cm

15.3 cm

S 16 Networks and 3D coordinates

3D coordinates

To locate a point in **two dimensions** we need **two axes** and **two coordinates** (**x, y**).

To locate a point in **three dimensions** we need **three axes** and **three coordinates** (**x, y, z**).

Coordinates like these are called **rectangular** or **Cartesian coordinates**.

In three dimensions, when the x- and y-axes are drawn as usual the **positive z-axis points upwards from the page**.

A plane has two dimensions. To locate a point on the plane, we need two numbers, the coordinates (x, y) of the point. These state how far the point is from a fixed origin in two perpendicular directions defined by the x-axis and the y-axis.

In three dimensions, we need three coordinates (x, y, z). The z-value indicates how far the point is above or below the plane.

The positive z-direction is conventionally defined as follows:

If the x- and y-axes are drawn on a page resting on a table, with the positive x-axis pointing to the right and the positive y-axis pointing up the page, then the positive z-axis points vertically up from the table.

Diagrammatically it can be represented in several ways. For example,

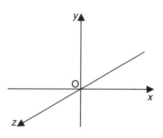

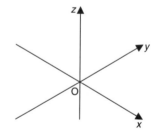

EXERCISE S45

1 The diagram shows a room with floor OABC.
OA = 6 m, OC = 4 m and the room is 3 m high. A light hangs 1 m below the centre of the ceiling. Relative to the axes shown, find the coordinates of

a the point B   **b** the point E

c the point F   **d** the mid point of FG

e the light

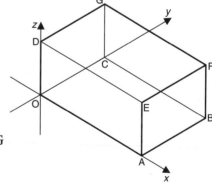

2 At midday a helicopter is at an altitude of 0.5 km and is 8 km north and 3 km west of the airport. It is flying at 120 km/h due south and is also climbing at 200 m/min. Taking the airport as the origin, east as the positive *x*-direction, north as the positive *y*-direction and up as the positive *z*-direction, find the coordinates of the helicopter

a at midday,   **b** 10 minutes later.

Calculating lengths and angles in 3D

Finding lengths and angles in three dimensions involves identifying suitable right-angled triangles and then using Pythagoras' theorem and the trigonometric ratios.

EXAMPLE 1

The diagram shows a cuboid. Given the coordinates of points A(2, 3, 2), B(7, 3, 2), D(2, 6, 2) and E(2, 3, 5) (units are cm), find **a** the length DF and **b** the angle between DF and the base ABCD.

a Angle DAB is a right angle.
AD = 3 cm and AB = 5 cm.
By Pythagoras on triangle ADB

$$DB^2 = 3^2 + 5^2$$
$$\Rightarrow \quad DB = \sqrt{34} \text{ cm}$$
$$= 5.831 \text{ cm}$$

Angle DBF is a right angle.

$$BF = 3 \text{ cm}.$$

By Pythagoras on triangle DBF

$$DF^2 = 3^2 + 5.831^2$$
$$\Rightarrow \quad DF = \sqrt{43}$$
$$= 6.557 \text{ cm}$$

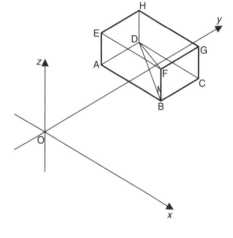

b The angle required is FDB.

$$\tan FDB = \frac{FB}{DB}$$
$$= 0.5145$$
$$\Rightarrow \quad \text{angle FDB} = 27.2°$$

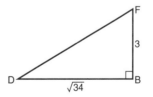

EXERCISE S46

1 The elastic of a catapult is attached to points A(9, 1, 1) and B(9, 5, 6) and is pulled back to the point C(2, 1, 1). (All measurements are in inches.) Calculate

a the total length ACB of the elastic

b the angle between the two parts of the elastic.

2 A vertical pole, 3 m tall, stands in horizontal ground. A second pole, 8 m tall, is placed at a point 12 m east and 7 m north of the first pole. A string joins the tops of the poles. Assuming that the string does not sag, calculate

a the length of the string

b the angle between the string and the taller pole.

Networks

Many real-life problems involve the ways in which a number of points are linked together and data about those links.

For example, a delivery firm will need to know how the various depots are connected and the distances or average journey times for those routes. Similarly, an oil company might have pumping stations connected by pipelines and each pipeline has a certain carrying capacity.

Problems like this can be analysed as networks. It is not necessary to have the geographical detail of the routes. The only important facts are what links exist and the data associated with each link.

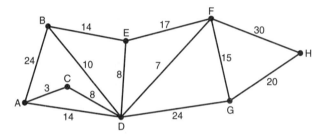

For example, this network shows places A to H connected by various routes. The numbers are the average journey times in minutes. The problem is to find the route from A to H with the shortest journey time.

Real problems can be very complex (even the above network has 29 possible routes) and require systematic and computerised solutions but simple problems, such as the one above, can be solved by trial-and-improvement methods. The shortest journey time is 48 minutes by route ACDFH.

EXERCISE S47

1 The network shows the main routes connecting five towns and the route distances in miles.

A delivery firm based in Bristol has to make deliveries to each of the other four towns and then return to Bristol. Identify the shortest round trip and state the total mileage.

2 This network shows water pipelines connecting a series of pumping stations. The figures indicate the maximum flow that each pipe can carry.

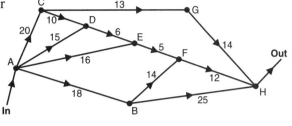

Water enters the system at A and leaves at H and can travel in the directions shown by the arrows. Find the largest flow which the system can deliver.

D 01 Collecting data

Data is classified as **numeric** (quantitative) data which can be expressed as numbers and **non-numeric** (qualitative or categorical) data which cannot.

Data is the term generally used to describe information which is collected and upon which decisions will be based. The data could be something as simple as finding out which colour workers prefer their workroom to be painted, or something as far reaching as a market-research postal-survey on what features people think are most important in car designs.

Data can be divided into two types: numeric and non-numeric.

Numeric data, also known as quantitative data, is concerned with information which can be assigned a numerical value, such as how many or what size.

Non-numeric data, also known as qualitative or categorical data, is concerned with attributes which cannot be given a numerical value, such as colour and nationality.

Numeric data is further classified as **discrete** or **continuous**.

Numeric data can be further divided into two types: continuous and discrete.

Continuous data is obtained by **measuring** and can take any value within a certain range, depending upon the accuracy of the measuring equipment.

Continuous data is found by measuring. There are no gaps within the range of values the data can take. Examples of continuous data are mass, height, time and speed.

Discrete data is obtained by counting and takes isolated values separated by distinct gaps.

Discrete data is obtained by counting, and there are definite gaps between the values the data can take. Examples of discrete data could include shoe size, the number of passengers in a car and the number of pages in a book.

It could be argued that the measurement of a person's height changes in steps of an inch or centimetre but that is only because of the way we record such data. It is true that a person's height is changing by tiny amounts throughout the day so it is impossible ever to say what someone's height is! Similarly if you attempt to say how old you are in years, months, days, hours, minutes, seconds, fractions of a second . . . by the time you have said it the information is inaccurate!

Continuous data can only be found approximately. Values to be recorded are rounded or truncated.

Height and time are two examples of continuous data. The value is usually **rounded** to the nearest unit (as with height) or **truncated** to the last whole number (as with age).

It is the nature of the variable which determines whether the data is discrete or continuous, NOT the way we record it.

EXERCISE D1

State whether each of the following is qualitative (categorical) or quantitative data. If quantitative, state whether it is discrete or continuous.

1 The number of pupils in a class.

2 The colour of cars in a car park.

3 The time spent by a motorist waiting at a red traffic light.

4 The styles of women's dresses available in a chain store.

5 The number of votes received by the candidates in an election.

6 The club of each of the members of the England football team.

7 The number of players from a club who play football for England.

8 The mass of a new born baby.

9 The number of words on a page of a book.

10 The duration of a hockey match.

D 02 Survey design

Sampling and bias

A **sample** is some portion of a **population** from which we collect information about that population. In statistics, the term 'population' does not mean the people who live in a certain place. Population refers to **all** of the items we are gathering information about. So a population could refer to the fish in a river, the loaves of bread produced at a bakery, or the houses which have green front doors.

A **census** is a survey which collects information from all members of a population. This is a rare event for many reasons:

- It costs too much.
- It takes too long.
- It could be silly: for example, if every match produced was tested to see if it lit when struck.
- It may be totally impossible: for example, to measure the length of all the earthworms in Wales.

To avoid these problems, information is collected about a population by taking a sample from that population. The sample must be **representative** of the population, that is it has as many as possible of the same characteristics as the population. A sample which is not representative of its population is **biased** and the results obtained from such a sample will not reflect the information within the population as a whole.

For example, television debates are currently popular and viewers can phone in to register their vote on the matter in hand. It would then be unwise to expect this fairly to represent the views of the nation, since the votes are only from those people who watch that sort of programme and who feel inclined to phone in.

One method of avoiding bias is to select the sample randomly. A true **random sample** is one where every member of the population has an equal chance of being selected. This is done simply by giving every member of the population a number and using a computer to generate random numbers. The sample size must be large enough to ensure that it is truly representative of the population it comes from.

There are other sampling techniques which can be used alongside random sampling.

A **sample** is a part of a population.

A **population** is the whole collection of items about which we are collecting information.

A **census** is a study of the whole population.

A sample is **representative** if it is effectively a small version of the population.

A sample is **biased** if its conclusions are not true for the population.

A **random sample** is one where, at each stage of the selection procedure, each remaining member has an equal chance of being selected.

A **stratified** sample is one where random samples are taken from different parts of the population in proportion to their size.

A **quota** sample is one in which the number of people to be interviewed in each category is decided in advance.

Stratified sampling is used to make sure that the sample contains similar proportions of members of relevant groups within the population. (If this information is known, a representative sample could be smaller than the size needed when a general random sample is used.) For example, a school may have 600 students, 100 of whom are in the sixth form. If we wanted a representative sample of 60 students, we would select a random sample of 10 from the sixth form and 50 from the rest of the school.

Quota sampling targets the proportion of certain categories which are to be included. For example, market research may have shown that the ages of people who each ice cream at the seaside are

under 14	30%
14 to 30	20%
31 to 55	10%
over 55	40%.

A survey of opinion on a new ice cream may therefore set quotas of 30, 20, 10 and 40 for every 100 people surveyed by the seaside to be in these same age groups.

This is similar to stratified sampling, but the sample is **not selected randomly**. Instead, the interviewer chooses the sample within the restrictions set by the quotas.

Designing a questionnaire

A lot of information obtained from random samples of people is collected by means of questionnaire. The following points should be kept in mind when designing a questionnaire.

- Avoid using long words where short words are easier to understand.
- Avoid technical terms or acronyms which require specialist knowledge.
- Avoid questions which are vague or require more than one response.
- Avoid questions which require the respondent to remember a lot or perform calculations.
- Avoid questions which lead to an expected answer.
- Make sure any multiple-choice answers cover all possible responses.

Here are some examples of bad practice.

Would you say that your current financial position and that of other contributors to your household budget enable you to divert more of your disposable income towards entertainment than you could within the last five years?

Do you agree that something should be done about the total moral corruption within the Government?

Would you find it anti-Europeanist if the value of the Ecu was closely allied to that of the German mark?

Do you think that the minimum age for buying cigarettes and driving a car should be raised?

There are two types of question which can be asked within a questionaire – open questions and closed questions.

An **open question** is one where the respondent answers in his/her own words.

Advantages:

- the respondent can express his/her own opinion rather than respond to suggested answers;
- allows the interviewer to ask further questions related to an earlier response.

Disadvantages:

- difficult to record answers fully;
- responses could be irrelevant to information sought;
- analysis of a whole survey may prove difficult to summarise.

A **closed question** is one where the respondent chooses an answer from a list of 'allowed' answers.

Advantages:

- answers easy to classify, analyse and summarise;
- makes sure that the answer is relevant.

Disadvantages:

- may have omitted some valid responses;
- may suggest answers which sway the respondent's opinion.

D03 Analysing qualitative and discrete data

Tally charts and frequency tables

Raw data is just a jumble of numbers or categories. We organise it by counting how many (the **frequency**) of each number or category we have. This may have been done directly on the observation sheet used when collecting the data, or it may need to be done at a later stage.

Raw data is unorganised data.

Frequency of a value is the number of times the value occurs.

Frequency table is a table of values with their frequencies.

Work through the data once and tally as you go. Do not search for all the 0s then all the 1s etc, as this makes errors more likely.

Every fifth tally mark should go through the previous four to make counting up easier.

Total your frequency column and check that it matches the number of data items.

EXAMPLE 1

The following data shows the number of goals scored in each of the 32 matches in the Gowforth Sunday League on 16 April 1996.

1, 4, 5, 2, 1, 6, 4, 3, 2, 2, 3, 2, 2, 2, 2, 1, 2, 2, 5, 2, 1, 2, 2, 3, 7, 0, 2, 3, 2, 5, 1, 5.

We organise them in a **frequency table**:

Goals scored	Tally	Frequency
0	/	1
1	////	5
2	//// //// ////	14
3	////	4
4	//	2
5	////	4
6	/	1
7	/	1
	Total	32

Pictograms

A pictogram illustrates a frequency table by using a symbol to represent each item or a number of items.

EXAMPLE 2

Suppose we had collected the goal data above for the whole season. We could present this in a pictogram as shown.

Frequency table

Goals	Frequency
0	40
1	175
2	394
3	210
4	132
5	65
6	38
7	21
8	14

Pictogram

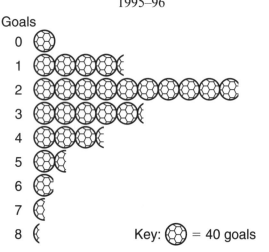

Goals per match – Gowforth Sunday League 1995–96

Key: = 40 goals

Bar charts

A bar chart is a diagram which consists of a series of blocks which are usually vertical but may be horizontal. Gaps are usually left between the blocks.

EXAMPLE 3

The following data show the methods of transport to school of a group of 80 children.

Mode of transport	Car	Bus	Cycle	Walk
Number of children	15	29	20	16

These can be shown as a bar chart.

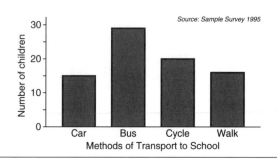

There are other varieties of bar chart to show more complex information. For example, we may have had more detail on the above data.

Mode of transport	Car	Bus	Cycle	Walk
Males	6	16	13	6
Females	9	13	7	10

We could present this as a dual bar chart or a sectional bar chart.

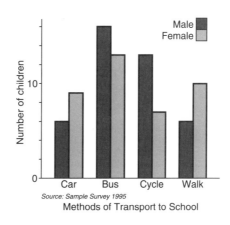

Source: Sample Survey 1995
Methods of Transport to School

A **dual** or **multiple bar chart** shows subtotals side by side.

A **sectional** or **component bar chart** shows the totals divided up into their subtotals. The subtotals are 'stacked' on top of each other.

There should be a **key** to identify the subtotals.

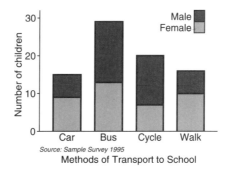

Source: Sample Survey 1995
Methods of Transport to School

Pie charts

A pie chart is used to show how a single total is shared among several categories. The total is represented by a circle and the subtotals of the different categories are represented by sectors whose angles are proportional to the subtotals. To draw a pie chart you may use

    A: an ordinary angle protractor which divides the circle into 360°;

or   B: a special pie chart protractor which divides the circle into 100%.

EXAMPLE 4

Using the school transport data from the previous page, methods A and B are as follows.

		Method A		Method B	
Car	15	$\frac{15}{80} \times 360°$	67.5°	$\frac{15}{80} \times 100\%$	18.75%
Bus	29	$\frac{29}{80} \times 360°$	130.5°	$\frac{29}{80} \times 100\%$	36.25%
Cycle	20	$\frac{20}{80} \times 360°$	90°	$\frac{20}{80} \times 100\%$	25%
Walk	16	$\frac{16}{80} \times 360°$	72°	$\frac{16}{80} \times 100\%$	20%
Total	80	Check total →	360°	Check total →	100%

(Of course you will use the method which suits the equipment you have.)

Then draw the pie chart.

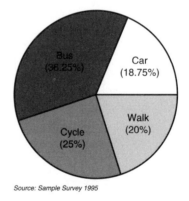

Source: Sample Survey 1995

Methods of transport to school

As with all diagrams, you should have

* **a title**
* **clear labelling**
* **the data source** (if known)

It is not uncommon to show the percentages or the actual subtotals for each category, but it is not usually helpful to show the angles of the sectors in degrees.

Interpreting pie charts

A pie chart gives an instant visual impression of the relative size of the groups of data represented without giving the actual frequencies of each category.

To get numerical information from a pie chart we need to know the angles or percentages for each sector and either the total represented or one of the subtotals.

EXAMPLE 5

This pie chart shows the types of
waterfowl using a certain lake on
one afternoon.

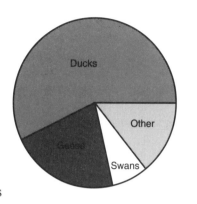

Suppose we know there were 50 ducks.
We measure the sector angle for ducks
and find it to be 200°.
We then know that each duck is
represented by

$$200 \div 50 = 4°$$

This means there were $360° \div 4° = 90$ birds
altogether.
Suppose we now wanted to know the number of geese.
We measure the sector angle for geese and find it to be 80°.
This means there were $80° \div 4° = 20$ geese.

Line graphs

When a quantity is measured at regular time intervals, the data form a **time
series**. We illustrate such data with a **line graph**.

EXAMPLE 6

Wafer-It is a company selling ice cream. They record their sales for each
quarter of the year for three years as follows.

Year	1992				1994				1994			
Quarter	1st	2nd	3rd	4th	1st	2nd	3rd	4th	1st	2nd	3rd	4th
Sales (£0 000s)	3.6	6.2	8.9	2.9	4.1	7.3	9.6	3.2	4.5	8.1	11	3.7

As usual there should be

- **a title**
- **clear labelling**
- **the data source** (if
known)

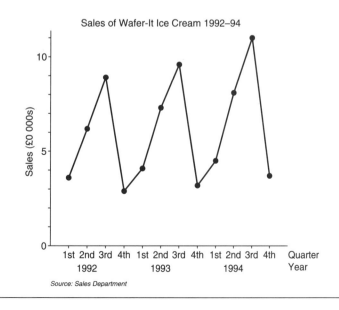

Sales of Wafer-It Ice Cream 1992–94

Source: Sales Department

Seasonal variation is a regular pattern of fluctuation in the time series.

Trend is a general upward or downward tendency of data after allowing for seasonal variations.

The advantage of a line graph is that regular patterns (**seasonal variations**) can be seen (in this case, there is an obvious yearly cycle).

It is also possible to get an idea of the underlying **trend** (in this case, the value of sales seems to be increasing year on year, though whether they are selling more ice cream or just raising prices is not clear).

Identifying such seasonal variations and trends would be important for the company because they form the basis for forecasting future sales. Decisions about buying stock, new equipment, etc depend on the reliability of such forecasts.

EXERCISE D2

1 A cafe sells tea, coffee, chocolate, milk and fruit juice. The first 40 drinks sold during one day were:

tea, coffee, coffee, juice, milk, coffee, tea, chocolate, tea, juice, coffee, coffee, juice, milk, chocolate, milk, juice, tea, tea, coffee, tea, coffee, coffee, juice, coffee, milk, coffee, tea, chocolate, coffee, milk, tea, coffee, juice, chocolate, coffee, milk, juice, coffee, tea.

  a Use tally marks to construct a frequency table for the data.
  b Draw a pictogram to illustrate the data.
  c Draw a bar chart to illustrate the data.
  d Draw a pie chart to illustrate the data.

2 The two diagrams relate to users of a sports centre. The bar chart shows the attendance for one week analysed by gender, and the pie chart shows the number of people engaged in different activities on one Saturday afternoon.

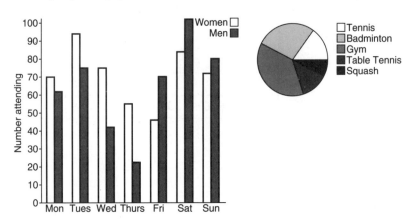

  a Which was the most popular day for **i** women, **ii** men?
  b How many people used the centre on the busiest day?
  c On the pie chart the sector for tennis is 60° and there were 25 people who played tennis that afternoon.
    i How many people used the centre altogether that afternoon?
    ii If the sector for the gym is 144°, how many people used the gym?

3 The numbers of students attending St Audacious Sixth-form College between 1987 and 1994 were as shown in the table. Illustrate these data by means of a line graph.

Academic year	1987–8	1988–9	1989–90	1990–1	1991–2	1992–3	1993–4
Number of students	675	742	698	788	825	889	914

Misleading diagrams

A poorly designed diagram can easily give a false impression of the data. There are several ways in which a diagram can be misleading. Two of the most common are shown below.

Pictograms using different-sized symbols

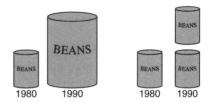

The diagram on the left gives the impression that sales in 1990 are much more than twice sales in 1980 because the area of the larger symbol is four times the area of the small symbol. (In fact, the large tin would hold eight times as many beans as the small tin!)

The diagram on the right gives the correct impression.

Scales which do not start at zero

Year	1990	1991	1992	1993
Number of cars sold	122	125	128	129

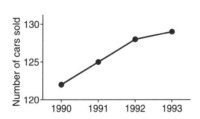 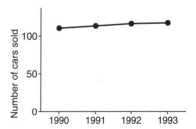

At first glance the graph on the left appears to show that sales are increasing rapidly, whereas the graph on the right shows the true situation that sales have hardly changed at all.

If you wish to start a scale somewhere other than zero, you should always show a break in the scale to warn the viewer that this has happened.

like
this
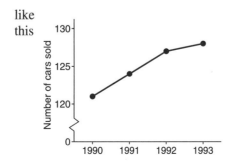

or
like
this
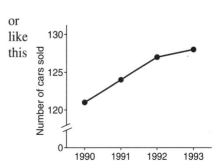

D 04 Analysing grouped and continuous data

Grouped discrete data

When a discrete variable takes a wide range of values, we can only produce a sensible frequency table by grouping the data into **classes**.

EXAMPLE 1

A student examining the writing style of different newspapers recorded the number of words in each of the first 50 sentences in an article, as follows: 8, 31, 43, 17, 83, 27, 11, 40, 17, 21, 27, 25, 27, 58, 37, 33, 13, 32, 17, 22, 44, 34, 12, 23, 30, 36, 16, 18, 24, 41, 23, 16, 24, 16, 29, 64, 20, 18, 9, 34, 19, 9, 26, 27, 51, 7, 8, 28, 17, 12.

These could reasonably be grouped as follows.

> Choose the classes so that they do **not overlap**. You must always be able to tell to which class a value belongs.

Number of words	Tally	Frequency
1–10	⧚	5
11–20	⧚ ⧚ ⧚	15
21–30	⧚ ⧚ ⧚	15
31–40	⧚ ///	8
41–50	///	3
51–60	//	2
61–70	/	1
71–80		0
81–90	/	1
	Total	50

These data could then be shown on a frequency diagram similar to a bar chart.

> A diagram like this is only acceptable if the **classes have the same width**. Using classes of varying widths would give a distorted and misleading picture of the data.

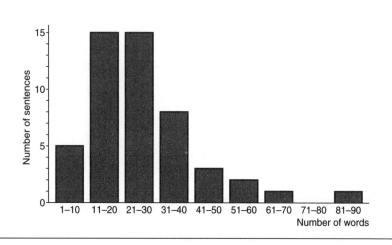

Stem-and-leaf diagrams

One problem with grouping data is that the detail of the original numbers is lost. A stem-and-leaf diagram enables us to display the data in a grouped fashion without losing the detail. The data may be **unsorted** or **sorted**. For example, the data on sentence length would appear as follows:

Stem plus **leaf** gives **data value.**

Stem	Leaf		Stem	Leaf
0	89978		0	78899
10	71737268668972		10	12236667777889
20	717572343490678		20	012334456777789
30	17324064		30	01234467
40	3041		40	0134
50	81		50	18
60	4		60	4
70			70	
80	3		80	3

Stem + Leaf = Data value e.g. 0 + 7 = 7

Unsorted stem-and-leaf diagram   Sorted stem-and-leaf diagram

Note that this stem-and-leaf diagram gives a slightly different set of frequencies from those in the grouped frequency table on the previous page because it has grouped the data as 0–9, 10–19, etc rather than as 1–10, 11–20, etc.

EXERCISE D3

1 The following shows the results of a survey counting the number of cars per minute passing along a busy stretch of road.

22, 28, 35, 31, 26, 37, 44, 42, 24, 28, 33, 35, 39, 41, 40,
30, 33, 27, 38, 39, 42, 31, 43, 28, 29, 20, 36, 29, 31, 36.

a Construct a frequency table using intervals 20–24, 25–29, 30–34, etc.
b Draw a frequency diagram to illustrate the data.

2 The entries for a 'guess the number of sweets in the jar' competition were as follows.

62, 86, 78, 94, 108, 69, 84, 92, 95, 76, 100, 99, 83, 77, 79, 69, 64, 112, 73, 115, 94, 86, 80, 72, 66, 68, 91, 110, 119, 75, 65, 68, 82, 92, 88, 101, 96, 88, 77, 70, 76, 81, 79, 69, 94, 116.

a Construct an unsorted stem-and-leaf diagram for the data.
b Construct a sorted stem-and-leaf diagram for the data.

3 Using the data from question 1, construct a sorted stem-and-leaf diagram in which the stems are 20, 25, 30, etc.

Continuous data

Continuous data is obtained by measuring, weighing, timing etc. and can in theory take any value. However, such data can only be stated to a given degree of accuracy, e.g. to two decimal places.

Frequency tables for continuous data are always grouped into class intervals. Even a statement such as 'the length was 8 cm to the nearest cm' really means 'the measurement was in the interval 7.5 cm to 8.5 cm'.

We must be clear where the boundaries of our classes are. The situation is different depending on how the values have been rounded.

Rounding 'to the nearest'

For example, when measuring the heights of plants, we might record the results 'to the nearest cm'. We might then group all the values recorded as being between 15 cm and 19 cm into a class interval labelled '15-19'.

Intervals labelled '10–', '20–' etc usually mean

$$10 \leqslant x < 20$$
$$20 \leqslant x < 30 \text{ etc}$$

If the values have been **rounded 'to the nearest'**, then intervals labelled '10–19', '20–29', etc mean

$$9.5 \leqslant x < 19.5$$
$$19.5 \leqslant x < 29.5 \text{ etc}$$

If the values have been **rounded down** (truncated), then intervals labelled '10–19', '20–29' etc mean

$$10 \leqslant x < 20$$
$$20 \leqslant x < 30 \text{ etc}$$

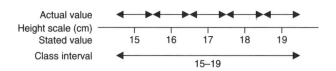

The actual height of a plant in this interval must be at least 14.5 cm and less than 19.5 cm. The class boundaries are 14.5 and 19.5.

A better way of labelling this interval would be $14.5 \leqslant x < 19.5$.

Rounding down (truncating)

For example, when recording people's ages, we would usually record 'completed years'. We might then group all the values recorded as being between 15 years and 19 years into a class interval labelled '15–19'.

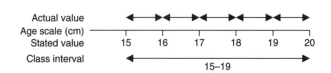

People with ages in this interval have had their 15th birthday but not yet had their 20th birthday. The class boundaries are 15 years and 20 years.

A better way of labelling this interval would be $15 \leqslant x < 20$.

Rounding down may also occur when values are obtained from digital equipment. For example, an object with a mass of 15.8 grams placed on scales with a digital display showing whole numbers of grams may well appear as 15 grams because it has 'triggered' the 15 but failed to trigger the 16.

Frequency diagrams for continuous data

A frequency diagram for continuous data differs from one for discrete data in that we use an ordinary graph scale on the horizontal axis and, as all values of the variable are possible, there should be **no gaps** between the bars.

EXAMPLE 2

The heights of 60 plants were recorded to the nearest cm and the following frequency table was constructed.

Height (nearest cm)	5–9	10–14	15–19	20–24	25–29
Number of plants	4	11	19	10	6

A frequency diagram for continuous data (a **histogram**) has

- an ordinary graph scale on the horizontal axis
- no gaps between the bars
- bars which start and finish at the true boundaries of the intervals.

The method shown is **only valid for intervals of equal width**.

This can be presented graphically, as below.

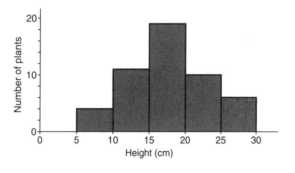

Notice that the boundaries of the intervals are 4.5, 9.5, 14.5, etc. and the bars are drawn at these boundaries.

A frequency diagram like this for continuous data is called a **histogram**. The details of drawing histograms in general are beyond the scope of this book, but you will not go wrong provided you use class intervals which are **all the same width**.

Frequency polygon

A **frequency polygon** is an alternative way of illustrating a set of continuous data. It can be drawn superimposed on the histogram or separately. The frequency polygon for the plant-height data looks like this.

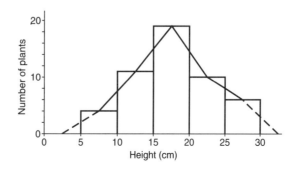

The points are plotted at the centre of the top of each bar of the histogram. We can find the position of each point by averaging the appropriate class boundaries. For example, the interval labelled 5–9 has boundaries at 4.5 and 9.5. The mid-point of this is at $\frac{1}{2}(4.5 + 9.5) = 7$.

You may wish to join the polygon to the mid-points of the intervals before and after those shown in the table, as shown by the broken lines. This is recommended by some statisticians and is usually acceptable unless it shows negative values for a variable which is obviously positive.

EXERCISE D4

1

Time (nearest second)	10–19	20–29	30–39	40–49	50–59	60–69
Number of people	8	13	24	29	19	12

This table shows the time taken by a number of people to complete a task. Illustrate this table using   **a** a frequency diagram (histogram), **b** a frequency polygon.

2

Age (years)	16–20	21–25	26–30	31–35	36–40
Number of people	18	35	50	23	10

This table shows the ages of people applying for sales jobs with a certain company. Illustrate these data by means of a histogram.

Cumulative frequency graphs

A **cumulative frequency** graph, or **ogive**, shows the running total of the frequencies as we go through the distribution. Each total is plotted on a graph against the **upper boundary** of the interval to which it refers. For example, using the data for heights of plants from the previous pages, we proceed as follows.

A cumulative frequency graph shows the number of observations which are **less than** the corresponding value of the variable.

The cumulative frequency values are plotted against the **true upper boundary** of the interval.

If the points clearly follow a curve, then we draw as smooth a curve as possible through the point – a **cumulative frequency curve** or **ogive**.

If the points clearly do not lie on a curve, we join them with straight lines. The graph is then called a **cumulative frequency polygon**.

The graph can be joined to the axis (i.e. zero cumulative frequency) at the true lower boundary of the first interval.

Height (cm)	Frequency	Upper boundary	Cumulative frequency
5–9	4	9.5	4
10–14	11	14.5	15
15–19	19	19.5	34
20–24	10	24.5	44
25–29	6	29.5	50

The cumulative frequency shows the number of values which were **less than** the corresponding upper bound, so in this case there were 4 values below 9.5, 15 below 14.5 and so on. We then draw the graph as follows.

Points to note

- There were no values below 4.5, so we join the graph to that point.
- The points clearly lie on a curve, so we draw a smooth curve through the plotted points – a **cumulative frequency curve**.

Reading information from a cumulative frequency graph

Each point on a cumulative frequency graph shows a value of the variable and the number of observations which were below that value.

> When drawing a cumulative frequency graph, you should choose your scales so that the central part of the curve is at an angle of about 45°. If it is too steep or too shallow, the accuracy with which you can read information from the graph will suffer.

EXAMPLE 3

For the plant-height data find   **a** the percentage of plants below 18 cm, and **b** the minimum height of the top 20% of plants.

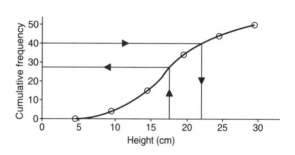

a From 18 cm on the height scale, we find the corresponding value (28) on the cumulative frequency scale, as shown above. Therefore, 28 of the 50 plants, or 56%, were below 18 cm.

b 20% of plants is 10 plants.
The top 20% correspond to the region 40–50 on the cumulative frequency scale.
From 40 on the cumulative frequency scale, we find the corresponding value (22 cm) on the height scale, as shown above. Therefore, the top 20% of plants were those over 22 cm high.

EXERCISE D5

The table shows the times, to the nearest second, taken by 200 trainees to complete a test task.

a Complete the cumulative frequency table.

b Draw a cumulative frequency graph for the data.

c From your graph estimate
  i how many completed in 43 seconds or less
  ii the pass standard if only 30% of the trainees passed.

Time	No. of trainees	Upper boundary	Cumulative frequency
10–19	15		
20–29	28		
30–39	46		
40–49	53		
50–59	33		
60–69	25		

D 05 Describing distributions: averages of discrete data

Describing a distribution

When describing a set of data, one of the questions we need to answer is 'What is a typical, middle-of-the-road value of the data?'

For this we need a measure of **average**. The term 'average' is used loosely to mean an ordinary or typical value but there are several ways in which such a value can be found. The most commonly used measures of average are the **mode**, the **median** and the **mean**.

Finding averages for discrete data

The mode

The **mode** or **modal value** is the value in the data set with the greatest frequency. It is the **most common value**.

The most **common value** in a data set is called the **mode** or the **modal value**. For example, the marks scored on a test by a group of students were

6, 4, 4, 6, 7, 8, 3, 6, 4, 7, 6, 9, 5

Putting these in order, we get

3, 4, 4, 4, 5, 6, 6, 6, 6, 7, 7, 8, 9

We can now see that the mode or modal score is 6 marks.

The median

The **median** is the middle value when the values are placed **in order of size**.

When the values in a data set are placed **in order of size**, the value at the middle of the list is the **median**.

When the number of data values is odd, the middle of the list falls on one of the values, as in the test score data above.

If there are n **data values**, we can find the **position** of the median as

$$\tfrac{1}{2}(n+1)$$

If n is **odd**, the **value** of the median is the data value at that position.

If n is **even**, the **value** of the median is **halfway** between the two central values.

Value	3	4	4	4	5	6	6	6	6	7	7	8	9
Position	1	2	3	4	5	6	7	8	9	10	11	12	13

↑ middle (under position 7)

The **position** of the median is 7. We can find this as $\tfrac{1}{2}(13+1)$.
The **value** of the median is 6.

When the number of data values is even, the middle of the list falls between two values, as follows.

Value	8	8	9	12	17	18	18	20
Position	1	2	3	4	5	6	7	8

↑ middle (between positions 4 and 5)

The **position** of the median is 4.5. We can find this as $\tfrac{1}{2}(8+1)$.
The **value** of the median is halfway between the 4th value (12) and the 5th value (17). This gives $\tfrac{1}{2}(12+17) = 14.5$ as the value of the median.

The mean

Properly called the **arithmetic mean**, this is the value which most people think of when they say 'average'.

To find the mean first **add up all the data values** then **divide this total by the number of values in the set**.

For example, find the mean of 5, 9, 14, 7, 8, 13, 10, 8.

Add up the values: $5 + 9 + 14 + 7 + 12 + 13 + 10 + 8 = 78$
There are 8 values, so the mean is $78 \div 8 = 9.75$

Notation: the mean of a set of values of a variable x is given by $\bar{x}$.

$$\text{Mean} = \frac{\text{Total of all values}}{\text{Number of values}}$$

We sometimes use Σ to mean 'the sum of', so for n numbers we write

$$\bar{x} = \frac{\Sigma x}{n}$$

Finding the mode, median and mean from a frequency table

EXAMPLE 1

The hours of overtime worked by staff in one week were as follows.

Hours overtime	0	1	2	3	4	5
Number of staff	3	7	12	6	3	2

The mode

The **mode** is the value having the **greatest frequency**.

The data values are 0, 1, 2, 3, 4, 5 hours.
The value which occurs most often is 2, which occurs 12 times.
The mode of this distribution is 2 hours.

The median

To find the median, we need the **cumulative frequency** – the running total of the frequencies.

Hours overtime	0	1	2	3	4	5
Cumulative frequency	3	10	22	28	31	33

Use cumulative frequency to help 'count along' to the position of the median.

The total number of values is 33.
The position of the median is $\frac{1}{2}(33 + 1) = 17$.
From the table, all the values from the 11th to the 22nd are 2 hours, so in particular the 17th value, i.e. the median, is 2 hours.

The mean

For a frequency table:
No. of values
   = Total frequency
Total of values
   = Sum of (frequency
      × value)
So

$$\text{Mean} = \frac{\text{Sum (frequency} \times \text{value)}}{\text{Total frequency}}$$

or

$$\bar{x} = \frac{\Sigma fx}{\Sigma f}$$

Hours (x)	Frequency (f)	fx
0	3	0
1	7	7
2	12	24
3	6	18
3	6	18
4	3	12
5	2	10
Total	33	71

There were 33 values – the total of the frequencies.
To find the total of those 33 values, we multiply each value by its frequency, e.g. the value 2 occurs 12 times, which contributes $12 \times 2 = 24$ to the total of the values.

$$\text{Mean} = \frac{\text{Total of values}}{\text{Number of values}}$$

$$\bar{x} = \frac{71}{33}$$

$$= 2.15 \text{ hours} \quad \text{or} \quad 2\,\text{h}\,9\,\text{min}$$

EXERCISE D6

1 Find the mode, median and mean for each of the following data sets.

   a 6, 3, 8, 8, 4, 6, 7, 8, 8, 2, 8, 4, 5, 9, 8

   b 12, 19, 15, 15, 16, 19, 13, 19, 14, 15, 18, 18

2 The table shows the number of flowers per plant in a study of dahlias. Find the mode, median and mean.

Number of flowers	8	9	10	11	12	13	14
Number of plants	6	14	25	28	32	21	12

3 The mean wage of the 10 day workers in a factory is £260 per week, and the mean wage of the 5 night workers is £296 per week.

   a Find the total money paid per week to   **i** the day workers,   **ii** the night workers

   b Find the mean wage for all 15 workers.

D06 Describing distributions: averages of grouped data

Finding the mode, median and mean for grouped data

When data is presented as a grouped frequency table, we do not know what the original data values were, only which class they belonged to. We cannot, therefore, calculate accurate values for the averages.

The mode

Modal class is the class interval with the **greatest frequency**.

We cannot find the mode of the data in a grouped frequency table, but we can state which class interval has the greatest frequency. This is called the **modal class**.

Height (nearest cm)	5–9	10–14	15–19	20–24	25–29
Number of plants	4	11	19	10	6

In the case of the data on plant heights, the modal class is 15–19 cm.

The median

We can estimate the median of the data in a grouped frequency table by making assumptions about how the data in each class is spread. There are two possible approaches, which may give slightly different estimates.

1 Using the cumulative frequency graph

We draw a cumulative frequency graph and assume that the data in each class follows the curve drawn through the known points. The estimate of the median is then the value corresponding to the point halfway up the cumulative frequency scale.

The cumulative frequency graph for the plant-height data from page 217 is shown below.

For a grouped frequency table, we can only **estimate** the median.

Using the cumulative frequency graph assumes that the data follows a smooth curve.

For grouped data, the position of the median is $\frac{1}{2}n$, not $\frac{1}{2}(n+1)$ as for ungrouped data. This is because we are now using a cumulative frequency scale from 0 to n, and the mid point of this is $\frac{1}{2}n$.

When calculating an estimate of the median, we assume that data in each interval is evenly spread out. (This would be equivalent to joining the points on the cumulative frequency graph with straight lines.)

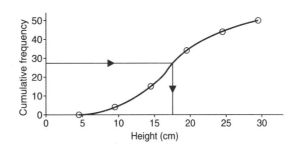

The total number of plants is 50.
The median position is where cumulative frequency is $\frac{1}{2} \times 50 = 25$.
The estimated median is the corresponding plant height, i.e. 17.5 cm.

2 Using the frequency table

To estimate the median directly from a frequency table, we assume that the data in each class interval is spread evenly through that interval.

Height (nearest cm)	Class boundaries	Frequency	Cumulative frequency
5–9	$4.5 \leqslant x < 9.5$	4	4
10–14	$9.5 \leqslant x < 14.5$	11	15
15–19	$14.5 \leqslant x < 19.5$	19	34
20–24	$19.5 \leqslant x < 24.5$	10	44
25–29	$24.5 \leqslant x < 29.5$	6	50
Total		50	

The median position is where the cumulative frequency = 25.
We can see from the table that this occurs in the 15–19 class.
At the lower boundary (14.5) of this class, the cumulative frequency = 15.
We need a further 10 values from the 19 values in the class.

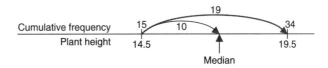

The width of the interval from 14.5 to 19.5 cm is 5 cm.
If the data is evenly spread we need to go forward by $\frac{10}{19}$ of the interval.
The median is

$$14.5 + \frac{10}{19} \times 5 = 17.1 \text{ cm}$$

The mean

To estimate the mean, we assume that the data in each class interval is spread evenly through that interval. This means that the average value of data in the interval falls at the interval mid-point. We then use this mid-point value in calculating the mean.

When calculating an estimate of the mean, we use the **interval mid-point** as our data values. (Remember we can find the mid-point by averaging the class boundaries – $\frac{1}{2}(4.5 + 9.5) = 7$, etc.)

Height (cm)	Class boundaries	Mid-point x	Frequency f	fx
5–9	$4.5 \leqslant x < 9.5$	7	4	28
10–14	$9.5 \leqslant x < 14.5$	12	11	132
15–19	$14.5 \leqslant x < 19.5$	17	19	323
20–24	$19.5 \leqslant x < 24.5$	22	10	220
25–29	$24.5 \leqslant x < 29.5$	27	6	162
		Total	50	865

$$\text{Estimated arithmetic mean } (\bar{x}) = \frac{\text{Sum of all the values}}{\text{Total number of values}}$$

$$= \frac{865}{50}$$

$$= 17.3 \, \text{cm}$$

EXERCISE D7

1

Journey time (nearest minute)	10–12	13–15	16–18	19–21	22–24	25–27
Number of journeys	8	15	29	14	9	5

The table shows the results of a survey of journey times on a certain bus route.

a State the modal class.

b Draw a cumulative frequency graph for the data and from it estimate the median journey time.

c Calculate an estimate of the mean journey time.

2

Age (years)	16–20	21–25	26–30	31–35	36–40	41–45	46–50
Number of people	5	12	26	47	34	25	11

The table shows the results of a sample survey by a company into the ages of its customers.

a State the modal class.

b Calculate an estimate of the median age.

c Calculate an estimate of the mean age.

Finding a mean using statistical functions on a calculator

Different calculator models have different approaches to this. If the following section does not make sense in relation to your calculator, you will need to consult your instruction manual or ask your tutor.

1 Put your calculator in the correct mode (SD or STAT).

2 Ensure statistical memories are cleared (SAC or KAC).

3 Data values are now entered using the key labelled x or DATA.

   a For individual data items the sequence is

   | Data value | DATA | Data value | DATA | etc |

   b For data in a frequency table the sequence is

   | Data value | × | Frequency | DATA | etc |

4 Once all the data has been entered we can obtain

   a The number of values – use key labelled n.

   b The total of the values – use key labelled Σx.

   c The mean – use key labelled $\bar{x}$.

   (It may be necessary to use **INV/SHIFT** or **KOUT** to access these functions.)

EXERCISE D8

Use the statistical functions on your calculator to find the mean of the following distributions.

1 28, 34, 36, 40, 23, 30, 31, 45, 28, 28, 37, 40, 41, 43, 38, 39, 29, 22

2

Exam mark	12	13	14	15	16	17	18	19	20
Number of pupils	3	7	15	42	49	31	23	14	8

3

Time (nearest second)	10–19	20–29	30–39	40–49	50–59	60–69	70–79	80–89
Frequency	26	56	73	89	64	40	25	19

Measures of average – advantages and disadvantages

Mode

For   Very easy to evaluate.

Not affected by extreme values.

Can be used for qualitative data (e.g. we could find the modal colour of car sold in a given month).

Against Doesn't take all the data values into account.

May be more than one mode.

Use for Qualitative data. Situations where we are asking for the 'most likely' value.

Median

For   Easy to find for ungrouped data, though grouped data needs a cumulative frequency graph or calculation.

Not affected by extreme values.

Against   Doesn't take all the data values into account.
                Not readily understood by many people.

Use for   Distributions with extreme values (e.g. average wage paid by a company).

Mean

For   Uses all the data values.
                It is the value most people mean by the term 'average'.
                If we are given the mean, we can calculate the expected total for a given number of data items.

Against   Usually requires a calculator.
                Easily distorted by extreme values, especially where the sample is small.

Use for   Reasonably symmetrical distributions. The mean is also used in the calculation of other statistical values.

An example for comparison

Suppose we are examining pay increases in a company.

A **mode** of £5 would tell us that more people received a £5 rise than any other value, but we would have no idea whether this was a good or bad rise in relation to others in the company.

A **median** of £5 would give an indication of the impact of the rise on individuals – we would know that half the employees received £5 or less and half £5 or more.

A **mean** of £5 would give an indication of the impact of the rise on the company – if we knew the number of employees, we could decide the effect of the rise on the overall wage bill.

D 07 Describing distributions: dispersion

Measures of dispersion

A **measure of dispersion** indicates how spread out the values in a data set are.

Consider the two data sets (a) 12, 15, 13, 16, 13 and (b) 2, 9, 23, 18, 17.
In each case, there are 5 data values and the mean of each data set is 13.8. However, the values in set (a) are closely grouped together, while those in set (b) are quite widely spread out.
A quantity which indicates how spread out the values in a data set are is called a **measure of dispersion**.

Range

Range = Largest value
– smallest value

This is the simplest measure of dispersion. We simply find the difference between the largest and the smallest values in the data set. For example,

     for set (a) 16–12 = 4, so the range is 4
     for set (b) 23–2 = 21, so the range is 21

The drawback with the range is that a single extreme value can have a large effect on the value of the range.

Interquartile range

The **first** or **lower quartile** (Q_1) is the value **one quarter** of the way along the distribution.

The **third** or **upper quartile** (Q_3) is the value **three quarters** of the way along the distribution.

Interquartile range = $Q_3 - Q_1$

We sometimes find at other fractional positions in the distribution. Common ones are:
- **Deciles** at intervals of one tenth of the distribution, e.g. the third decile would be three tenths of the way along the distribution.
- **Percentiles** at intervals of one hundredth of the distribution, e.g. the 28th percentile would be twenty-eight hundredths of the way along the distribution.

We can avoid the problem of extreme values by ignoring the data at each end of the distribution.

In the same way that we found the median as the value halfway along the distribution, we can find:

- the **first (lower) quartile (Q_1)** – the value one quarter of the way along, and
- the **third (upper) quartile (Q_3)** – the value three quarters of the way along.

(The second quartile is, of course, the median.)

We then find the **interquartile range** as the difference between the upper and lower quartiles. For example, for the plant height data used previously (page 217), we have

$$\text{position of } Q_1 \text{ is } \tfrac{1}{4} \times 50 = 12.5$$

$$\text{position of } Q_3 \text{ is } \tfrac{3}{4} \times 50 = 37.5$$

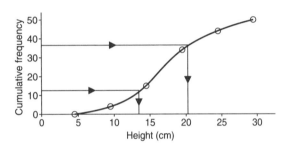

Reading from the cumulative frequency graph, we get

$$\text{value of } Q_1 = 14 \, \text{cm}$$
$$\text{value of } Q_3 = 20.8 \, \text{cm}$$

Interquartile range is $20.8 - 14 = 6.8 \, \text{cm}$

Box-and-whisker diagrams

A **box-and-whisker diagram** is a way of illustrating a distribution to show dispersion.

For example, for the plant height data, we have

$$\text{lower extreme} = 4.5 \, \text{cm}$$
$$\text{lower quartile} = 14 \, \text{cm}$$
$$\text{median} = 17.5 \, \text{cm}$$
$$\text{upper quartile} = 20.8 \, \text{cm}$$
$$\text{upper extreme} = 29.5 \, \text{cm}$$

We draw the box-and-whisker diagram with a central box between the quartiles, a vertical line in the box to show the median, and whiskers extending each side to the extremes.

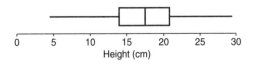

Standard deviation

This is the most sophisticated measure of dispersion. There are two ways to calculate it, illustrated in the following example.

EXAMPLE 1

Find the standard deviation of the values 5, 7, 7, 8, 8, 9, 12, 15, 19, 20.

METHOD 1

Step 1 Find the mean.
There are 10 values totalling 110, so the mean $= 110 \div 10 = 11$.

Step 2 Find the difference between each value and the mean.

x	5	7	7	8	8	9	12	15	19	20
$(x - 11)$	-6	-4	-4	-3	-3	-2	1	4	8	9

Step 3 Square these differences.

x	5	7	7	8	8	9	12	15	19	20
$(x - 11)$	-6	-4	-4	-3	-3	-2	1	4	8	9
$(x - 11)^2$	36	16	16	9	9	4	1	16	64	81

Step 4 Find the mean of these squares.
The total of the squares is 252, so the mean $= 252 \div 10 = 25.2$

Step 5 Take the root of this result to give the standard deviation.
Standard deviation $= \sqrt{25.2} = 5.02$ (to 3 sf)

METHOD 2
This more efficient method avoids the need to find the individual differences from the mean.

Step 1 Find the mean of the data. This is 11, as before.

Step 2 Square all the data values.

x	5	7	7	8	8	9	12	15	19	20
x^2	25	49	49	64	64	81	144	225	361	400

Step 3 Find the mean of these squares.
The squares total 1462, so mean of square $= 1462 \div 10 = 146.2$

Step 4 Subtract the square of the mean of the data values.
$$146.2 - 11^2 = 25.2$$

Step 5 Take the square root of this result.
Standard deviation $= \sqrt{25.2} = 5.02$ (to 3 sf)

Standard deviation from a frequency table

This is best done using the second method. The only modification is that we must allow for the frequencies when calculating the totals of x and x^2.

If the table is grouped, we estimate the standard deviation using the mid-points of the class intervals in the same way as for the mean.

For example, for the plant height data:

Height (nearest cm)	Class boundaries	Mid-point x	Frequency f	fx	fx^2
5–9	$4.5 \leqslant x < 9.5$	7	4	28	196
10–14	$9.5 \leqslant x < 14.5$	12	11	132	1 584
15–19	$14.5 \leqslant x < 19.5$	17	19	323	5 491
20–24	$19.5 \leqslant x < 24.5$	22	10	220	4 840
25–29	$24.5 \leqslant x < 29.5$	27	6	162	4 374
			Total	50	865	16 485

For a frequency table:

Standard deviation =

$$\sqrt{\left(\frac{\Sigma fx^2}{n} - \bar{x}^2\right)}$$

Standard deviation $= \sqrt{(\text{mean of squares} - \text{square of mean})}$

$$= \sqrt{\left[\frac{16485}{50} - \left(\frac{865}{50}\right)^2\right]}$$

$$= 5.51\,\text{cm (to 3 sf)}$$

Finding a standard deviation using a calculator statistical function
If your calculator has a statistical mode, it will calculate standard deviation.

1 Set the calculator in statistics mode (SD or STAT).
2 Enter the data in the same way as for finding the arithmetic mean (see page 223).

The symbol σ (the Greek lower case letter sigma) is often used for standard deviation.

3 You can now obtain the standard deviation using the key marked σ_n, $x\sigma_n$ or s. You will probably need to use the INV/SHIFT or KOUT keys to access this.

Note You will also have a key marked σ_{n-1}, $x\sigma_{n-1}$ or σ. This gives a quantity closely related to the standard deviation of your data set but which you will not need unless you study statistics in greater depth.

Some calculators have other procedures for finding standard deviation. If yours is one, you should consult your instruction manual or your tutor.

Interpreting standard deviation
Standard deviation is the most widely used measure of dispersion because it makes the fullest use of the available data and gives a very clear impression of the distribution in most cases.
Most distributions have a fairly symmetrical shape, with most of the data items near the mean and a few further away on each side. The standard deviation tells us how many data items to expect in various regions:

Approximately $\frac{2}{3}$ of the distribution lies in the interval

Mean $\pm$ 1 SD

• Approximately two thirds of the data items can be expected to fall within one standard deviation of the mean.
• Approximately 95% of the data items can be expected to fall within two standard deviations of the mean.

Approximately 95% of the distribution lies in the interval

Mean ± 2 SD

Approximately 99% of the distribution lies in the interval

Mean ± 3 SD

● Almost all the data items will fall within three standard deviations of the mean. A value which is more than three standard deviations from the mean is such a rare event that we would suspect that either the data was wrongly recorded or that the nature of the data had changed.

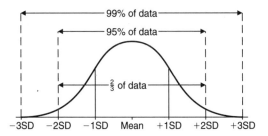

EXERCISE D9

1 Alma and Bernice recorded the distance in miles that they travelled per day in their cars for a period of 20 days. The results were:

Alma	28, 37, 34, 23, 29, 40, 36, 45, 27, 30, 33, 42, 49, 44, 36, 29, 31, 22, 38, 47
Bernice	16, 12, 34, 56, 28, 62, 32, 18, 36, 54, 27, 20, 51, 69, 43, 37, 34, 38, 29, 46

For each of these sets of data find   **a** the mean,   **b** the range,   and **c** the standard deviation. Use your results to compare the two sets of data.

2 To compare two types of golf ball, a golfer hit 80 drives with balls of each type and recorded the distance in metres which each ball travelled. The results are shown in the table.

Distance (nearest metre)	100–119	120–139	140–159	160–179	180–199	200–219	220–239
Number of shots (ball A)	0	7	15	23	19	10	6
Number of shots (ball B)	8	14	15	20	12	11	0

a Draw cumulative frequency graphs for the two sets of data. From your graphs estimate   **i** the median,   **ii** the lower quartile,   **iii** the upper quartile, and   **iv** the interquartile range.

b Draw a box-and-whisker diagram to compare the data for the two types of ball.

3 Calculate estimates of the mean and standard deviation of the data for the two types of ball in question 2. Comment on what they show about the performances of each type.

4 A manufacturer claims that its brand of light bulb will last for an average of 500 hours with a standard deviation of 28 hours.

a Explain why you would be justified in complaining that a bulb which only lasted 410 hours was faulty.

b A consumer watchdog organisation tested 10 bulbs and obtained lifetimes of

510, 452, 470, 526, 543, 578, 430, 508, 520, 544

The organisation decide to complain to the manufacturer that their bulbs are not as consistent in quality as their claim suggests. Explain why the organisation came to this conclusion.

D 08 Correlation

Scatter graphs

To study the relationship between two sets of data, we can plot their corresponding values on one graph. The result is called a **scatter graph**.

EXAMPLE 1

Class 5AM took tests in both French and German after studying both subjects for exactly four terms. The results are given below

Student	French	German
Simon Ambrosi	67	52
Pat Langley	76	56
Jake Lepegg	78	72
Nadim Mohamed	93	84
Neville Norris	65	43
Sally O'Brien	61	78
Megan Seymour	56	67
Marilyn Thompson	38	34
Walter Vernon	54	62
Lotti Williams	72	77
Brendan Zorbb	84	84

Plot this information on a scatter graph.

The point marked with a cross is the point showing the scores of Lotti Williams: French 72, German 77

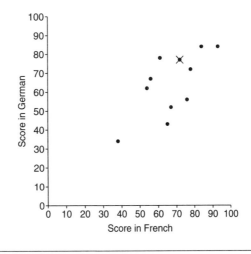

Line of best fit

The line of best fit might not pass through **any** of the points on the scatter graph and it doesn't have to.

The idea is to draw a line which shows the general location of all the points.

Drawing the line of best fit
• Draw it through the point plotted to show the mean of each set of data
• Does it represent the pattern of points on the scatter graph?
• Are there roughly the same number of points on each side of the line?

After plotting data as points on a scatter graph, we can see how the two sets of data might be related. It is possible that the relationship is **linear**, that is, one which can be represented by straight line. It is unlikely that the points will lie exactly in a straight line so we draw the **line of best fit**. This is done 'by eye', trying to get the best straight line which represents the trend of the pattern seen in the points.

There is no right or wrong answer to drawing the line like this, since not everyone will judge the best position of the line to be in the same place. There are statistical techniques for calculating this line which are not within the scope of this book. Whichever method you use, the line should pass through the point representing the mean of each set of data. You should always calculate the mean of each set of data and include this point on your scatter graph before drawing the line of best fit through it.

EXAMPLE 2

Draw the line of best fit to represent the data in the example on page 229.

Calculate the mean of the French results.

   Total = 744   Mean = 744 ÷ 11 = 68 to nearest whole number

Calculate the mean of the German results.

   Total = 709   Mean = 709 ÷ 11 = 64 to nearest whole number

Plot this point on the scatter graph and draw the line of best fit through it by eye.

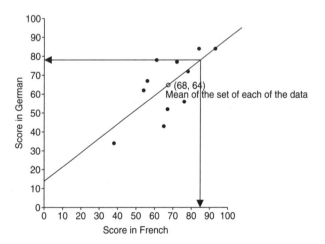

Once we have a line of best fit, we can use it to obtain estimates within the data.

For example, Sue Palfrey scored 85 in the French test but missed the German test due to illness. Use the line of best fit to estimate Sue's score in German.

The estimate of Sue's German score from the line of best fit is 78.

It is important to realise that the estimate is based on the rest of the data and not Sue's ability in German.

Calculating the equation of the line of best fit

The line of best fit is a straight line and, as with all straight lines, will have an equation of the form $y = mx + c$. The gradient of the line is given by the value of m, and c is the point at which the line crosses the vertical axis (y-axis).

Calculating the gradient

Choose two points **on the line** of best fit.

You must be wary of choosing any points plotted on the scatter diagram, even if it looks as though your line of best fit goes through them.

You can always use the point which is plotted at the mean value of each set of data because this point is always on the line.

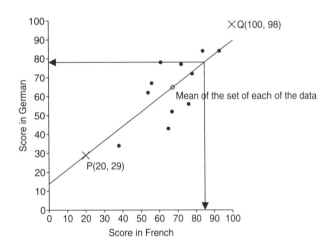

In this case, we have P(20, 29) and Q(100, 89).

$$\text{Gradient} = \frac{\text{Difference in the } y\text{-coordinates}}{\text{Difference in the } x\text{-coordinates}} = \frac{89 - 29}{100 - 20}$$

$$= 0.75$$

You can make some of the calculation easier by choosing two points whose x-coordinates are whole numbers and therefore their difference is a whole number.

The intercept can be read off the vertical axis if the point (0, 0) is the origin of your graph. This is not always the case and often is not necessary, particularly if there are no points near (0, 0) to be plotted. It is always better to **calculate the intercept**. (If it **can** be read off, it is a good check of your other calculations.)

Choose one of the points on the line, in this case P.

Substitute the values of x, y and m into $y = mx + c$, to give

$$29 = 0.75 \times 20 + c$$

$$\Rightarrow \quad c = 29 - 15$$

$$c = 14$$

Once we have the equation of the line, we can use it instead of the graph to find any estimates within the data.

The equation of the line of best fit is $y = 0.75x + 14$

The estimate of Sue Palfrey's German score can now be **calculated** to be

$$0.75 \times 85 + 14 = 77.75 \quad \text{or} \quad 78 \text{ to the nearest whole number}$$

EXERCISE D10

For each of the following sets of data

a plot the data on a scatter graph

b calculate the mean of each set of data and plot this point on the scatter graph

c draw the line of best fit through this point

d calculate the equation of the line of best fit.

1 An experiment was carried out to see whether the distance a discus was thrown by Year 10 boys was related to their height. The results were

Height, x	123	126	131	137	146	157	159	164	165	167
Distance, y	44	39	53	54	26	55	57	61	62	66

e Estimate the distance which a Year 10 boy who is 150 cm tall could throw the discus.

2 A hospital carried out research amongst its patients, comparing the number of years they had smoked to the percentage of tissue damage to their lungs. The results are given below.

Years smoked, x	8	16	21	28	32	35	38	40	47
Damaged %, y	11	31	49	55	59	63	69	72	78

e Estimate the number of years smoking which would show 50% damage to the lungs.

3 In a survey of population density, the number of people on the electoral register whose postal address was within a suburb was recorded with the distance of that suburb from the city centre. The results are given below.

Thousands of people, x	53	12	67	23	45	37	41	19
Distance in km, y	0.8	4.1	1.6	3.6	2.3	2.8	1.3	3.1

e Estimate the distance from the city centre that a suburb of 30 000 residents might be.

Correlation

Correlation is the term used to describe how well the points on a scatter graph will be represented by a line. When the points are all close to a line, there is **high correlation** between the variables. The more scattered the points are, the lower is the degree of correlation. When the points are so scattered that it would not be sensible to try to fit them to a line, there is no correlation at all.

When **both variables are increasing** as the points are plotted, the line of best fit will slope up from left to right and its gradient will be **positive**. The correlation between the variables is **positive** to some degree.

Using the line of best fit to estimate an unknown quantity **within the range of values plotted on the scatter graph** is accepted practice. This is called **interpolation**.

It is very **unreliable** to use the estimates 'predicted' by the line of best fit **outside of the range of values** used to produce the line in the first place. This is called **extrapolation**.

The degree of correlation depends on how closely the points follow the line. The 'closeness' can be measured and given a value but the mathematics of this is beyond the scope of this book.

When **one variable increases as the other decreases**, the line of best fit will slope down from left to right and its gradient will be **negative**. The correlation between the variables is **negative** to some degree.

We talk of 'high' and 'low' degrees of correlation depending on how closely points fit with the line.

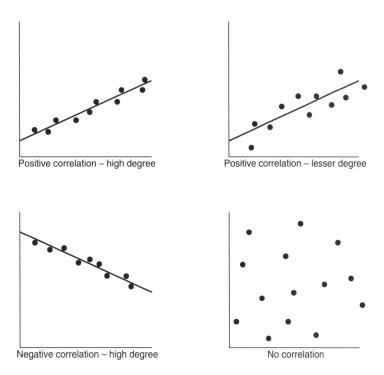

Positive correlation – high degree

Positive correlation – lesser degree

Negative correlation – high degree

No correlation

EXERCISE D11

Describe the correlation between the variables in each of the questions in Exercise D10.

D 09 Estimating probability

Outcomes and events

An experiment can have several possible **outcomes**.

An outcome is a single, separate result which does not overlap with other results.

For example, if we are studying eggs produced on a farm, the outcomes of examining an individual egg might be

small white	medium white	large white
small brown	medium brown	large brown

Notice that no egg could fall into more than one category.

An **event** is a set of one or more outcomes.

For example,

brown egg	contains 3 of the outcomes listed
large egg	contains 2 of the outcomes listed.

An **outcome** is a single, separate result that does not overlap with any other outcome.

Given a list of outcomes, a result could not belong to more than one category in the list.

An **event** is a set of one or more outcomes.

What is probability?

When a situation has several possible outcomes, we cannot be sure which will occur.

We use words such as **probability**, **chance**, **likelihood** and **risk** to describe how rare or common an outcome is.

If we repeat an experiment a large number of times, an outcome or event which is

- impossible   will never happen
- unlikely   will not happen very often
- likely   will happen more often
- certain   will happen every time

We use a **probability scale** from **0 to 1** (or **0% to 100%**) to give a value to how likely an outcome or event is.

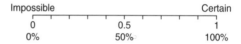

Events that are unlikely will have probabilities towards the left-hand end of the scale. More likely events have probabilities towards the right-hand end.

If we expect that, on average, an event will occur seven times out of ten, the expected probability of the event happening will be

$$\frac{7}{10} \quad \text{or} \quad 0.7 \quad \text{or} \quad 70\%$$

Estimating probability

There are many events for which you have an idea from your own experience of how likely they are to happen. For example,

How likely is it to rain tomorrow?
How likely is it that a tossed coin will come down heads?
How likely is it that a hot drink you make tomorrow will be made incorrectly?
How likely is it that the next traffic light you come to will be red?

In most places in Britain, there are more dry days than wet ones and so the answer to the first question will be a probability of less than 0.5. Say 0.3.

You can be more sure about the second question. The coin can only come down heads or tails and, if it is not biased, you will expect an equal number of each. This probability is 0.5.

If you often make hot drinks, you get into habits and make them without thinking. You are unlikely to make a mistake and so this probability is going to be close to 0.

The terms **probability**
           chance
           likelihood
           risk

are all used to talk about how rare or common an event or outcome is.

Event is	Probability
Impossible	**0 or 0%**
Certain	**1 or 100%**

It will depend where that traffic light is situated. At the junction of a major road with a minor road, the light on the major road will show green for longer than that on the minor road. If you are on the main road, you would expect a probability of less than 0.5. If you were on the minor road, you would expect a probability of greater than 0.5. If both roads have green for the same length of time, there still has to be time for traffic to cross after the green light changes and so there is more red than green. This probability will be greater than 0.5 – say 0.7.

You can give a better estimate of the probability of an event by keeping a check yourself on how many times something happens and how many times you test it. For example, as you travel by road, how many times do you meet a traffic light? How often is it at red?

At this level, all you need is a rough estimate of the figures.

EXERCISE D12

1 A bag contains 3 red sweets (strawberry, raspberry and cherry), 2 green (lime and kiwi) and 1 orange. Joanna selects two without looking.

   a List all the possible outcomes.

   b List the outcomes which make up the event 'both sweets are flavoured with fruits that do not have stones or hard pips'.

2 Estimate the probability of the following events.

   a The next vehicle to pass you will be a bus.

   b The number plate of the next car to pass you will have a 3 on it.

   c Given a group of 30 friends, two of them will share a birthday.

Relative frequency

In order to obtain a better estimate of probability, we need to gather information.

In a survey of the transport methods used by 24 college students, the results were: 12 travelled by bus, 6 by car, 4 cycled and 2 walked.

$$\text{The proportion of students travelling by car to college} = \frac{6}{24} = 0.25 \text{ (or 25\%)}$$

This is called the **relative frequency**.

$$\text{Relative} \atop \text{frequency} = \frac{\text{Frequency of the event}}{\text{Total sample size}}$$

$$\textbf{Relative frequency} = \frac{\textbf{Frequency of the event}}{\textbf{Total sample size}}$$

The relative frequency of an event provides an estimate of the probability. Note that:

- It is only an estimate.
- A larger sample size would provide a more reliable estimate.

EXAMPLE 1

A group of 40 students were asked where they ate lunch. The responses were as follows:

12 brought packed lunch   12 used the college snack bar
8 ate outside college   5 did not eat lunch
3 went home for lunch.

Estimate the probability that a student, chosen at random, would use the college snack bar for lunch.

$$\text{Relative frequency} = \frac{\text{Frequency of the event}}{\text{Total sample size}}$$

$$= \frac{12}{40} = 0.3 \text{ (or 30\%)}$$

EXERCISE D13

1 In the survey about student transport, above, estimate the probability that a student, chosen at random, will travel   **a** by bus, **b** by cycle, **c** on foot.

2 From the survey of students eating habits, estimate the probability that a student, chosen at random, will eat   **a** packed lunch, **b** outside college, **c** at home.

3 Tree seeds are very difficult to germinate. In a conservation project, 500 seeds were planted and only 32 produced shoots.

   a Estimate the probability that a randomly chosen seed will germinate.

   b The project needs 200 saplings. How many seeds should be planted to ensure that they have enough?

D 10 Calculating probability

Equally likely outcomes

A set of outcomes are **equally likely** if each has the same probability of occuring.

When we have a set of equally likely outcomes, we can calculate the **theoretical probability** of an event occuring.

If a situation has n equally likely outcomes, the probability of each outcome is $\frac{1}{n}$.

If a situation has n equally likely outcomes, the probability of each outcome is $\frac{1}{n}$

EXAMPLE 1

Each of 5 cards has a different picture drawn on it. The pictures are a tennis ball, a football, a rugby ball, a squash ball and a basketball. The cards are shuffled and one is chosen at random. What is the probability that the selected card shows a football?

If the 5 cards are all identical in size and shape, then each is equally likely to be chosen. The probability that the football card is chosen is therefore $\frac{1}{5}$.

EXAMPLE 2

Five toy building bricks, all the same size, are put into a bag. There are 3 red ones and 2 white ones. John wrote his name on one of the red bricks. One is selected at random. What is the probability of selecting **a** the brick with John's name on it, **b** a red brick?

a Since there are 5 bricks, each has a probability of being selected of $\frac{1}{5}$.

b Since there are 3 red bricks, the probability of selecting one of them is $\frac{3}{5}$

In **b**, each of the red bricks constitutes an outcome. Collectively, they constitute an **event** consisting of 3 equally likely outcomes.

$$\text{Probability of an event} = \frac{\text{Number of outcomes in the event}}{\text{Total number of possible outcomes}}$$

or

$$\text{Probability of an event} = \frac{\text{Number of possible successful outcomes}}{\text{Total number of possible outcomes}}$$

Notation

The **possibility space** is the set of all possible outcomes.

If   S   is the **set of all possible outcomes**
           (called the **possibility space**)
      R   is the **desired event** (a collection of desired outcomes)

      $n(R)$ is the **number of outcomes in the event R**
      $n(S)$ is the **number of outcomes in S**

and $P(R)$ is the **probability of event R**

$P(R) = \dfrac{n(R)}{n(S)}$

then $P(R) = \dfrac{n(R)}{n(S)}$

EXAMPLE 3

A digit is picked at random from all the digits, 0 to 9. Find the probability that it is a prime number.

The set of all possible outcomes $S = \{0, 1, 2, 3, 4, 5, 6, 7, 8, 9\}$
If A is the event 'prime number' $A = \{2, 3, 5, 7\}$

Then $n(S) = 10$ and $n(A) = 4$

So $P(A) = \dfrac{n(A)}{n(S)} = \dfrac{4}{10} = 0.4$

EXERCISE D14

1 A pack of cards is shuffled and one card is dealt at random. Find the probability that the card

   a shows a number less than 7

   b is a picture card

   c is a black card.

2 A letter is picked at random from the word MISSISSIPPI. Find the probability that it is   **a** I,   **b** P,   **c** T.

3 Three red balls, five blue and two green are placed in a bag. A ball is picked at random. Find the probability that it is   **a** a blue ball,   **b** a green ball, **c** a red ball.
A blue ball is selected from the bag and not replaced. Then a second ball is selected from the bag. Find the probability that it is   **d** a blue ball, **e** a green ball,   **f** a red ball.

4 Thirty balls, numbered 1–30, are placed in a bag and one is chosen at random. Find the probability that the chosen ball has a prime number written on it.

Conditional probability

A **conditional probability** is based on a restricted part of the sample. This part is defined by the condition placed upon it.

When only part of a sample is used to estimate a probability, what we have is a **conditional probability**. We place a condition upon which part of the sample we are interested in.

EXAMPLE 4

A survey of sporting preferences produced the results shown in the table.

	Prefer		
	Outdoor sports	Indoor sports	Totals
Boys	25	15	40
Girls	18	12	30
Totals	43	27	70

Estimate the following probabilities.

a A student will prefer indoor sports to outdoor sports.

b A boy, chosen at random, will prefer outdoor sports to indoor.

c A girl, chosen at random, will prefer indoor sports to outdoor.

a Of all 70 students, 27 prefer indoor sports.

Probability $= \dfrac{27}{70} = 0.386$ (or 38.6%)

b Of all 40 **boys**, 25 prefer outdoor sports.

Probability $= \dfrac{25}{40} = 0.625$ (or 62.5%)

c Of all 30 **girls**, 12 prefer indoor sports.

Probability $= \dfrac{12}{30} = 0.3$ (or 30%)

In this example, **b** and **c** are conditional probabilities since they are based upon a restricted part of the sample.

Expected frequencies

Expected frequency = Probability × Sample size

If we have an estimate of the probability of an event, we can use it to predict what will happen in a given situation (see Exercise D13, question 3b, page 236).

Expected frequency = Probability × Sample size

EXAMPLE 5

A manufacturer of cat food has a promotion in which a voucher is printed on the back of the label. They claim that there is a 40% chance of getting a 10 p voucher and a 5% chance of getting a £1 voucher. Approximately how much would be won if 40 tins of cat food were bought?

Expected frequency of 10 p vouchers $= 0.4 \times 40 = 16$
Expected frequency of £1 vouchers $= 0.05 \times 40 = 2$

Value of expected 10 p vouchers $= 16 \times 10\,\text{p} = £1.60$
Value of expected £1 vouchers $= 2 \times £1 = £2.00$

Total expected receipts $= £3.60$

EXERCISE D15

1 In a holiday survey, people were asked where they went and how they got there. The results are shown in the table.

	Rail	Road	Air	Ferry	Totals
UK	15	45	0	0	60
Europe	0	0	60	40	100
USA	0	0	20	0	20
Other	0	0	30	0	30
Totals	15	45	110	40	200

a Estimate the probability that a person chosen at random and holidaying in Europe will travel by ferry.

b Estimate the probability that a person chosen at random, holidaying in UK will travel by road.

c Estimate the probability that a person chosen at random, travelling by air will have their holiday in the USA.

d Estimate the probability that a person chosen at random will be having a holiday other than in UK, Europe or USA.

e Estimate the probability that a person chosen at random will be travelling by air for a holiday in Europe.

2 When a die is thrown, the probability of getting a six is one-sixth. How many sixes would you expect to get if you threw the die 80 times?

3 An opinion poll shows that the probability of a voter voting Labour is 48%, Conservative is 23%, and Liberal Democrat is 21%. In an election, 8000 people voted. How many votes would you expect each party to get?

4 A pack of cards consists of the following:

	Hearts	Clubs	Diamonds	Spades	Total
Picture cards	3	3	3	3	12
Plain cards	10	10	10	10	40
Total	13	13	13	13	52

a Calculate the probability that if a heart is chosen then it will be a picture card.

b Calculate the probability that if a picture card is chosen than it will be a heart.

c Calculate the probability that if a card is chosen at random then it will be a plain card.

d Calculate the probability that if a card is chosen at random then it will be a red card (hearts or diamonds).

Multiple component outcomes

Some outcomes have more than one component. This happens, for instance, when you toss two dice. The outcome consists of two values, one value from each die. We may even choose to combine these together in some way, for example, to add them or find their difference.

Listing outcomes in a table

When a test consists of two items, the results can be shown in a table. The table shows the possibility space for two dice but any two-item possibility space can be shown in a similar way.

If you wish to combine the two components in any way – perhaps by adding them – you can fill in the table with the sums of the two dice.

A two-item possibility space

	Second die					
First die	1	2	3	4	5	6
1						
2						
3						
4						
5						
6						

If three or more items are required for an outcome, a two-dimensional table like this is no help.

	Second die					
First die	1	2	3	4	5	6
1						
2						
3						
4						
5						
6						

EXAMPLE 6

A cubic die (6 sides) is thrown with a tetrahedral die (4 sides) and the scores are added. Find the probability that the total is **a** even, **b** 7 or more.

You could construct a three-item table by making layers, each layer representing a different value in the third item.

Be very systematic about how you list the possibilities when you have more than two items.

Step 1
Draw up a table showing the possibility space

Step 2
Fill in the table with the required information

		Cubic die					
		1	2	3	4	5	6
Tetrahedral die	1	2	3	4	5	6	7
	2	3	4	5	6	7	8
	3	4	5	6	7	8	9
	4	5	6	7	8	9	10

a

Step 3
Select the relevant elements in the table

Step 4
Do the calculations

$$P\,(\text{even}) = \frac{12}{24} = 0.5$$

		Cubic die					
		1	2	3	4	5	6
Tetrahedral die	1	2	3	4	5	6	7
	2	3	4	5	6	7	8
	3	4	5	6	7	8	9
	4	5	6	7	8	9	10

b

Step 3
Select the relevant elements in the table

Step 4
Do the calculations

$$P\,(\text{even}) = \frac{10}{24} = 0.42$$

		Cubic die					
		1	2	3	4	5	6
Tetrahedral die	1	2	3	4	5	6	7
	2	3	4	5	6	7	8
	3	4	5	6	7	8	9
	4	5	6	7	8	9	10

EXERCISE D16

1 I throw a cubic die and toss a coin.
  a Construct a possibility space table for this situation.
  b What is the probability of getting a head and an even score on the die?

2 Two coins are tossed.
  a Construct a possibility space table for this situation.
  b What is the probability of getting two heads?
  c What is the probability of getting one head and one tail?
  d What is the probability of getting three tails?

3 Two cubic dice are thrown.
  a Construct a possibility space table for this.
  b Find the probability of throwing a total of 7.
  c Find the probability of throwing a total of 6.
  d Find the probability of throwing a double.

e Find the probability of throwing either a double or a total of 7.

f Find the probability of throwing either a double or a total of 6.

g Which total is the most likely when two cubic dice are thrown?

4 Three coins are tossed. Write down all members of the possibility space. What is the probability of getting **a** three heads, **b** two heads and one tail?

5 Three boys are playing a game tossing pennies. The rules state that the odd one out wins all three pennies.

   a What is the probability of Simon winning a particular game?

   b What is the probability that there is no winner of a particular game?

6 Two cubic dice are thrown. What is the probability of throwing either a six or a total of six?

D 11 Probability for combined events: (1) Addition rules

Combining events

Ten cards are numbered 1–10. They are shuffled and one is selected at random.

Event A is 'Pick an odd number'.
Event B is 'Pick a prime number'.

The set, S, of equally likely outcomes is $\{1, 2, 3, 4, 5, 6, 7, 8, 9, 10\}$.

   $n(S) = 10$

We can illustrate the possibility space with a diagram.

This type of diagram is called **Venn diagram**

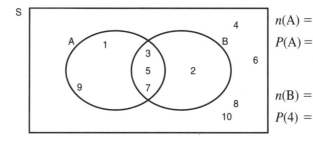

$n(A) = 5$

$P(A) = \dfrac{5}{10}$

$n(B) = 4$

$P(4) = \dfrac{4}{10}$

And, ∩
Some of the outcomes – $\{3, 5, 7\}$ – satisfy both events.

This is a new event,

   (A **and** B)   'Both an odd number **and** a prime number'

We use the symbol ∩ to represent the word **and**. We write **A ∩ B**.

(A **and** B)
(**A ∩ B**)

consists of the outcomes belonging to **both A and B**

• (**A ∩ B**) consists of the outcomes belonging to **both A and B**.

Or, ∪

We can form another event using the connective word **Or** – symbol ∪.

(**A or B**)   '**Either** an odd number **or** a prime number **or both**'

The outcomes in this event are {1, 2, 3, 5, 7, 9}.

● (**A ∪ B**) consists of the outcomes belonging to **either A or B or both**.

Not, '

We can form yet another event using the connective word **Not** – symbol '.

Not A   **A'**   **Not** an odd number'

The outcomes in this event are {2, 4, 6, 8, 10}.

● **A'** consists of those outcomes which **do not belong to A**.

We can use the notation to describe other events.

A' ∩ B means	(Not **A**) and **B**	Outcome is not an odd number but is a prime number = {2}
A' ∪ B means	(Not **A**) or **B**	Outcome is either not an odd number or is a prime number = {2, 3, 4, 5, 6, 7, 8, 10}
(**A ∪ B**)' means	Not (**A** or **B**)	Outcome is neither an odd number nor a prime number = {4, 6, 8, 10}

Side notes (left margin):

(A or B)
(A ∪ B)   consists of the outcomes belonging to **either A or B or both**

In mathematics, the term **or** includes **both**

Not A
A'   consists of the outcomes which **do not belong to A**

EXERCISE D17

1 Two cubic dice, one red and one green are thrown.
   Event A is 'The sum of the two dice is 8'.
   Event B is 'The red die shows an even number'.

   Compound events are created as follows:

a A	**b** B	**c** A ∩ B	**d** A ∪ B	**e** A'
f A' ∩ B	**g** A' ∪ B	**h** B'	**k** A ∩ B'	**m** A ∪ B'
n (A ∩ B)'	**p** (A ∪ B)'	**q** A' ∪ B'	**r** A' ∩ B'	

   i Express each of the events in words.
   ii List the outcomes satisfying each of the events.
   iii Find the probability of each of the events.

2 Chocolates are produced with cream, toffee or nut centres. Chocolates that are malformed are sold at a reduced price as seconds in gift packs of 3 chocolates. The mixing process is such that the different combinations possible in a bag are all equally likely.

   a Create a possibility space listing to show the possible contents of a bag.
      Event A is 'The three chocolates are all the same type'.
      Event B is 'The pack contains at least one cream'.

   Express each of the following combined events in symbol form and find the probability of each.

   b The pack contains all cream chocolates.

   c The pack contains three chocolates that are not all the same and includes at least one cream.

   d The pack contains no cream chocolates and they are not all the same.

   e The 3 chocolates are either not all the same or contain at least one cream.

Mutually exclusive events

Ten cards are numbered 1–10. They are shuffled and one is selected at random.

Event A is 'Pick an odd number'.

Event B is 'Pick a multiple of 4'.

The set, S, of equally likely outcomes is $\{1, 2, 3, 4, 5, 6, 7, 8, 9, 10\}$.

The Venn diagram illustrating this is shown below.

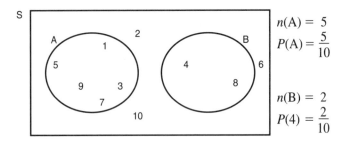

$n(A) = 5$
$P(A) = \dfrac{5}{10}$

$n(B) = 2$
$P(4) = \dfrac{2}{10}$

Mutually exclusive events cannot take place at the same time.
$n(A \cap B) = 0$

Events A and B have **no outcomes in common**. They cannot both take place at the same time. Events like this are called **mutually exclusive**.

- The event A ∩ B **contains no members** so $n(A \cap B) = 0$.

Exhaustive events

Event A is 'Pick a number less than 8'.

Event B is 'Pick a number greater than 4'.

The set, S, of equally likely outcomes is $\{1, 2, 3, 4, 5, 6, 7, 8, 9, 10\}$.

The Venn diagram illustrating this is shown below.

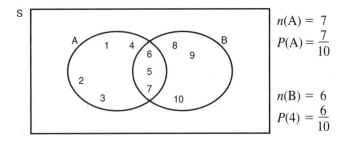

$n(A) = 7$
$P(A) = \dfrac{7}{10}$

$n(B) = 6$
$P(4) = \dfrac{6}{10}$

Events A and B are **exhaustive** if **at least one of them must happen.**
$A \cup B = S$

Events A and B contain all possible outcomes. One or both of them must happen. Events like this are called **exhaustive**.

- The event A ∪ B **contains all members** so A ∪ B = S.

Probabilities for mutually exclusive events

In the first example opposite, $n(A) = 5$ and $n(B) = 2$.
Also $n(A \cup B) = 7$.

These events were mutually exclusive.

For **mutually exclusive events**, A and B

$$n(A \cup B) = n(A) + n(B)$$

Also, since $P(A) = \dfrac{n(A)}{n(S)}$

$$P(A \cup B) = P(A) + P(B)$$

Note: this is **only true** when A and B are **mutually exclusive**.

For mutually exclusive
events, A and B

$n(A \cup B) = n(A) + n(B)$

and

$P(A \cup B) = P(A) + P(B)$

Probabilities for exhaustive events

If events A and B are exhaustive, then $A \cup B = S$.

So, for **exhaustive events** $n(A \cup B) = n(S)$

Also, since $P(A) = \dfrac{n(A)}{n(S)}$ $P(A \cup B) = P(S) = 1$

Note; this is **only true** when A and B are **exhaustive**.

For exhaustive events, A and
B

$n(A \cup B) = n(S)$

and

$P(A \cup B) = P(S) = 1$

Events which are both mutually exclusive and exhaustive

When two (or more) events are both mutually exclusive and exhaustive, we can combine these results to give

$$P(A \cup B) = P(A) + P(B) = 1$$

• **When a set of events are both mutually exclusive and exhaustive their total probability is 1.**

When a set of events are
both **mutually exclusive**
and **exhaustive** their
total probability = 1

Probability of A′

Event A and event not A (A′) are both mutually exclusive and exhaustive and so

$$P(A) + P(A') = 1$$

or $P(A') = 1 - P(A)$

$P(A') = 1 - P(A)$

Events which overlap

The expression $P(A \cup B) = P(A) + P(B)$ only applies when the events A and B are mutually exclusive. In the example of the ten cards.

> Event A is 'Pick an odd number'.
> Event B is 'Pick a prime number'.

The events A and B do overlap.

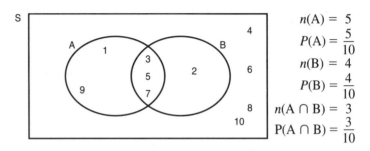

$$n(A) = 5$$
$$P(A) = \frac{5}{10}$$
$$n(B) = 4$$
$$P(B) = \frac{4}{10}$$
$$n(A \cap B) = 3$$
$$P(A \cap B) = \frac{3}{10}$$

In order to find $P(A \cup B)$, we first need to find $n(A \cup B)$. The expression for this is

$$n(A \cup B) = n(A) + n(B) - n(A \cap B)$$

The correction factor $-n(A \cap B)$ is introduced because when we find $n(A) + n(B)$, we count the overlapping section, $n(A \cap B)$, twice.

From this, dividing by $n(S)$ gives

$$P(A \cup B) = P(A) + P(B) - P(A \cap B)$$

EXERCISE D18

1 Two cubic dice are thrown. Three events are defined.
Event A is 'The scores on the dice are equal'.
Event B is 'The sum of the scores on the dice is 7'.
Event C is 'The sum of the scores on the dice is 6'.

Find the following probabilities:

  a $P(A)$ **b** $P(B)$ **c** $P(C)$ **d** $P(A \cap B)$

  e $P(A \cup B)$ **f** $P(A \cap C)$ **g** $P(A \cup C)$ **h** $P(B \cap C)$

  k Show from the results above that $P(A \cup B) = P(A) + P(B)$.

  m Why is $P(A \cup C)$ not equal to $P(A) + P(C)$?

2 The college snack bar offers three potato options to accompany the main choices for lunch. The probability that a student will choose chips is 0.42, baked potatoes 0.28, and creamed 0.18.

Find the probability that a student will

  a order either chips or baked potato

  b not order creamed potato

  c not order potato.

3 When I am feeling peckish in the evening, the probability that I eat some crisps is 0.3. The probability that I eat some cheese on biscuits is 0.5. The probability that I eat both is 0.1.

When events overlap

$$P(A \cup B) =$$
$$P(A) + P(B) - P(A \cap B)$$

When events are mutually exclusive

$$P(A \cap B) = 0$$

and the formula becomes the same as that for the mutually exclusive case.

Use the above information to define two events.
Express the following compound events in terms of the single events you have defined and find the probability of each.

a I have crisps but no cheese.

b I have cheese but no crisps.

c I have crisps or cheese or both.

d I have neither crisps nor cheese.

4 Use the Venn diagram and the results from question 2 to show that

  a $P(A \cap B)' = P(A' \cup B')$ 　　　　 **b** $P(A \cup B)' = P(A' \cap B')$

5 Of the students on a PE course, there is a probability of 75% that a student chosen at random will wish to specialise in football and a probability of 57% that a student chosen at random will wish to specialise in cricket. If there is a probability of 49% that a student chosen at random will wish to specialise in both sports, what is the probability that a student will wish to specialise in neither?

6 After a visit to a safari park, a group of children were asked which of three areas they enjoyed. The probability that a child, chosen at random, would enjoy a particular area was

didn't like any	2%
monkeys, big cats and grazing animals	4%
monkeys and big cats	5%
big cats and grazing animals	17%
monkeys and grazing animals	11%
grazing animals but not big cats nor monkeys	18%
monkeys but not big cats nor grazing animals	30%

What is the probability that a child, chosen at random, would enjoy

a big cats but not grazing animals nor monkeys

b big cats

c monkeys?

D 12 Probability for combined events: (2) Multiplication rules

Dependency

Events A and B are **dependent** when the probability of one event **changes according to whether or not the other event has happened.**

We met this example of sporting preferences before.

Event A is 'subject prefers outdoor sports'.
Event B is 'subject is a boy'.

	Prefer		
	Outdoor sports	**Indoor sports**	**Totals**
Boys	25	15	40
Girls	18	12	30
Totals	43	27	70

> Events A and B are **dependent** when the probability of one event **changes according to whether or not the other event has happened.**

The conditional probability

P(A given B) is usually written

$$P(A|B)$$

We know that $P(A) = \dfrac{43}{70} = 0.614$ and $P(B) = \dfrac{40}{70} = 0.571$

Also $P(A \text{ given } B) = \dfrac{25}{40} = 0.625$

and $P(A \text{ given } B') = \dfrac{18}{30} = 0.6$

Clearly, the three results $P(A)$, $P(A|B)$ and $P(A|B')$ are all different. The probability of A happening depends upon whether B has happened.

The events A and B are dependent events.

Events A and B are **independent** when the probability of one event is not affected by whether or not the other event has happened.
When

$$P(A) = P(A|B) = P(A|B')$$

and

$$P(B) = P(B|A) = P(B|A')$$

then

Events A and B are independent

Events A and B are **independent** when the probability of one event is **not affected by whether or not the other event has happened**.

When

$$\mathbf{P(A) = P(A|B) = P(A|B')}$$

and

$$\mathbf{P(B) = P(B|A) = P(B|A')}$$

then

Events A and B are independent

If A and B are **independent events** composed of **equally likely** outcomes, then

$$n(A \cap B) = n(A) \times n(B)$$

and

$$P(A \cap B) = P(A) \times P(B)$$

Note that $P(A)$ and $P(B)$ are both less than 1. When they are multiplied together, the result will be **smaller** than either of them.

Suppose we toss two dice, one cubic and red, the other tetrahedral and green, and

Event A is 'The red score is 3 or more'.
Event B is 'The green score is 3 or less'.

Then these two events are independent. The possibility space is as shown.

Since there are 6 possibilities for the cubic die and 4 for the tetrahedral die, there $6 \times 4 = 24$ possible equally likely pairs of values in the possibility space.

		Cubic die					
		1	2	3	4	5	6
Tetrahedral die	1	1,1	2,1	3,1	4,1	5,1	6,1
	2	1,2	2,2	3,2	4,2	5,2	6,2
	3	1,3	2,3	3,3	4,3	5,3	6,3
	4	1,4	2,4	3,4	4,4	5,4	6,4

Since $n(A) = 4$ and $n(B) = 3$, there must be $4 \times 3 = 12$ pairs satisfying the event $(A \cap B)$. That is

$$n(A \cap B) = n(A) \times n(B).$$

Also

$$P(A \cap B) = \frac{n(A \cap B)}{n(S)} = \frac{4 \times 3}{6 \times 4} = \left(\frac{4}{6}\right) \times \left(\frac{3}{4}\right) = \frac{12}{24}$$

So $P(A \cap B) = P(A) \times P(B)$

EXAMPLE 1

For breakfast, I have something to eat and something to drink. The probability that I choose cereal to eat is 0.25. The probability that I choose coffee to drink is 0.2. What is the probability that I have both cereal and coffee for breakfast?

Event A is 'I choose cereal', and $P(A) = 0.25$
Event B is 'I choose coffee', and $P(B) = 0.2$

Provided that the **choices of food and drink are independent**, then

$P(A \cap B) = 0.25 \times 0.2 = 0.05$

EXAMPLE 2

Three coins are tossed. What is probability that there are two heads and one tail?

Event A is 'The first coin shows a head', so $P(A) = 0.5$
Event B is 'The second coin shows a head', so $P(B) = 0.5$
Event C is 'The third coin shows a tail', so $P(C) = 0.5$

These events are independent and so

$$P(A \cap B \cap C) = P(A) \times P(B) \times P(C)$$
$$= 0.5 \times 0.5 \times 0.5$$
$$= 0.125$$

However, the combination '2 heads and 1 tail' could be achieved not only in the order HHT, but also as HTH or THH.

$P(A \cap B' \cap C') = 0.125$ $P(A' \cap B \cap C') = 0.125$

The events HHT, HTH and THH are mutually exclusive and so the probabilities must be added.

$$P[(A \cap B \cap C) \cup (A \cap B' \cap C') \cup (A' \cap B \cap C')]$$
$$=\quad 0.125 \quad + \quad 0.125 \quad + \quad 0.125$$
$$= 0.375$$

EXERCISE D19

1 Which of the following pairs of events are independent?

Trial   Two dice are thrown
a Event A: A score of 3 on the first die.
Event B: A score of 5 on the second die.

b Event A: A score of 1 on the first die.
Event B: A total of 7 on the two dice.

c Event A: A score of 2 on the first die.
Event B: A score of 8 on the two dice.

d Trial   A car is chosen at random on a motorway.
Event A: The car is exceeding the speed limit.
Event B: The car has an engine capacity greater than $1800 \, \text{cm}^3$.

2 In an examination, the probability that a student will forget to take a ruler is 0.08, and the probability that he/she will forget to take a calculator is 0.03. Assuming that these are independent events, find the probability that a student, chosen at random, will

   a forget to take both ruler and calculator

   b forget to take the ruler but remember the calculator

   c remember to take both ruler and calculator.

3 A card is drawn from a standard pack and a cubic die is thrown. Find the probability that the combination is

   a a picture card and an even number

   b a red card and a prime number.

4 A bag, A, contains 3 red, 2 green and 1 white balls. A second bag, B, contains 2 red, 5 green and 2 white balls. A ball is selected at random from each bag. Find the probability that

   a they are both white

   b they are both red

   c one is red and one is green.

5 A football game is played by throwing two cubic dice, a red one for the home team and a green one for the visiting team. The red die is numbered 0, 1, 1, 2, 2, 3 while the green die is numbered 0, 0, 1, 1, 2, 3.
Find the probability that

   a the home team will win

   b the game will be drawn

   c the visiting team will be victorious.

Albion Rovers play two games against Benchwood Athletic, one at home and one away. Find the probability that

   d Rovers win both games

   e Rovers win one game out of two

   f Rovers gain more points from the two matches than their opponents.

Combining dependent events

Suppose we draw a coloured ball from a bag and then draw a second one without replacing the first, the contents of the bag will be different for the second draw trial from what they were in the first, and so the probabilities will have changed.

Any events defined for the two draws will be **dependent**.

EXAMPLE

Six coloured balls are placed in a bag. There are 4 red and 2 green balls. A ball is taken from the bag and not replaced. A second ball is taken from the bag. What is the probability that both balls are red?

Event A is 'The first ball is red'.
Event B is 'The second ball is red'.

What we really want in the second draw is
'The second ball is red, **given that the first ball is red**' or $P(B|A)$

Draw 1 $n(S_1) = 6$, $n(A) = 4$ giving $P(A) = \dfrac{4}{6}$

Draw 2 $n(S_2) = 5$, $n(B|A) = 3$ giving $P(B|A) = \dfrac{3}{5}$

$$P(A \cap B) = P(A) \times P(B|A)$$

$$= \frac{4}{6} \times \frac{3}{5} = \frac{2}{5}$$

For dependent events, the probability of **both events** is the **probability of the first event** multiplied by the **probability of the second event** *assuming that the first event has happened.*

When A and B are **dependent** events

$$P(A \cap B) = P(A) \times P(B|A)$$

For **dependent events** the probability of **both events** is the **probability of the first event** multiplied by the **probability of the second event** *assuming that the first event has happened.*

When A and B are **dependent** events

$$P(A \cap B) = P(A) \times P(B|A)$$

EXERCISE D20

1 If it is raining today, the probability that it will rain tomorrow is 40%. If it is dry today, the probability that it will be dry tomorrow is 50%. If it is raining today, what is the probability that only one day in the next two will be dry?

2 Three chocolates, 2 toffees and 5 boiled sweets are in a bag. Two are chosen. What is the probability that

a both are boiled sweets

b one is chocolate and the other is toffee?

D 13 Probability: Tree diagrams and using probability

Probability trees

Probability trees are useful in solving problems involving two (or more) trials, either one after the other or all at the same time. For example, mathematically, there is no difference between throwing three dice together or throwing them one after the other.

Each set of branching points represents a trial.
In this example, there are three trials and a set of final results.
Trees can be any size. This tree also has only two options at each trial. You could have a tree with more options.

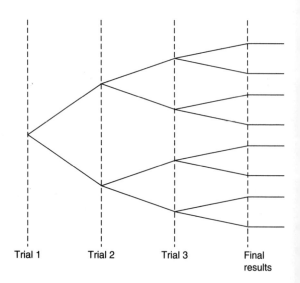

On each branch we write the probability of branching that way. These will depend upon having reached that point. We then use the probability rules to calculate the probability of reaching each possible end point. To find this, multiply together all the probabilities on the route.

EXAMPLE 1

Six coloured balls are placed in a bag. There are 4 red and 2 green balls. A ball is taken from the bag and not replaced. A second ball is taken from the bag. What is the probability that one ball of each colour is selected?

TRIAL 1
We choose the top branch to represent a red outcome and the bottom branch to represent a green outcome

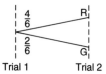

$$P(R) = \frac{4}{6} \qquad P(G) = \frac{2}{6}$$

If the ball were replaced
after noting its colour, the
probabilities for this trial
would be exactly the same
as the original ones.

TRIAL 2

If the first outcome were red, the balls remaining would be

$n(R) = 3$
$n(G) = 2$
$n(S) = 5$

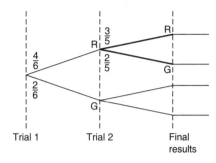

If the first outcome were green, the balls remaining would be

$n(R) = 4$
$n(G) = 1$
$n(S) = 5$

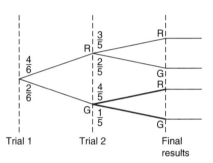

Now we can calculate the final results by multiplying, for example

$$P(R \text{ and } R) = \frac{4}{6} \times \frac{3}{5}$$

$$= \frac{12}{30}$$

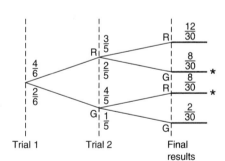

Note that the branches at
the end represent every
possible outcome. The sum
of these probabilities is 1.

The other results are calculated in a similar way.

Finally, answer the question. There are two routes that correspond to the
event 'one ball of each colour is selected' (indicated by *).

$$P(\text{one of each colour}) = \frac{8}{30} + \frac{8}{30} = \frac{16}{30} = \frac{8}{15}$$

EXAMPLE 2

Three coins are tossed. What is the probability of getting two heads and one tail?

Step 1
Draw the probability tree

Step 2
Fill in the probabilities

Step 3
Multiply to calculate the final results

Step 4
Select the required outcomes*

Step 5
Find probability by adding these together

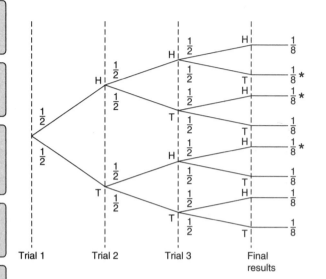

$$P(\text{Two heads and one tail}) = \frac{3}{8}$$

EXERCISE D21

1 A machine relies upon three electronic components A, B and C. The probability of a fault in A is 0.3. If A is working, the probability of a fault in B is 0.25; otherwise it is 0.6. If A and B are both working, the probability of a fault in C is 0.4; otherwise it is 0.5. The machine only works if C is working. Draw a tree diagram to represent this situation.

What is the probability that

a the machine is working

b all three components have failed

c only one component has failed?

2 Three cards are taken from a pack. What is the probability that they are

a three kings,   **b** two kings and an ace?

3 Five red, three green and two yellow balls are placed in a bag. Two balls are chosen at random without replacement. What is the probability that

a they are both red

b there is one red in the pair

c there is one green and one yellow ball in the pair?

4 On a road there are three sets of traffic lights. The probability that a set is at red or red/amber is 0.4. The probability that a set is at green is also 0.4 and the probability that a set is at amber is 0.2. I can only proceed if the light shows green. What is the probability that

a each set will be red when I arrive

b all will be green

c I will be stopped by at least one of them?

5 The letters of the word MISSISSIPPI are printed on cards, one letter to each card, and jumbled up. What is the probability that the first three letters drawn will be MIS in that order?

6 In a production process, three components, X, Y and Z, are assembled on a circuit board. It is known that the probabilities of these being fault-free are: X 95%, Y 98%, and Z 90%.
The boards are tested and if just component Y is faulty, they can be used for another purpose. What is the probability that the boards are

a completely fault-free, **b** suitable only for this second purpose?

7 A student oversleeps with a probability of 0.4. If he oversleeps, the probability that he is late for college is 0.7. If he does not oversleep, the probability that he is late for college is 0.3. What is the probability that he is not late for college?

D 14 Testing hypotheses

Null hypothesis (H_0) is a statement of the situation when nothing unusual is happening, written in the form 'something equals something' (in the example, $p = 0.5$). We examine the evidence to see if there are sufficient grounds for rejecting H_0.

Alternative hypothesis (H_1) is a statement of the situation if H_0 were false.

Critical region is the set of outcomes of the survey or experiment which will cause us to reject H_0.

Hypothesis testing is the process of determining whether or not some statement is true by collecting and examining data.

For example, 'Most dogs prefer Bow-Chow to other dog foods!'

To test this claim, we might give a number of dogs the choice of Bow-Chow or some other food and record the results. If p is the probability that a dog chooses Bow-Chow, we are interested in distinguishing between two situations:

- the **null hypothesis H_0**: 'each dog is equally likely to choose Bow-Chow or the other food', i.e. $p = 0.5$

- the **alternative hypothesis H_1**: 'each dog is more likely to choose Bow-Chow than the other food', i.e. $p > 0.5$.

Suppose we used 10 dogs. The number of dogs choosing Bow-Chow could be any number between 0 and 10. We need to decide which results will be sufficient to convince us that we should reject H_0 and accept H_1. These results are called the **critical region**.

Obviously 6 dogs choosing Bow-Chow would not be very convincing because this could easily happen by chance if H_0 were true. On the other hand, 9 dogs choosing Bow-Chow is quite unlikely unless they really do have a preference for it. We might decide to draw the line as follows:

								Critical region		
0	1	2	3	4	5	6	7	8	9	10
			Accept H_0						Accept H_1	

This means that unless at least 8 of the dogs choose Bow-Chow, we will not find the evidence sufficiently convincing.

There is always a chance that we will make the wrong decision as a result of the test. Even if the dogs have no preference (H_0 true) it is possible that 8 or more of them might choose the Bow-Chow purely by chance.

The probability that we mistakenly accept H_1 when in fact H_0 is true is called the **significance level** of the test. The calculation of this probability is outside the scope of this book, but for the above test is about $5\frac{1}{2}\%$.

It is usual to try to design the test so that the significance level is about 5%.

If 8 or more dogs chose Bow-Chow in the above test, we would say that the result was **significant at the $5\frac{1}{2}\%$ level**. This means that we have decided that most dogs do prefer Bow-Chow, but that there is a $5\frac{1}{2}\%$ chance that our decision is wrong.

Significance level is the probability that in rejecting H_0 we have made the wrong decision.

EXERCISE D22

1 A local politician claims that 60% of the electorate support the building of a new bypass. The local newspaper believes that it is an overestimate and sets out to test it.

   a State the null and alternative hypotheses they should use.

   They test the hypotheses by asking a random sample of 200 people for their opinions.

   b How many people would they expect to be in favour if the null hypothesis is correct?

   They set the critical region as 108 people or less in favour, which they calculate gives the test a 5% significance level. In fact, 107 people in their sample are in favour of the bypass.

   c What conclusion should they come to based on this result?

   d Explain the meaning of the 5% significance.

2 A gambler offers to sell you a coin which he says is biased so that heads are more likely than tails. You decide to test it by tossing it 4 times and accepting his claim if it gives 3 or 4 heads.

   a State the null and alternative hypotheses for this test.

   b State the critical region.

   c Calculate the probability of getting 3 or 4 heads with a fair coin.

   d If the gambler's coin gave 3 heads and you therefore accepted his claim that it was biased, what would be the significance level of the test?

   e Explain what the significance level in **d** means and give reasons why the test you carried out was not a very good one. How would you improve the test?

Answers

Exercise N1

1 a i 1, 2, 3, 4, 6, 9, 12, 18, 36
    ii 1, 2, 3, 4, 5, 6, 10, 12, 15, 20, 30, 60
    iii 1, 2, 4, 5, 8, 10, 16, 20, 40, 80
    iv 1, 3, 5, 15, 25, 75
    v 1, 2, 3, 4, 6, 8, 12, 16, 24, 32, 48, 96
    vi 1, 2, 3, 6, 7, 14, 21, 42
b 1, 2, 3, 4, 6, 12   **c** 12

2 14

3 a prime   **b** neither   **c** square
    d square   **e** neither   **f** prime

4 a $2^2 \times 3^2$ **b** $2 \times 3^2 \times 5$
    c $2^6 \times 3 \times 5^2$

5 a 72   **b** 98 000

6 a i 3, 6, 9, 12, 15, 18, 21, 24
    ii 9, 18, 27, 36, 45, 54, 63, 72
    iii 10, 20, 30, 40, 50, 60, 70, 80
    iv 15, 30, 45, 60, 75, 90, 105, 120
    b 30, 60, 90, 120, 150, 180, 210, 240
    c 30

7 a 126   **b** 60

8 HCF $= 2^3 \times 3 \times 5^2$
    LCM $= 2^4 \times 3^3 \times 5^3 \times 7$

Exercise N2

1 a 3901   **b** 17 176   **c** 311 563
    d 307 584

2 a 8055   **b** 134 489   **c** 72 045
    d 5379 rem 6

3 a 2561 rem 2   **b** 9113 rem 6
    c 71 385 rem 51

Exercise N3

1 $^-7, \, ^-5, \, ^-2, 0, 2, 4, 8$

2 a 7   **b** $^-11$ **c** 15   **d** $^-11$
    e $^-7$ **f** $^-18$ **g** $^-25$

3 a $^-12$ **b** $^-40$ **c** 77   **d** $^-4$
    e 8

4 a 24   **b** 1   **c** $^-15$ **d** 31

Exercise N4

1 a 6   **b** 24   **c** 3   **d** 12   **e** 15

2 a $\frac{27}{4}$ **b** $\frac{13}{3}$ **c** $\frac{17}{5}$ **d** $\frac{35}{6}$ **e** $\frac{79}{7}$

3 a $4\frac{2}{3}$ **b** $8\frac{1}{2}$ **c** $2\frac{1}{6}$ **d** $2\frac{5}{7}$
    e $5\frac{3}{5}$

4 a 33   **b** 33   **c** 55   **d** 44

5 a $\frac{2}{3}$ **b** $\frac{3}{4}$ **c** $\frac{3}{5}$

6 a 9   **b** 24   **c** 12

7 a $\frac{3}{5}, \frac{5}{8}$ **b** $\frac{5}{9}, \frac{7}{12}$ **c** $\frac{3}{5}, \frac{2}{3}, \frac{7}{10}$

Exercise N5

1 i $\frac{7}{8}$ **ii** $\frac{1}{2}$ **iii** $\frac{11}{24}$ **iv** $1\frac{7}{24}$ **v** $\frac{9}{10}$

2 i $\frac{20}{63}$ **ii** $\frac{3}{20}$ **iii** $\frac{11}{12}$ **iv** 4   **v** $2\frac{2}{3}$

3 i $\frac{8}{9}$ **ii** $\frac{6}{7}$ **iii** $3\frac{3}{4}$ **iv** $1\frac{1}{2}$ **v** $\frac{2}{9}$

4 i $3\frac{1}{6}$ **ii** $\frac{5}{18}$ **iii** $\frac{9}{10}$ **iv** $2\frac{3}{10}$

Exercise N6

1 a 9 tens   **b** 7 tenths
    c 8 thousandths   **d** 4 hundredths

2 a $2\frac{7}{10}$ **b** $\frac{6}{25}$ **c** $35\frac{1}{20}$ **d** $\frac{7}{8}$
    e $1\frac{17}{20}$ **f** $\frac{3}{40}$

3 a 0.3   **b** 0.37   **c** 3.9   **d** 14.249

4 a 0.4   **b** 0.625   **c** 0.56   **d** $0.\dot{3}$
    e $0.58\dot{3}$

5 a 0.8125   **b** $0.5\dot{1}$ **c** $0.\dot{7}1428\dot{5}$
    d 3.5   **e** $0.0\dot{3}\dot{7}$

6 a 208.17   **b** 33.495   **c** 16.186
    d 19.8899

Exercise N7

1 349.02   **2** 1986.3
3 2620   **4** 0.034
5 6.795   **6** 0.005 93
7 3.9   **8** 0.000 006 17
9 205.2   **10** 0.369
11 0.004 95   **12** 0.000 582 4
13 42.297   **14** 910.675
15 0.041 08   **16** 7.7425

Exercise N8

1 £38.50   **2** 8%   **3** £225
4 15%   **5** £13.50

Exercise N9

1 $\frac{1}{20}$ **2** $\frac{11}{20}$ **3** $1\frac{1}{4}$ **4** $\frac{1}{3}$ **5** $\frac{13}{20}$
6 $5\frac{3}{10}$ **7** $\frac{21}{40}$ **8** $\frac{4}{5}$ **9** $\frac{1}{8}$ **10** $\frac{19}{100}$

Exercise N10

1 0.11   **2** 0.5   **3** 0.09   **4** 0.653
5 0.083   **6** 0.515   **7** 1.25   **8** $2.1\dot{3}$

Exercise N11

1 35%   **2** 30%   **3** 87.5%
4 36%   **5** 60%   **6** 225%
7 85%   **8** $91\frac{2}{3}\%$ **9** 65.32%
10 $66\frac{2}{3}\%$

Exercise N12

1 $\frac{7}{9}$, 0.875, 88%   **2** $\frac{2}{5}$, $\frac{4}{9}$, 45%, 0.49
3 $\frac{3}{7}$, 0.44, 54%   **4** $\frac{11}{13}$, 85%, 0.881

Exercise N13

1 1000   **2** 100   **3** 1000   **4** 10
5 100 000

Exercise N14

1 c 800 g   **2 b** 100 g
3 a 20 m   **4 c** 330 ml

Exercise N15

1 214 m   **2** 356 cl
3 3.826   **4** 1560 kg
5 45.6 cm   **6** 3.298 l
7 2430 ml   **8** 56 390 g
9 2698 m   **10** 8 ft 2 in
11 19 yd   **12** 152 lb
13 5 gal 5 pt   **14** 4 lb 12 oz
15 1 mile 1240 yd

Exercise N16

1 25 800 cm^2 **2** 6240 mm^2
3 28.351 245 km^2 **4** 59.82 cm^2
5 3 280 000 m^2 **6** 4382.9561 m^2
7 9 730 000 cm^2 **8** 53 901
9 62.851 m^3 **10** 432 in^2
11 306 ft^2 **12** 21 yd^2
13 3240 in^2 **14** 17.5 yd^3
15 162 ft^3

Exercise N17

1 a 1524   **b** 2048   **c** 0054
2 a 12.25 am   **b** 7.38 pm
    c 7.42 am
3 7 h 23 min

Exercise N18

1 a 2.86 h **b** 7.4 h **c** 23.6 h

2 a 2 h 39 min **b** 9 h 27 min **c** 19 h 42 min

3 a 4 h 53 min **b** 5 h 2 min **c** 3 h 57 min

Exercise N19

1 a 5 673 900 **b** 5 670 000 **c** 6 000 000

2 a 9 573 900 **b** 9 570 000 **c** 10 000 000

3 a 4 657 400 **b** 4 660 000 **c** 5 000 000

4 a 7 438 900 **b** 7 440 000 **c** 7 000 000

5 a 2 344 700 **b** 2 340 000 **c** 2 000 000

6 a 3 141 600 **b** 3 140 000 **c** 3 000 000

Exercise N20

1 a 18.46 **b** 18.5 **c** 18.463

2 a 1.41 **b** 1.4 **c** 1.414

3 a 452.18 **b** 452.2 **c** 452.176

4 a 7.34 **b** 7.3 **c** 7.335

5 a 112.79 **b** 112.8 **c** 112.786

6 a 85.75 **b** 85.7 **c** 85.747

7 a 394.86 **b** 394.9 **c** 394.857

8 a 25.73 **b** 25.7 **c** 25.726

9 a 3.14 **b** 3.1 **c** 3.142

10 a 34.64 **b** 34.6 **c** 34.638

11 a 2.72 **b** 2.7 **c** 2.718

12 a 923.68 **b** 923.7 **c** 923.685

Exercise N21

1 a 83 000 **b** 80 000 **c** 82 700

2 a 0.84 **b** 0.8 **c** 0.837

3 a 35 **b** 30 **c** 35.0

4 a 0.019 **b** 0.02 **c** 0.0195

5 a 9.8 **b** 10 **c** 9.79

6 a 440 **b** 400 **c** 438

7 a 82 **b** 80 **c** 81.7

8 a 150 000 **b** 100 000 **c** 148 000

9 a 0.0084 **b** 0.008 **c** 0.008 36

Exercise N22

1 3 hours **2** 200 miles

3 3 m^2 **4** 1.414

Exercise N23

1 0.5 cm **2** 0.5 pt **3** 50 people

Exercise N24

1 40 000 **2** 0.02

3 30 **4** 80

5 10 **6** 5

7 29.262 604 **8** 0.004 170 576 4

9 52.262 36 **10** 93.751 445

11 115 207.22 **12** 0.168 983 7

13 714.996 63 **14** 219.2577

15 £5 000 000

Exercise N25

1 7.37 **2** 0.707 **3** 0.618

4 1.618 **5** 1

Exercise N26

1 a 7 : 9 **b** 1 : 3 **c** 9 : 5

2 a 2 : 7 **b** 80 : 13 **c** 1 : 120

3 a 19 : 7 **b** 11 : 5

4 a 2 : 3 : 4 **b** 1.5 kg

Exercise N27

1 6 h sleeping, 8 h working, 10 h leisure

2 Aneena £350, Baljit £500, Carlos £250

3 63 m^2 **4** 35 kg

Exercise N28

1 a 1 : 60 000 **b** 1 : 30 000 **c** 1 : 10 000

2 a 1 : 800 000 **b** 3 cm

Exercise N29

1 441 miles **2** £14.88 **3** $833\frac{1}{3}$ g

4 a 2575 lire to £1 **b** 193 125 lire

5 £130.21

Exercise N30

1 $7\frac{1}{2}$ h **2** 15 days

3 2 min – the number of people in the band and the time taken are not inversely proportional!

4 6 h **5** 4 h 12 min

Exercise N31

1 a £3 **b** £91 **c** £12.40

2 1.05 litres **3** 1394

4 £42.50 **5** £9000

Exercise N32

1 a 25% **b** 35% **c** $28\frac{1}{3}$%

2 55%

Exercise N33

M-plan 81%, N-plan 75% so the M-plan is more effective

Exercise N34

1 £8755 **2** £8100 **3** 54 p **4** £936

Exercise N35

1 15% **2** 60%

3 20% **4** 18.2% (3 sf)

Exercise N36

1 28 **2** 200 **3** £11 700 **4** £1256

Exercise N37

1 £141.59 **2** £41.48

Exercise N38

1 a £70 **b** £153.39 **c** 43 p **d** £2537.50

2 £44.81 **3** £30.41

Exercise N39

1 £102.53 **2** Scheme 2, £1879

Exercise N40

1 a £7800 **b** £376.85

2 a £78 000 **b** £610.74

Exercise N41

1 £403.20 **2** £184.50

Exercise N42

1 £131

2 a £89.25 **b** £93.04

3 a £55.20 **b** £66.24 **c** £23.92

Exercise N43

1 55% **2** 30% **3** £2.56

4 £10.14, 52%

Exercise N44

1 £158.76   **2** 39 hours

3 £280.60   **4** £18 336

5 a £3062.50   **b** £1371.67

6 a £31 980   **b** £2665   **c** £615

Exercise N45

1 £27.30   **2** £10 366.80

3 £147.25   **4** £65.75

Exercise N46

1 a i £19 985   **ii** £4640.40
   b i £11 445   **ii** £2590.80
   c i £14 340   **ii** £3285.60
   d i £32 015   **ii** £8570
   e i £7485   **ii** £1640.40

2 a £18.62   **b** £128.30   **c** £27.12
   d £40.62

3 a £20 370   **b** £4732.80   **c** £394.40
   d £2195.83   **e** £176.00   **f** £1625.43

Exercise N47

1 64 km/h   **2** 423 m   **3** 4 h

4 375 m min^{-1} or 6.25 m s^{-1} or 22.5 km/h

5 2.96 h or 2 h 57 min 36 s

Exercise N48

1 40.6 mph   **2** 5.4 mph

3 Stage 1   5
   Stage 2   10
   Stage 3   12
   —————————
   Total   17
   (Note: on Stage 2 he should wait for
   the correct time before checking in;
   otherwise there will be an extra
   4 point penalty.)

Exercise N49

1 −10 m s^{-2} **2** 87 m/s (or m s^{-1})

Exercise N50

1 55.6 m^3 **2** 1296 g   **3** 8500 kg/m^3

4 Ice 211.1 cm^3, Al 207.4 cm^3

Exercise N51

1 322 miles   **2** 7 h 21 min

3 422 km

Exercise N52

1 a 1.82 kg/cm^2 **b** 1.19 kg/cm^2
   c 3.78 kg/cm^2

2 a 4.4   **b** 90.92   **c** 28.18 or 28.19

Exercise N53

1 £19.51   **2** £790.68   **3** £2.37

4 10 p   **5** £4.85   **6** £33 169.92

7 £3422.44

Exercise N54

1 19.55   **2** 08.57

3 a 21.27   **b** 17.42

4 a 08.28   **b** 17.26   **c** 49 min
   d 9 h 54 min

5 54.3 km/h (3 sf)

Exercise N55

1

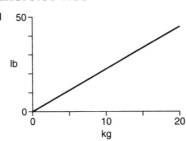

a 32 lb   **b** 11.9 kg

2

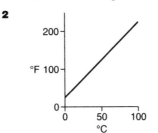

a 133°F   **b** 38°C

3 a

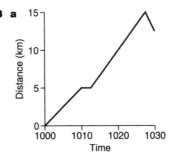

b Distance = 17 km,
   displacement = 13 km
c Av. speed = 34 km/h,
   av. vel. = 26 km/h

4 a

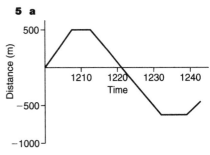

b 7.4 s, 33.3 s, 100 s
c 8 m/s   **d** 1 m/s

5 a

b 46.5 m/min   **c** −9.3 m/min

Exercise N56

1 1024   **2** 1024   **3** 729

4 729   **5** 1 000 000   **6** 125

7 128   **8** 2401   **9** 512

Exercise N57

1 12   **2** 1   **3** 256

4 $\frac{1}{6}$ **5** $\frac{1}{4}$ **6** 8

7 6^5 **8** 9^{-2} **9** 5^{15}

10 $3^{\frac{5}{2}}$ **11** 4^4 **12** 2^{15}

13 2^1 **14** 3^9 **15** 4^6

16 9^2 **17** $4^{\frac{5}{2}}$ **18** $9^{\frac{9}{2}}$

Exercise N58

1 4.6329×10^4 **2** $1.573\,81 \times 10^{-2}$

3 $7.853\,942 \times 10^6$ **4** 1.365×10^{-4}

5 $4.562\,83 \times 10^2$ **6** $1.428\,57 \times 10^{-1}$

7 6 400 000   **8** 67 000

Exercise N59

1 a 1.2×10^9 **b** 3×10^4
   c 7.5×10^2 **d** 4×10^7
   e 2.048×10^7 **f** 5×10^1
   g 2.5×10^5 **h** 3.6×10^{-5}

2 a 4.03×10^5 **b** $4.199\,88 \times 10^6$
   c 5.015×10^{-2} **d** -9.6×10^3
   e 6.432×10^4 **f** 1.47×10^{-3}

3 h, j, f, d, a, g, e, b, c

4 5.997×10^{24} kg

Exercise A1

1 A : 9, 12, 15, 18, 21, 24

2 1, 8, 27, 64, 125, 216, 343

3

N	10	9	8	7	6	5	4	3	2	1	0
A	20	18	16	14	12	10	8	6	4	2	0
B	4	3.6	3.2	2.8	2.4	2	1.6	1.2	0.8	0.4	—

Exercise A2

a i 1 **ii** 6 **b i** 7 **ii** 4

Exercise A3

1 13 **2** 5 **3** 19 **4** 22

5 1 **6** 6 **7** 37 **8** 259

9 5 **10** -102

Exercise A4

1 3 **2** 5 **3** 2

4 14 **5** 1 **6** 1

Exercise A5

1 10 **2** 1

3 6 **4** -13

5 20 **6** 144

7 23 **8** 4

9 -52 **10** 11

11 89 **12** $\frac{3}{29}$ or 0.103 (3 sf)

13 91 **14** -4

15 9

Exercise A6

1 $4a$ **2** $4b - 2a$

3 $2d - 3$ **4** $4m + 4n$

5 $7p + 5q$ **6** $r^2 + 3 - 2s$

7 $-2pq - 1$ **8** $-ab + 5$

9 $3pqr + pq$ **10** $5xy + 3x^2$

11 t^2 **12** $10a + 2ab$

13 $5 - 3y + xy$ **14** $3mm + 6m - n$

Exercise A7

1 a 68 p **b** £2.38
  c $34x$ pence or £$0.34x$

2 a 17 **b** 27 **c** $12 + y$

3 a 47 p **b** 52 p **c** $x - 5$ pence

4 a 25 **b** 20 **c** $32 - r$

5 a 5 oz **b** 3 oz **c** $\frac{1}{2}M$ or $0.5M$ oz

6 a £$(28 - x)$ **b** £$(18 + z)$
  c £$(36 + n - m)$

Exercise A8

1 $1400 - 17a$

2 $\frac{125}{100}x$ or $\frac{5}{4}x$ or $1.25x$

3 £$\left(2h + \frac{4}{100}g\right)$ or $200h + 4g$ pence

4 $500 - 10y$ pence or £$\left(5 - \frac{y}{10}\right)$

Exercise A9

1 Add 4; 21, 25, 29

2 Multiply by 4; 1024, 4096, 16 384

3 Subtract 2; $-7, -9, -11$

4 Multiply by -3; $-486, 1458, -4374$

5 Multiply by 2 then add 3; 125, 253, 509

6 Divide by 2; $\frac{1}{2}, \frac{1}{4}, \frac{1}{8}$

7 Add $\frac{1}{3}$; $2, \frac{7}{3}, \frac{8}{3}$

8 Multiply by -2 then add 4; 44, -84, 172

Exercise A10

1

2

3

4

Exercise A11

1 $x \rightarrow x + 4$ **2** $x \rightarrow \frac{1}{2}x$

3 $x \rightarrow x - 5$ **4** $x \rightarrow 2x - 1$

5 $x \rightarrow 3x + 1$ **6** $x \rightarrow 2x$

Exercise A12

1 $2n + 1$, 19 **2** $3n - 2$, 25

3 $n + 6$, 15 **4** $4n$, 36

5 $2n - 3$, 15 **6** $n + 10$, 19

7 $4n - 3$, 33 **8** $-2n + 9$, -9

Exercise A13

1 $n^2 + 1$, 50 **2** $3n^2 - 1$, 146

3 $n^2 - 5$, 44 **4** $n^2 - 2$, 47

5 $2n^2 - 3$, 95

Exercise A14

1 $a = 15$ **2** $b = 9$

3 $c = -9$ **4** $e = 31$

5 $f = -5$ **6** $g = -6$

7 $h = 6$ **8** $k = 5$

9 $m = 9$ **10** $n = 3$

11 $p = 5$ **12** $q = 7$

13 $r = 20$ **14** $s = 54$

15 $t = 21$ **16** $v = 18$

17 $w = 40$ **18** $x = 36$

Exercise A15

1 $a = 8$ **2** $b = 4$

3 $c = -3$ **4** $e = 8$

5 $f = 7$ **6** $g = 7$

7 $h = 7$ **8** $k = -3$

9 $m = 6$ **10** $n = 2$

11 $p = 11$ **12** $q = -6$

13 $r = -10$

Exercise A16

1 $n = 6$ **2** $p = 4$ **3** $q = -3$

4 $r = 7$ **5** $t = 7$ **6** $v = 9$

7 $w = 5$ **8** $x = -3$ **9** $y = -3$

Exercise A17

1 $3p - 6$ **2** $-4a - 20$

3 $10x - 6$ **4** $20m + 10n$

5 $30a - 40b$ **6** $p - 3q$

7 $-18g + 6h$ **8** $-2x + 4y$

Exercise A18

1 $ab - a^2$ **2** $2x^2 + 2xy$

3 $6mn - 15m^2$ **4** $-3gh + h^3$

5 $-12xy - 3x^2$ **6** $28q^2 - 21pq$

Exercise A19

1 $7x - 2xy$ **2** $-b - 3a$

3 $3m + mn + 2n$ **4** $6q - 2pq$

5 $27 + 4a$ **6** $-21a - 4b$

7 $5x - y$ **8** $2mn - m$

9 $6r + rs + 4s^2$ **10** $-ab + 9ac$

Exercise A20

1 $4(a - b)$ **2** $3(2x + 3y)$

3 $5(p + 2q)$ **4** $7(e + 4f)$

5 $11(m - n)$ **6** $2(7f - g)$

7 $3(6x + y)$ **8** $6(7v - 6w)$

9 $54(a + 2b)$ **10** $12(6r - 11s)$

Exercise A21

1 $a(2b + 3c)$ **2** $y(5x - 2z)$

3 $p(7q - 1)$ **4** $m(4 + 11k)$

5 $3a(b - c)$ **6** $3y(1 + 2z)$

7 $5b(3a - 5c)$ **8** $14m(n + 2p)$

9 $5a(a - 4b)$ **10** $6y(5x^2 + 8z)$

Exercise A22

1 $(3x - 2y)(m + n)$

2 $(4a + 7b)(x - y)$

3 $(a - 2)(b - c)$

4 $(3p + 2q)(4s - 3t)$

5 $(12n - 13)(p + 2q)$

6 $(5p - 3q)(a + b)$

7 $(5w - 3v)(w - v)$

8 $(11x + 12)(3u - v)$

9 $(2x + 3)(y - z)$

10 $(s + r)(2t - w)$

Exercise A23

1 $(a + b)(c + d)$

2 $(2x + y)(w - z)$

3 $(3m + 2n)(4p - q)$

4 $(5c - d)(2f - q)$

5 $(d - c)(4a - 3b)$

6 $(4y + 5z)(2w + 3x)$

Exercise A24

1 $x = 2$ **2** $y = -1$ **3** $z = 3$

4 $x = 5$ **5** $p = -4$ **6** $t = -2$

7 $w = 1$ **8** $t = 4$ **9** $h = -3$

Exercise A25

1 $x = 4$ **2** $x = -3$ **3** $x = 1$

4 $x = 2$ **5** $x = -1$ **6** $x = -4$

7 $x = 3$ **8** $x = -2$

Exercise A26

1 $x = 6$ **2** $y = 15$ **3** $z = 21$

4 $x = 12$ **5** $p = 7$ **6** $t = 5$

7 $m = 4$ **8** $r = 2$ **9** $k = 4$

Exercise A27

1 $x = 20$ **2** $x = 24$ **3** $x = 8$

4 $x = 15$ **5** $x = 18$ **6** $x = 20$

7 $x = 9$ **8** $x = 7$ **9** $x = 15$

10 $x = 5$ **11** $x = 12$

Exercise A28

1 $a^2 - a - 6$ **2** $b^2 + 7b + 12$

3 $c^2 - 4c - 12$ **4** $d^2 - 11d + 24$

5 $6e^2 - 13e + 6$ **6** $8f^2 - 14f - 15$

7 $3g^2 - 10g - 8$ **8** $6h^2 + 22h + 16$

9 $12k^2 + 7k - 12$

Exercise A29

1 $6a^2 - 13ab + 6b^2$

2 $6c^2 - 7cd - 20d^2$

3 $3e^2 + 10ef + 8f^2$

4 $12g^2 + gh - 6h^2$

5 $6k^2 - 22km + 20m^2$

6 $6p^2 + 7pq - 20q^2$

7 $x^2 + 2xy + y^2$

8 $x^2 - 2xy + y^2$

9 $x^2 - y^2$

Exercise A30

1 $9a^2 + 6ab + b^2$

2 $c^2 - 8cd + 16d^2$

3 $e^2 + 4ef + 4f^2$

4 $9g^2 - h^2$

5 $k^2 - 16m^2$

6 $4p^2 + 20pq + 25q^2$

7 $9r^2 - 24rs + 16s^2$

8 $4t^2 - 36u^2$

9 $25v^2 - 9w^2$

Exercise A31

1 $S = \dfrac{D}{T}$ **2** $D = \dfrac{C}{\pi}$

3 $\theta = \dfrac{a}{r}$ **4** $a = \dfrac{F}{m}$

5 $x = \dfrac{y - c}{m}$ **6** $s = \dfrac{v^2 - u^2}{2a}$

7 $g = \dfrac{ma + T}{m}$ **8** $h = \dfrac{A}{2\pi r} - r$

9 $F = \dfrac{9C}{5} + 32$

Exercise A32

1 $p = \dfrac{(q - r)^2}{2g}$ **2** $r = \sqrt{\dfrac{A}{\pi}}$

3 $a = \sqrt{(h^2 - b^2)}$ **4** $r = \sqrt[3]{\dfrac{3V}{4\pi}}$

5 $t = \sqrt{\dfrac{2s}{a}}$ **6** $L = \dfrac{T^2 g}{4\pi^2}$

7 $R = \sqrt[3]{\dfrac{A}{P}} - 1$ **8** $u = \sqrt{(v^2 - 2as)}$

9 $v = \sqrt{\dfrac{2E}{m}}$

Exercise A33

1 $m = \dfrac{T}{g - a}$ **2** $r = \dfrac{A}{\pi(s + 2h)}$

3 $c = \dfrac{n}{4 + 2r}$ **4** $a = \dfrac{S}{r^2 + r^3}$

5 $u = \sqrt{\dfrac{2gd}{1 - e^2}}$ **6** $v = \dfrac{fu}{u - f}$

7 $r = \sqrt{\dfrac{3V}{\pi(h + 3H)}}$ **8** $v = \dfrac{2E}{v^2 + 2gh}$

Exercise A34

1 20, 21, 22   **2** 6 cm

3 8   **4** 5 cm

5 120 g   **6** £600 000

Exercise A35

1 16   **2** Child £3, Adult £8

3 24°, 78°, 78°   **4** 10

Exercise A36

1 16   **2** 28

3 Carrots 20 p   **4** Anne   £12 000
   Potatoes 24 p   Bernard £7000
    Charles £5000

5 3, 6   **6** 16

Exercise A37

1 a True **b** False **c** True

2 a > **b** < **c** >

3 a
2

b
−1

c
5

Exercise A38

1 $a > -2$
−2

2 $b < 9$
9

3 $c \leq 2$
2

4 $e \leq 4$
4

5 $-5 \leq f$
−5

6 $g < 4$
4

7 $h \geq 6$
6

8 $k > -5$
−5

9 $m \geq 9$
9

10 $n > -3$
−3

11 $p \leq -5$
−5

12 $q > 7$
7

13 $r > -20$
−20

14 $s \geq 54$
54

15 $t \leq -21$
−21

16 $v < -18$
−18

17 $w \leq 40$
40

18 $x > 36$
36

Exercise A39

1 $a < 8$
8

2 $b \geq 4$
4

3 $c > -3$
−3

4 $e \leq -8$
−8

5 $f < 7$
7

6 $g \leq 7$
7

7 $h < 8$
8

8 $k < -3$
−3

9 $m \leq -6$
−6

10 $n > 2$
2

11 $p \leq 11$
11

12 $q > -6$
−6

13 $r \geq -10$
−10

Exercise A40

1 $x > 2$
2

2 $y \leq -1$
−1

3 $z \leq 3$
3

4 $x < 12$
12

5 $p \leq 7$
7

6 $t > 5$
5

7 $x \geq 9$
9

8 $x > -3$
−3

9 $x > 15$
15

Exercise A41

1 $3 - f < 2$
  $f > 1$

2 $50 \leq c \leq 250$
50   250

3 $w \geq 15$ **4** 66.667 miles
  $l \leq 65$
  $w \leq l$

15 w 40 l 65

5

Exercise A42

1

x	−4	−3	−2	−1	0	1	2
y	14	3	−4	−7	−6	−1	8

a −5.7 **b** −3.1, 1.6

2

x	−4	−3	−2	−1	0	1	2	3	4
y	−8	16	22	16	4	−8	−14	−8	16

$x = -3.75$, 0.31 and 3.44

3

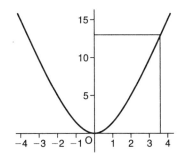

$\sqrt{13} = 3.6$

4 a $y = \dfrac{4}{x-2}$ **b** $y = x^3 - 9x$

c $y = 3 + 2x - x^2$

Exercise A43

1 a Not linear
  b Linear **i** 5   **ii** (0,3) **iii** Increasing
  c Linear **i** −2 **ii** (0,7) **iii** Decreasing
  d Linear **i** 3   **ii** (0,4) **iii** Increasing

2 **A** and **D** are parallel, **B** and **E** are parallel

3 a $y = \frac{1}{2}x + 3$ **b** $x = 8$
  c $y = 5 - 2x$ **d** $y = -3$

4 $y = 6x - 15$

5 a

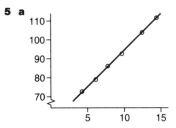

b $y = 4x + 57$
c i 57 cm   **ii** 137 cm

Exercise A44

1 a

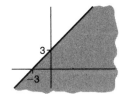

b

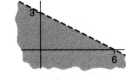

c

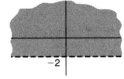

d

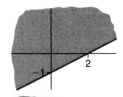

2 a

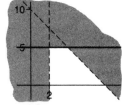

b

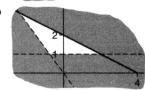

3 a $y \leqslant x$
$x + y > 2$
$y \leqslant 2$
$y \geqslant \frac{1}{3}x$
$x + y \leqslant 5$

b

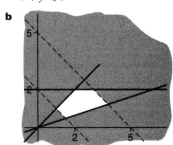

4 $x + y \geqslant 10$
$y > x$
$x + 2y < 18$

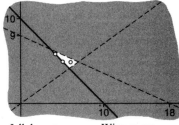

Jellybeans	Wine gums
3	7
4	6
5	6

Exercise A45

1 $x = 3, y = 1$

2 $x = 1, y = 3$

3 $x = -2, y = 4.5$

4 $x = 2.5, y = -0.5$

5 $x = -1.2, y = -1.6$

6 $x = -1.5, y = -2.3$

Exercise A46

1 $x = 4, y = 19$ **2** $x = 6\frac{2}{3}, y = 1\frac{2}{3}$

3 $a = 2, b = -1$ **4** $m = 3, n = 4$

5 $x = 1, y = 1$ **6** $x = -2, y = 0.5$

Exercise A47

1 $x = 5, y = 3$ **2** $x = -4, y = 3$

3 $x = 3, y = 2$ **4** $x = 5, y = -2$

5 $x = 1, y = -1$ **6** $x = -1, y = 1$

Exercise A48

1 $5x + 3y = 105, 4x + 5y = 123$
Oranges are 12 p, lemons are 15 p

2 Let x be running speed and y be walking speed.
$x + 2y = 22, 1\frac{1}{2}x + 4y = 39$
Running speed is 10 km/h, walking speed is 6 km/h

3 Let x be Nirmal's age and y be Naresh's age
$x = 4y, x - 2 = 5(y - 2)$
Nirmal is 32 years old, Naresh is 8 years old

4 Let s be the contents of a small can and l be the contents of a large can
$s + l = 500, 7s + 6l = 10s + 41$
A small can contains 200 g, a large can contains 300 g

5 Let x be the distance AB and y be the distance BC
$\dfrac{x}{48} + \dfrac{y}{50} = 4, \dfrac{x}{108} + \dfrac{y}{90} = 2$
AB = 96 km, BC = 100 km

Exercise A49

1 $y = 1.5x$ **a** $y = 45$ **b** $x = 52$

2 3321 N   **3** 20 oscillations

4 $p = 97.65625$ **4** 15 N

Exercise A50

1 a^4 **2** b^9 **3** c^9

4 $d^5 e^4$ **5** $15f^5$ **6** $24g^5 h^7$

Exercise A51

1 k^2 **2** m^3 **3** n^{-5}

4 p^4 **5** q^{-2} **6** $3r^2 s^2$

Exercise A52

1 $2t^4 u$ **2** $2v^2 w$

3 $\frac{1}{2}ab^2$ **4** $x^2 y - xy^2 + xyz$

Exercise A53

1 x^{12} **2** $4y^8$ **3** z^6 **4** a^3

5 b^3 **6** c^{-2} **7** $\frac{1}{18}$ **8** $2ab^{-5}$

Exercise A54

1 1.90

2 a $\cos x = \tan x$ **b** 38.17°

3 -1.43

Exercise A55

$x >= 1.43$

Exercise A56

1 a Converges to 0.6
 b $2.5x^2 - 1.5x = 0$

2 a Diverges
 b $2.5x^2 - 1.5x = 0$

3 a Oscillates between 0.823 603 289
   and 0.479 427 02
 b $3.3x^2 - 2.3x = 0$

4 a Converges to 1.414 213 562
 b $x^2 - 2 = 0$

Exercise A57

1 $(x+3)(x+4)$ **2** $(x+2)(x+7)$

3 $(x+4)(x-3)$ **4** $(x-7)(x+2)$

5 $(x-3)(x-5)$ **6** $(x-5)(x-6)$

7 $(x+5)(x-3)$ **8** $(x-4)(x-7)$

9 $(x+1)(x+20)$ **10** $(x+7)(x-7)$

11 $(x-9)(x+2)$ **12** $(x+6)(x+7)$

Exercise A58

1 $(2x+1)(x+2)$ **2** $(2x+1)(x-2)$

3 $(3x+7)(x+2)$ **4** $(7x+2)(x-3)$

5 $(2x-1)(3x-4)$

6 $(5x+2)(2x-3)$

7 $(3x-4)(2x+1)$

8 $(2x+5)(2x-5)$

9 $(7x+6)(2x+1)$

10 $(3x+2)^2$

11 $(5x+1)(x+4)$

12 $(3x-4)(7x+2)$

Exercise A59

1 a $x = -3.37$ or 2.37
 b $x = -3.70$ or 2.70

2 a $x = -3$ or -5 **b** $x = 1$ or -2
 c $x = 0$ or -7 **d** $x = \frac{1}{2}$ or $-\frac{2}{3}$

3 a $x = 1$ or 3 **b** $x = 4$ or 7
 c $x = -2$ or -3 **d** $x = 3$ or 9
 e $x = 8$ or -3 **f** $x = 9$ or -7
 g $x = 6$ or -3 **h** $x = 1$ or $\frac{1}{2}$
 i $x = -1\frac{1}{2}$ or $\frac{1}{4}$ **j** $x = \frac{1}{2}$
     (repeated root)

Exercise A60

1 $x = -3.414$ or -0.586
2 $x = 1.721$ or -0.387
3 no real roots
4 $x = -1.531$ or 0.131
5 $x = -5.646$ or -0.354
6 $x = 3.436$ or -0.436
7 no real roots
8 $x = 1$ or $-\frac{1}{4}$
9 $x = -4$ or $\frac{1}{2}$

Exercise A61

1 7 and 11 **2** 36 cm
3 90 km/h **4** $AB = 6$ m

Exercise S1

1 a Acute **b** Acute **c** Obtuse
 d Obtuse **e** Acute

2 a 6.4 cm **b** 53° **c** 87° **d** 273°

3 a 16.2 cm **b** 17.7° **c** 37.3°
 d 342.3°

4 a 10 cm **b** 106°

5 23°, 34°, 123°

6 a 30° **b** 140° **c** 110° **d** 220°

Exercise S2

1 $a = 55°$ **2** $b = 39°$

3 $c = 47°$ **4** $d = 38°$

5 $e = 132°$ **6** $f = 203°$

7 $g = 78°$ **8** $h = 61°$

9 $j = 132°$ **10** $(p = 30°)$ $m = 60°$
 $k = 48°$ $2p = 60°$ $n = 120°$
        $4p = 120°$

11 $(q = 20°)$ **12** $r = 72°$
 $4q = 80°$
 $6q = 120°$

Exercise S3

1 $a = 125°$ **2** $e = 138°$
 $b = 55°$ $f = 42°$
 $c = 55°$ $g = 138°$
 $d = 125°$ $h = 42°$

3 $j = 61°$ **4** $n = 50°$
 $k = 61°$ $p = 50°$
 $m = 119°$ $q = 130°$
        $r = 50°$
        $s = 130°$

5 $t = 123°$ **6** $v = 72°$
 $u = 117°$ $w = 36°$

7 $x = 36°$ **8** $(y = 20°)$
 $2x = 72°$ $4y = 80°$
        $5y = 100°$

9 $z = 26°$

Exercise S4

1 1 line of symmetry

2 Rot. sym. order 4

3 2 lines of symmetry
   Rot. sym. order 2

4 Rot. sym. order 4

5 5 lines of symmetry
   Rot. sym. order 5

6 4 lines of symmetry
   Rot. sym. order 4

7
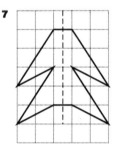

8
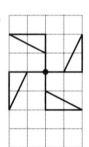

9

10
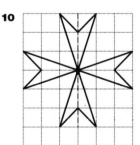

Exercise S5

1 Scalene
2 Right-angled scalene
3 Isosceles
4 Right-angled scalene
5 Scalene
6 Equilateral

Exercise S6

1 $a = 27°$ 2 $b = 70°$
3 $c = 35°$ 4 $d = 70°$
5 $e = 73°$ 6 $f = 86°$
7 $g = 68°$ 8 $h = 54°$
9 $j = 42°$ 10 $m = 35°$
  $k = 106°$
11 $n = 84°$ 12 $p = 56°$
              $q = 69°$

Exercise S7

1 $a = 20°$ 2 $b = 60°, c = 30°$
3 $d = 65°$ 4 a $e = 75°$ b 4
5 a $f = 90°$ $g = 30°$
  b Rot. sym. order 2
6 No in all cases

Exercise S8

1 $a = 69°$ 2 $b = 70°$
3 $c = 99°$ 4 $d = 36°$
              $2d = 72°$
              $3d = 108°$
              $4d = 144°$
5 $e = 105°$ 6 $h = 36°$
  $f = 75°$ $j = 144°$
  $g = 75°$
7 $k = 35°$ 8 $n = 116°$
  $m = 117°$ $p = 32°$
9 $q = 110°$ 10 $r = 63°$
              $s = 126°$
              $t = 63°$
11 $u = 129°$ 12 $w = 118°$
  $v = 147°$ $x = 62°$
13 $y = 146°$
  $z = 112°$

Exercise S9

3 90°   4 54°
5 22.5°, 22.5°, 135°
6 a 130°   c 55°   d 35°, 30°, 115°

Exercise S10

1 139°   2 78°   3 112°
4 a 108°   b 120°   c 135°
5 a 12   b 8   c 20
6 a 8   b 18   c 24
7 36°
10 $x = 22.5°$ $y = 45°$

Exercise S11

1 Will   2 Will   3 Will not
4 a Angle is not a factor of 360°
  b 36° and 144°
5 a Yes   b Yes   c Yes   d No
6 Square, rectangle, parallelogram, rhombus
7 a No   b Yes

Exercise S12

1 a 51.52 cm   b 21.33 cm
2 a 50.8 cm   b 20.71 cm
  c 33.56 cm
3 a 376.99 cm   b 20.42 cm
4 a 157.08 m   b 100 rev

Exercise S13

1 29.76 cm^2 2 24.38 cm^2
3 5.64 cm^2 4 65.205 cm^2
5 97.79 m^2 6 113.1 m^2
7 59.45 cm^2 8 72.38 ft^2
9 70 cm^2 10 255.15 m^2

Exercise S14

1 a 108.52 cm^2 b 44.265 m^2
  c 75.43 m^2
2 27 m^2

Exercise S15

1 5.39 m   2 8.94 cm
3 13.7 cm   4 11.5 cm
5 12.7 cm   6 16.3 cm
7 10.8 m   8 32.4 m
9 43.1 m   10 20.8 m

Exercise S16

All answers to 3 sf
1 9.17 cm   2 13.1 cm   3 8.49 cm
4 BD = 15.1 cm AD = 25.9 cm
5 9.22 cm
6 BC = 47.7 cm AD = 35.7 cm
7 13.0 cm
8 BC = 8.54 cm AB = 16.1 cm

Exercise S17

1 A(−4, 4) B(4, 3) C(1, −1) D(0, −3)
  E(−2, −4) F(−5, −2) G(−4, 0)
  H(−2, 2)

2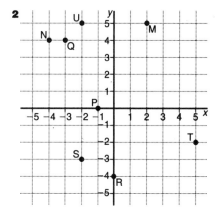

Exercise S18

1 a (1, 4)   b (−5, 2)   c (−3, 7)
2 a $\begin{pmatrix} -2 \\ -2 \end{pmatrix}$ c B′(−3, −4) C′(2, −4)
3 a $\begin{pmatrix} 3 \\ 5 \end{pmatrix}$ b $\begin{pmatrix} 1 \\ 4 \end{pmatrix}$ c $\begin{pmatrix} -6 \\ -3 \end{pmatrix}$
  d $\begin{pmatrix} -2 \\ 6 \end{pmatrix}$

Exercise S19

a A′(2, 1) B′(3, −2) C′(−1, −1)
b A′(−4, 1) B′(−5, 4) C′(−1, 3)
c A′(2, 1) B′(1, 4) C′(5, 3)

Exercise S20

1 a P′(−1, 1) Q′(−2, 3) R′(−4, 2)
  b P′(−1, −1) Q′(−1, 0) R′(0, −2)
  c P′(4, 0) Q′(3, 2) R′(1, 1)
  d P′(−3, −3) Q′(−5, −4)
    R′(−4, −6)
2 Rotation 180° about (0, 0)

Exercise S21

1 a X′(1.5, 1.5) Y′(4.5, 3) Z′(3, 6)
  b X′(−3, −7) Y′(3, −4) Z′(−1, −1)
  c X′(0, 0) Y′(4, 2) Z′(2, 6)
2 a Scale factor + 2 from (2, 3)
  b Scale factor + 3 from (0, 0)
  c Scale factor + 2 from (−4, 3)

Exercise S22

1 a A′(−3, 2) B′(−1, 2) C′(−1, 1)
  D′(−3, 1)
  b A′(3, −2) B′(1, −2) C′(1, −1)
  D′(3, −1)

2 a P′(0, 1) Q′(1, 2) R′(1, 1)
  b P′(−2, −2) Q′(−9, −8)
  R′(−9, −2)

3 Scale factor 0.5 from (−4, −4)

4 Scale factor −3 from (−1, 1)

Exercise S23

1 20 cm **2** 9 cm **3** 17.5 m

4 a 28 cm **b** 30 cm

5 a 28.8 m **b** 31.2 m

Exercise S24

1
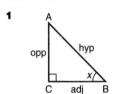

2

3
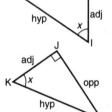

4
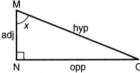

5
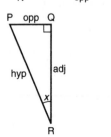

6

7
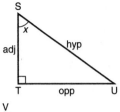

8
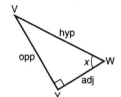

Exercise S25

1 a 0.920 504 853 **b** 11.430 052 3
  c 0.996 194 698 **d** 0.559 192 903
  e 0.965 925 822 6 **f** 0.267 949 192
  g 0.5 **h** 1

2 a 14.477 512 19° **b** 48.240 911 53°
  c 77.161 431 86° **d** 75.963 756 53°
  e 19.034 434 35° **f** 82.924 727 07°

Exercise S26

All answers to 3 sf

$a = 48.2°$ $b = 51.5°$ $c = 36.9°$
$d = 28.8°$ $e = 55.2°$ $f = 49.6°$
$g = 18.0°$ $h = 37.9°$

Exercise S27

All answers to 3 sf

1 4.59 cm **2** 18.1 m **3** 24.2 m

4 13.6 m **5** 48.1 cm **6** 102 m

Exercise S28

All answers to 3 sf

1 10.9 m **2** 5.61 cm **3** 7.64 cm

4 12.1 m **5** 44.2 cm **6** 17.0 m

Exercise S29

All answers to 3 sf

1 59.0° **2** 2.51 cm **3** 14.6 m

4 23.4 m **5** 15.3 cm **6** 29.1°

7 16.8 m **8** 24.4 cm **9** 34.2 m

Exercise S30

All answers to 3 sf

1 101 m **2** 2270 m

3 1180 m **4** 184 m

Exercise S31

All answers to 3 sf

1 a 975 m **b** 1.62 km

2 a 72.8 m **b** 12.1 m

3 a 7740 m **b** 11500 m

4 66.2 m

5 a 1.43 km **b** 7.40°

6 a 1.18 km **b** 187 m

Exercise S32

1 a 045° **b** 000° **c** 315°

2 a 053° **b** 299° **c** 214°
  d 162° **e** 325° **f** 254°

Exercise S33

1 000° **2** 132° **3** 338°

4 312° **5** 016° **6** 175°

7 312° **8** 251° **9** 013°

Exercise S34

All answers to 3 sf

1 a 235 km **b** 407 km

2 a 133 km **b** 205 km

3 a 773 km **b** 746 km

4 a 91.4 km **b** 58.7 km

5 a 290° **b** 362 km

6 a 122° **b** 13.0 km

Exercise S35

All answers to 3 sf

1 a 54.0 km **b** 89.8 km

2 a 374 km **b** 414 km

3 a 22.4 km **b** 157°

4 a 271° **b** 78.7 km

5 a 69.5 miles **b** 65.8 miles
  c 52.4 miles **d** 90.6 miles
  e 143 miles **f** 271°

Exercise S36

1 5 cm by 15 cm

2 10 km

3 4.3 m

4 15 cm, 10 cm, 18 cm
  Angles are unchanged

5 a 200 by 100 m **b** 0.08 cm²
  c 20 000 m² **d** 1 : 250 000 000 0

Exercise S37

1 a 40 km   **b** 099°   **c** 279°

2 210°

3 3.66 – 4.51 miles from A

4 596 m, 088°

5 Cargo ship gets there first

Exercise S38

No answers to this exercise

Exercise S39

1

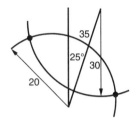

2 The tree can be planted anywhere in the hatched region

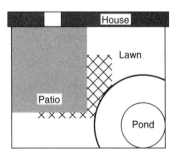

3 The goat can graze the shaded area

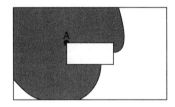

4 The locus of M is an arc of the circle as shown.

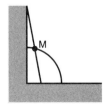

Exercise S40

1 A horizontal line

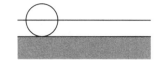

2

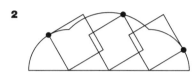

3

4

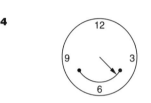

5 The locus shown is only approximately correct

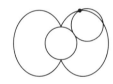

Exercise S41

1

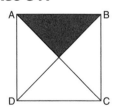

2

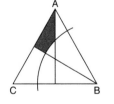

3

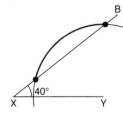

Exercise S42

1 14.92 cm   **2** 6 cm
3 8.04 cm   **4** 5.48 cm

Exercise S43

1 a

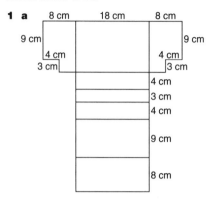

b 888 cm²

2 1910.1 cm²

3 a AB = 13 in
b

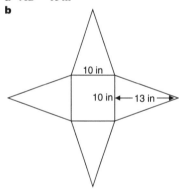

c 360 in²

4 2682.9 cm²

Exercise S44

1 a 358.72 m³   **b** 76.245 cm³
   c 168 ft³   **d** 1546.4 m³
   e 252 cm³   **f** 378.65 cm³

2 579.6 cm³

Exercise S45

1 a (6, 4, 0)   **b** (6, 0, 3)   **c** (6, 4, 3)
   d (3, 4, 3)   **e** (3, 2, 2)

2 a (−3, 8, 0.5)   **b** (−3, −12, 2.5)

Exercise S46

1 a 16.49 in   **b** 42.5°

2 a 14.76 m   **b** 70.2°

Exercise S47

1 Bristol – Birmingham – Sheffield –
Nottingham – Leicester – Bristol,
335 miles

2 36

Exercise D1

1 Quantitative – discrete

2 Qualitative

3 Quantitative – continuous

4 Qualitative

5 Quantitative – discrete

6 Qualitative

7 Quantitative – discrete

8 Quantitative – continuous

9 Quantitative – discrete

10 Quantitative – continuous

Exercise D2

1 a
Tea	*NN ////	9
Coffee	*NN NN ////	14
Chocolate	////	4
Milk	*NN /	6
Juice	*NN //	7
		40

b Choice of drinks in cafe –
sample of 40 drinks

Tea	▽▽▽▽▽▽▽▽▽
Coffee	▽▽▽▽▽▽▽▽▽▽▽▽▽▽
Chocolate	▽▽▽▽
Milk	▽▽▽▽▽▽
Juice	▽▽▽▽▽▽▽

Key: ▽ = One purchase

c Choice of drinks in cafe –
sample of 40 drinks

d Choice of drinks in cafe –
sample of 40 drinks

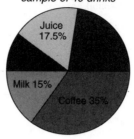

2 a i Tuesday **ii** Saturday
b 184 **c i** 150 **ii** 60

3 St Audacious Sixth-form College –
student numbers 1987–94

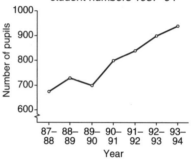

Exercise D3

1 a
No. of cars		Frequency
20–24	///	3
25–29	*NN //	7
30–34	*NN /	6
35–39	*NN ///	8
40–44	*NN /	6

b

Results of survey – cars per minute

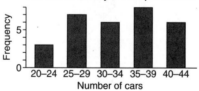

2 a
60	2 9 9 4 6 8 5 8 9
70	8 6 7 9 3 2 5 7 0 6 9
80	6 4 3 6 0 2 8 8 1
90	4 2 5 9 4 1 2 6 4
100	8 0 1
110	2 5 0 9 6

b
60	2 4 5 6 8 8 9 9 9
70	0 2 3 5 6 6 7 7 8 9 9
80	0 1 2 3 4 6 6 8 8
90	1 2 2 4 4 4 5 6 9
100	0 1 8
110	0 2 5 6 9

3
20	0 2 4
25	1 2 3 3 3 4 4
30	0 1 1 1 3 3
35	0 0 1 1 2 3 4 4
40	0 1 2 2 3 4

Exercise D4

1 a, b

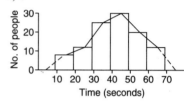

2

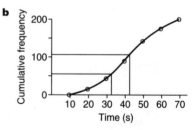

Exercise D5

a
Upper boundary	Cumulative frequency
19.5	15
29.5	43
39.5	89
49.5	142
59.5	175
69.5	200

b

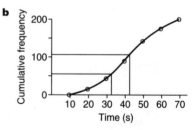

c i Approx. 108 **ii** Approx. 33 s

Exercise D6

1 a Mode = 8, Median = 7,
Mean = 6.27
b Mode = 15 or 19, Median = 15.5,
Mean = 16.08

2 Mode = 12, Median = 11,
Mean = 11.28

3 a i £2600 **ii** £1480 **b** £272

Exercise D7

1 a 16 – 18   **b** Median ≈ 17.3 min
   c Mean ≈ 17.6 min

Upper boundary	Cumulative frequency
12.5	8
15.5	23
18.5	52
21.5	66
24.5	75
27.5	80

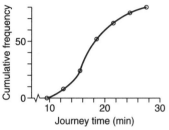

2 a 31–35 yr   **b** Median ≈ 34.9 yr
   c Mean ≈ 34.6 yr

Exercise D8

1 34   **2** 16.24   **3** 45.3 s

Exercise D9

1 a A 35 miles, B 37.1 miles
   b A 27 miles, B 57 miles
   c A 7.6 miles, B 15.2 miles
   Means similar, so they travel about the same distance per year, but Bernice's daily usage varies much more than Alma's.

2 a

Upper boundary	Cum. frequency	
	A	B
119.5	0	8
139.5	7	22
159.5	22	37
179.5	45	57
199.5	64	69
219.5	74	80
239.5	80	80

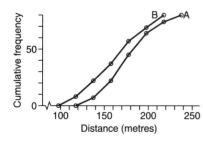

   i A 175.2 m, B 162.5 m
   ii A 156.8 m, B 136.6 m
   iii A 195.3 m, B 184.5 m
   iv A 38.5 m, B 47.9 m

b

B ⊢━━━━━━━━━━━━┤
A ━━━━━━━━┤

100   150   200
Distance (metres)

3 Ball A – mean = 176.5 m, standard deviation = 27 m
   Ball B – mean = 161.25 m, standard deviation = 30.4 m
   Ball B travels on average 15 m less than ball A and its performance is also slightly more variable.

4 a We would expect 99% of the bulbs to last between $500 \pm 3 \times 28$ hours, that is between 416 and 584 hours. A bulb which last only 410 hours would be very rare and so our bulb is almost certainly faulty.
   b From the manufacturer's data they would have expected $\frac{2}{3}$ of the bulbs to be in the range 500 ± 28 hours, that is between 472 and 528 hours, but only four of the tested bulbs are in this range. This suggests that the bulbs vary more in quality than the manufacturer claims (in fact, the standard deviation of the tested bulbs is 43 hours). The consumer watchdog should be careful about its conclusion, however, as 10 bulbs is a very small sample on which to base its decision.

Exercise D10

Answers to **d** and **e** will depend upon where you draw your line of best fit in **c**. So your answers will probably be different from these to some extent.

1 b x mean = 147.5 cm, y mean = 51.7 m
   d $y = 0.44x - 13.4$
   e $y = 52.8$ m when $x = 150$ cm

2 b x mean = 29.4 yr, y mean = 54.1%
   d $y = 1.67x + 5.02$
   e $x = 27$ yr when $y = 50\%$

3 b x mean = 37125, y mean = 2.45 km
   d $y = -0.053x + 4.43$
   e $x = 2.83$ km when $x = 30$ (thousand)

Exercise D11

1 Positive   **2** Positive   **3** Negative

Exercise D12

1 a

Straw/Rasp	Straw/Cherry
Straw/Lime	Straw/Kiwi
Straw/Orange	Rasp/Cherry
Rasp/Lime	Rasp/Kiwi
Rasp/Orange	Cherry/Lime
Cherry/Kiwi	Cherry/Orange
Lime/Kiwi	Lime/Orange
Kiwi/Orange	

   b Straw/Rasp   Straw/Kiwi
      Rasp/Kiwi

2 a 0.02   **b** 0.27   **c** 0.6
   These answers are approximate. Yours may be different.

Exercise D13

1 a $\frac{1}{2}$ (0.5)   **b** $\frac{1}{6}$ (0.167)
   c $\frac{1}{12}$ (0.083)

2 a $\frac{3}{10}$ (0.3)   **b** $\frac{2}{10}$ (0.2)
   c $\frac{3}{40}$ (0.075)

3 a $\frac{8}{125}$ (0.064)   **b** 3125

Exercise D14

1 a $\frac{6}{13}$ (0.46)   **b** $\frac{3}{13}$ (0.23)
   c $\frac{1}{2}$ (0.5)

2 a $\frac{4}{11}$ (0.36)   **b** $\frac{2}{11}$ (0.18)   **c** 0

3 a $\frac{1}{2}$ (0.5)   **b** $\frac{1}{5}$ (0.2)   **c** $\frac{3}{10}$ (0.3)
   d $\frac{4}{9}$ (0.44)   **e** $\frac{2}{9}$ (0.22)   **f** $\frac{1}{3}$ (0.33)

4 $\frac{1}{3}$ (0.33)

Exercise D15

1 a $\frac{2}{5}$ (0.4)   **b** $\frac{3}{4}$ (0.75)
   c $\frac{2}{11}$ (0.18)   **d** $\frac{3}{20}$ (0.15)
   e $\frac{3}{10}$ (0.3)

2 13

3

Cons	1840
Lab	3840
Lib Dem	1680

4 a $\frac{3}{13}$ (0.23)   **b** $\frac{1}{4}$ (0.25)
   c $\frac{10}{13}$ (0.77)   **d** $\frac{1}{2}$ (0.5)

Exercise D16

1 a

6		
5		
4		
3		
2		
1		
	H	T

   b $\frac{1}{4}$ (0.25)

2 a

	H	T
H		
T		

b $\frac{1}{4}$ (0.25)   **c** $\frac{1}{2}$ (0.5)   **d** 0

3 a

	1	2	3	4	5	6
1						
2						
3						
4						
5						
6						

b $\frac{1}{6}$ (0.167)   **c** $\frac{5}{36}$ (0.139)

d $\frac{1}{6}$ (0.167)   **e** $\frac{1}{3}$ (0.333)

f $\frac{5}{18}$ (0.278)   **g** 7

4 HHH HHT HTH HTT
THH THT TTH TTT
a $\frac{1}{8}$ (0.125)   **b** $\frac{3}{8}$ (0.375)

5 a $\frac{1}{4}$ (0.25)   **b** $\frac{1}{4}$ (0.25)

6 $\frac{4}{9}$ (0.444)

Exercise D17

1 a i The sum of the 2 dice is 8
  ii (2,6), (3,5), (4,4), (5,3), (6,2)
  iii $\frac{5}{36}$

b i The red die shows an even number
  ii (2,1), (2,2), (2,3), (2,4), (2,5), (2,6); (41), (4,2), (4,3), (4,4), (4,5), (4,6); (6,1), (6,2), (6,3), (6,4), (6,5), (6,6)
  iii $\frac{1}{12}$

c i The total is 8 *and* the red die shows an even number
  ii (2,6), (4,4), (6,2)
  iii $\frac{1}{12}$

d i Either the total is 8 *or* the red die is even
  ii All of **b** plus (3,5), (5,3)
  iii $\frac{5}{9}$

e i The total is not eight
  ii All 36 cases *except* those in **a**
  iii $\frac{31}{36}$

f i The total is not 8 *and* the red is even
  ii (2,1), (2,2), (2,3), (2,4), (2,5); (4,1), (4,2), (4,3), (4,5), (4,6); (6,1), (6,3), (6,4), (6,5), (6,6)
  iii $\frac{5}{12}$

g i Either the total is not 8 *or* the red is even
  ii All 36 cases *except* (3,5), (5,3)
  iii $\frac{17}{18}$

h i The red die is odd
  ii (1,1), (1,2), (1,3), (1,4), (1,5), (1,6); (3,1), (3,2), (3,3), (3,4), (3,5), (3,6); (5,1), (5,2), (5,3), (5,4), (5,5), (5,6)
  iii $\frac{1}{2}$

k i The total is 8 *and* the red die is odd
  ii (3,5), (5,3)   **iii** $\frac{1}{18}$

m i Either the total is 8 *or* the red die is odd
  ii All of **h** plus (2,6), (4,4), (6,2)
  iii $\frac{7}{12}$

n i It is not the case that the total is eight *and* the red die is even
  ii All 36 cases *except* (2,6), (4,4), (6,2)
  iii $\frac{11}{12}$

p i It is not the case that either the total is eight *or* the red die is even
  ii (1,1), (1,2), (1,3), (1,4), (1,5), (1,6); (3,1), (3,2), (3,3), (3,4), (3,6); (5,1), (5,2), (5,4), (5,5), (5,6)
  iii $\frac{4}{9}$

q i Either the total is not 8 or the red die is not even
  ii All 36 cases *except* (2,6), (4,4), (6,2)
  iii $\frac{11}{12}$

r i The total is not 8 and the red die is not even
  ii (1,1), (1,2), (1,3), (1,4), (1,5), (1,6); (3,1), (3,2), (3,3), (3,4), (3,6); (5,1), (5,2), (5,4), (5,5), (5,6)
  iii $\frac{4}{9}$

2 a CCC CCT CCN CNT TTT
TTN TTC NNN NNC CNT

b A ∩ B $\frac{1}{10}$ **c** A′ ∩ B $\frac{1}{2}$

d A′ ∩ B $\frac{1}{5}$ **e** A′ ∪ B $\frac{4}{5}$

Exercise D18

1 a $\frac{1}{6}$ **b** $\frac{1}{6}$ **c** $\frac{5}{36}$ **d** 0   **e** $\frac{1}{3}$

f $\frac{1}{36}$ **g** $\frac{5}{18}$ **h** 0   **k** $\frac{1}{3} = \frac{1}{6} + \frac{1}{6}$

m The events are not mutually exclusive

2 a 0.70   **b** 0.82   **c** 0.12

3 a 0.2   **b** 0.4   **c** 0.7   **d** 0.3

4 No answer is given for this question

5 0.17

6 a 25%   **b** 43%   **c** 42%

Exercise D19

1 a Yes   **b** Yes   **c** No   **d** No

2 a 0.0024   **b** 0.0776   **c** 0.8924

3 a 0.115   **b** 0.25

4 a $\frac{1}{27}$ **b** $\frac{1}{9}$ **c** $\frac{19}{54}$

5 a $\frac{17}{36}$ **b** $\frac{9}{36}$ **c** $\frac{5}{18}$ **d** $\frac{85}{648}$

e $\frac{79}{162}$ **f** $\frac{413}{1296}$

Exercise D20

1 54%   **2 a** $\frac{2}{9}$ **b** $\frac{2}{15}$

Exercise D21

1 a 0.315   **b** 0.09   **c** 0.3575

2 a 0.00018   **b** 0.00109

3 a $\frac{2}{9}$ **b** $\frac{5}{9}$ **c** $\frac{2}{15}$

4 a 0.064   **b** 0.064   **c** 0.936

5 0.016

6 a 0.8379   **b** 0.0171

7 0.54

Exercise D22

1 a If p is the probability that a person will be in favour of the bypass, then
Null hypothesis $H_0 : p = 0.6$
Alternative hypothesis $H_1 : p < 0.6$
  b 120
  c They should reject H_0 and therefore conclude that the politician was overestimating the support for the bypass.
  d There is a 5% chance that the decision in **c** is the wrong one.

2 a If p is the probability that the coin shows head, then
Null hypothesis $H_0 : p = 0.5$
Alternative hypothesis $H_1 : p > 0.5$
  b The critical region is 3 or 4 heads.
  c The possibly outcomes are HHHH, HHHT, HHTH, HTHH, THHH, HHTT, HTTH, TTHH, HTHT, THHT, THTH, HTTT, THTT, TTHT, TTTH, TTTT. Of these five have 3 or 4 heads, so probability is $\frac{5}{16}$ or $31\frac{1}{4}$%.
  d The significance level is $31\frac{1}{4}$%.
  e This means that our conclusion that the coin is biased has a $31\frac{1}{4}$% chance of being wrong. This is a very high probability of being wrong and so the test is very unreliable. To improve on the test, we should toss it a much larger number of times and set the critical region so that the significance level is more like 5%.

Index